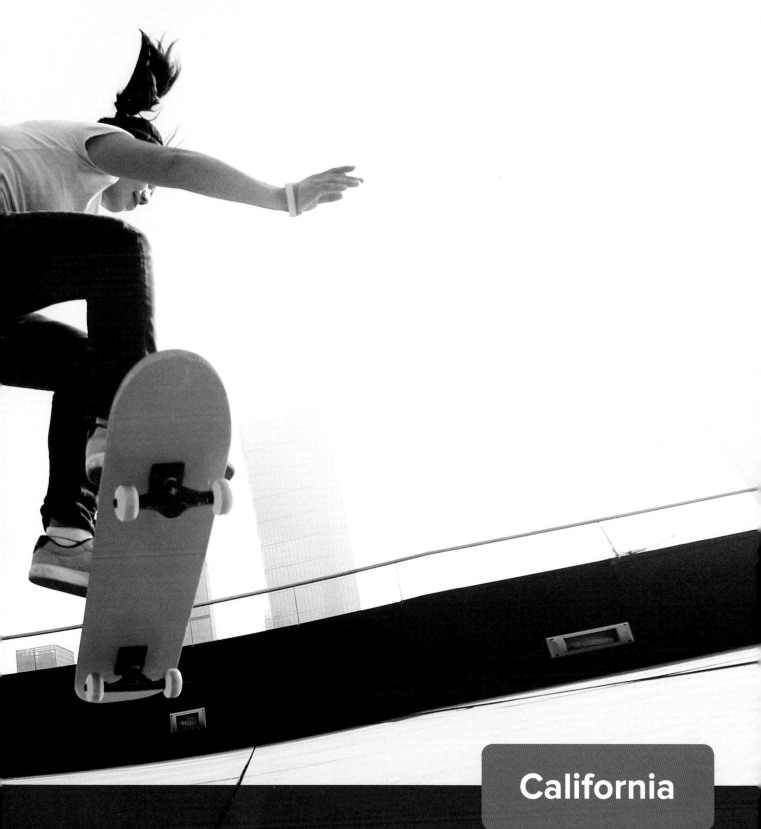

California

Discovery EDUCATION | **SCIENCE TECHBOOK**

Physics of the Universe

To obtain permission(s) or for inquiries, submit a request to:
Discovery Education, Inc.
4350 Congress Street, Suite 700
Charlotte, NC 28209
800-323-9084
Education_Info@DiscoveryEd.com

ISBN 13: 978-1-68220-651-5

Printed in the United States of America.

2 3 4 5 6 7 8 9 10 WAL 23 22 21 20 19   B

Acknowledgments
Acknowledgment is given to photographers, artists, and agents for permission to feature their copyrighted material.

Cover and inside cover art: lzf / Shutterstock.com

Table of Contents

Letter to the Student   v

Letter to the Parent/Guardian   vi

UNIT 1 | Forces and Motion

Concept 1.1 Understanding and Describing Motion   1

Concept 1.2 Newton's Laws   14

Concept 1.3 Using Vectors and Scalars to Describe Motion   32

Concept 1.4 Solving Motion Problems   48

Concept 1.5 Conservation of Momentum   84

UNIT 2 | Forces at a Distance

Concept 2.1 Fundamental Forces   106

Concept 2.2 Nuclear Forces   126

Concept 2.3 Electric Forces   138

Concept 2.4 Gravity   150

Concept 2.5 Movements in Space   177

UNIT 3 | Energy Conversion and Renewable Energy

Concept 3.1 Types of Energy   205

Concept 3.2 Conservation of Energy   226

Concept 3.3 Laws of Thermodynamics   252

Concept 3.4 Electricity and Magnetism   269

Concept 3.5 Conductors and Insulators   288

UNIT 4 | Nuclear Processes

Concept 4.1 Nuclear Physics   304

Concept 4.2 Radiometric Dating   323

UNIT 5 | Waves and Electromagnetic Radiation

Concept 5.1 Wave Characteristics	340
Concept 5.2 Reflection and Refraction	386
Concept 5.3 Seismic Waves	406
Concept 5.4 Earthquakes and Their Impacts	422

UNIT 6 | Stars and the Origins of the Universe

Concept 6.1 Understanding the Universe	443
Concept 6.2 Stars and Galaxies	456

Glossary	471
Index	497

Dear Student,

You are about to experience science like you never have before! In this class, you'll be using California Science Techbook™—a comprehensive science program developed by the educators and designers at Discovery Education. Science Techbook is full of Explorations, videos, Hands-On Activities, digital tools, reading passages, animations, and more. These resources will help you learn scientific concepts and procedures, and apply them to the world around you. California Science Techbook allows you to work at your own pace and investigate questions you may have related to science. You'll even be able to monitor your progress in real time using the Student Learning Dashboard.

The Student Edition accompanies the digital Science Techbook. You have access to Science Techbook's core text—the key ideas and details about each scientific concept—even when you do not have access to a device or the Internet. You can use this resource to explore important ideas, make connections to the digital content, and develop your own scientific understanding.

This Student Edition is organized by concept and includes the following:

- OVERVIEW: What's it all about? Lesson Questions, Lesson Objectives, and key vocabulary will help you prepare for each science concept.

- ENGAGE: What do you already know about the topic? Follow a link to uncover your prior knowledge about each concept.

- EXPLORE: What are the main ideas in the concept? The Explore pages include core text and images to help you answer each of the concept's Lesson Questions. Use evidence to write a scientific explanation and answer questions to check for understanding.

- STEM IN ACTION: How is science used in the real world and in STEM careers? Read more in this section to find out how the knowledge you're building applies to real-world situations—both today and in the future.

Throughout this Student Edition, you'll find QR codes that take you to the corresponding online section of Science Techbook for that concept. To use the QR codes, you will need a QR reader. Readers are available for almost any device. The reader will scan the code and direct you to the correct page or resource in Science Techbook.

Enjoy this deep dive into the exciting world of science!

Sincerely,

The Discovery Education Science Team

Dear Parent/Guardian,

This year, your student will be using California Science Techbook™, a comprehensive science program developed by the educators and designers at Discovery Education. Science Techbook is an innovative program that offers engaging, real-world problems to help your student master key scientific concepts and procedures. In class, students experience dynamic content, Explorations, videos, digital tools, and game-like activities that inspire and motivate scientific learning and curiosity.

This Student Edition allows students to explore the core Techbook content when the Internet is not available. Students are encouraged to use this resource to read about key ideas, seek connections, think about scientific questions, and develop their own scientific understanding.

This Student Edition is organized by concept and includes the following:

- OVERVIEW: Students preview a concept's Lesson Questions, Lesson Objectives, and key vocabulary to help them make connections to the science content.

- ENGAGE: Students answer questions to activate their prior knowledge of a concept's essential ideas, and begin making connections to the Explain Question.

- EXPLORE: Students deepen their understanding of the concept by exploring the core text related to each Lesson Question. Online, students have access to additional resources, Hands-On Activities, and interactives. They will also complete scientific explanations and answer questions to check for understanding.

- STEM IN ACTION: Students connect the skills and knowledge they are building in each concept with real-world applications. Online, they can explore related videos and resources, and complete additional activities.

Within this resource, you'll find QR codes that take you and your student to a corresponding section of Science Techbook. Once in Techbook, students will have access to the Core Interactive Text of each concept, as well as thousands of resources and activities that build deep conceptual scientific understanding. Additionally, tools and features such as the Interactive Glossary and text-to-speech functionality allow Science Techbook to target learning for students of a variety of abilities.

To use the QR codes, you'll need a QR reader. Readers are available for phones, tablets, laptops, desktops, and virtually any device in between.

We encourage you to support your student in using California Science Techbook. Together, may you and your student enjoy a fantastic year of science!

Sincerely,

The Discovery Education Science Team

Understanding and Describing Motion

LESSON OVERVIEW

Lesson Questions

- What are frames of reference, and how do they relate to motion?
- How can physicists use Newton's laws of motion and universal gravitation to predict objects' motions?

Lesson Objectives

By the end of the lesson, you should be able to:

- Use frames of reference to describe motion.
- Model Newton's laws of motion and universal gravitation to predict the motion of most objects.

Key Vocabulary

Which terms do you already know?

- [ ] acceleration
- [ ] acceleration due to gravity
- [ ] data
- [ ] directly proportional
- [ ] displacement (vector)
- [ ] distance
- [ ] force
- [ ] frame of reference
- [ ] gravitational force
- [ ] gravity
- [ ] inertial frame of reference
- [ ] inversely proportional
- [ ] mass
- [ ] measurement
- [ ] motion
- [ ] Newton's law of universal gravitation
- [ ] Newton's laws
- [ ] non-inertial frame of reference
- [ ] observation
- [ ] speed
- [ ] velocity

dlc.com/ca11008s

Glacier Movement

dlc.com/ca11009s

During the most recent Ice Age, scientists estimate nearly 32% of the Earth's land was covered with ice; however, currently, only about one-tenth of Earth's surface is covered in ice. As the ice melts, where does it go, and how quickly is the ice melting each day?

GLACIER IN MOTION

As a glacier moves down a valley toward the ocean, its motion can be predicted. How do scientists predict the motion of moving objects?

EXPLAIN QUESTION

How can we describe the motion of glaciers and the forces that cause the movement of glaciers?

What Are Frames of Reference, and How Do They Relate to Motion?

Frames of Reference: Coordinate Systems

Physicists describe the positions of objects with respect to frames of reference. A **frame of reference** provides a system of coordinates for identifying an object's location.

For example, suppose a student drops a ball straight down from the top of a tall building. A vertical axis along the ball's path could be chosen as a frame of reference. The ball's changing positions can be measured relative to an origin at ground level.

It would have been entirely reasonable to choose another frame of reference. For example, the release point at the top of the building could be chosen as the origin.

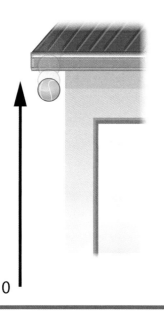

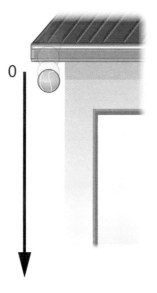

CHOOSING A FRAME OF REFERENCE

When a ball is dropped from a rooftop, it might make sense to choose the ground or the release point as the origin of the frame of reference. How do these choices make relevant calculations easier?

Reference frames can also be moving. In the example of the falling ball, a frame of reference could be chosen to be at the ball's center. For observers within this frame of reference, the ball would remain stationary while the surroundings would move. For outside observers, the frame itself would be accelerating toward the ground.

FRAMES OF REFERENCES FOR A SPACECRAFT

NASA used a frame of reference, that moves with the spacecraft, for spacecraft orbiting bodies in space. What are the advantages to using this type of frame of reference?

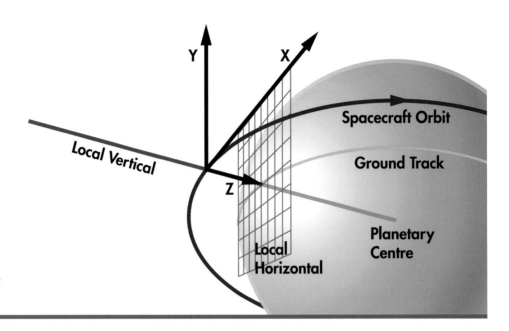

Using Rooms as Frames of Reference

In the lab, physics **motion** studies might use the room itself as a convenient reference frame. One corner at the floor or a particular spot on a piece of equipment can act as a reference frame's origin. The three axes of the frame can lie parallel to the room's three dimensions of length, width, and height. These three axes are typically at 90° to one another.

FRAME OF REFERENCE IN A ROOM

The position of the butterfly at a given instant can be specified using a reference frame aligned with the room. What do the frame of reference for a room and the frame of reference for the spacecraft (shown earlier) have in common?

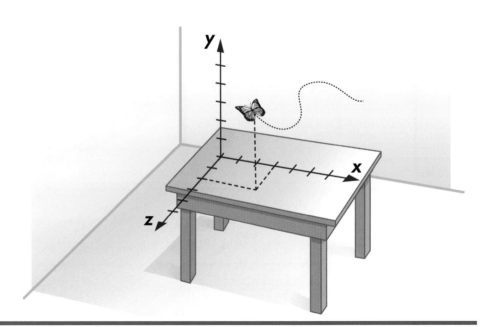

Using x-, y-, and z-Axes

In diagrams of motion experiments, the axes commonly have labels such as x, y, and z and include the relevant units. Usually, the vertical axis will be labeled y or z.

An object's location can be given using a set of coordinates in a frame of reference. For example, the ordered triplet (3, 4, 2) could mean that at a certain instant, a fly in the room might be 3 m from one wall, 4 m from the wall at a right angle to the first, and 2 m up from the floor.

Objects sometimes move along only one or two axes. For example, students might observe an object falling straight down along a vertical axis. Neither horizontal coordinate changes so the students might only record the change in the object's vertical coordinate. Physicists describe this kind of motion as one-dimensional.

As another example, a toy cannon might launch a projectile at an angle. The projectile would move along both vertical and horizontal axes in two-dimensional motion. Two coordinates would be necessary to describe its position at a given time, but the third might be omitted because it is constant.

Inertial and Non-inertial Frames of Reference

Physicists distinguish between two types of frames of reference: inertial and non-inertial. The difference has to do with the first of **Newton's laws** of motion, which are discussed in detail in another section. The first law applies in the case that there are no unbalanced forces acting on an object. It says that objects remain motionless if they are at rest, and the motion of an object will continue in a straight line at a constant **speed** if it is already moving.

An **inertial frame of reference** is one that acts in accordance with the first law. It has a constant **velocity**, which could have zero magnitude. Its velocity does not change in magnitude or direction. Objects moving within the inertial reference frame may accelerate, but the frame itself does not.

For example, imagine a train traveling in a straight line on a smooth track. It has a constant nonzero velocity. The train acts as an inertial frame of reference. People inside place drinks on tables in the dining car. Snack carts roll down the aisles only when pushed. Falling objects accelerate straight down toward Earth just as they do when the train is sitting still at the station. In fact, if the window shades were down, there would be no motion experiment that passengers could perform inside the train car that could prove whether the train was moving (if the tracks were perfectly smooth).

However, if the speed or direction of the train changed, the frame of reference would become non-inertial. Suddenly it might seem as if outside forces were pushing drinks onto the floor and rolling carts around the car.

Physicists often consider Earth to be an inertial frame of reference. However, Earth itself moves with non-constant velocity, because the direction of its motion is always changing. It rotates on its axis. It moves along its orbit around the sun. It is a part of a moving solar system and galaxy. Newton's first law does not precisely apply, so Earth is not truly an inertial reference frame. Fortunately, the effects of its changing motion on the human-scale experiments on Earth are usually small. The results from using Newton's laws are usually very good approximations.

RAILWAY STATION
A train that has been moving at a constant speed must slow as it enters a railway station. How does the frame of reference for a person inside the train change as the train enters the station?

How Can Physicists Use Newton's Laws of Motion and Universal Gravitation to Predict Objects' Motions?

Forces on Objects

Using a given **frame of reference**, physicists can analyze and predict changes in objects' positions over time—their **motion**. Under most ordinary circumstances, they can use laws of motion developed by the brilliant scientist Sir Isaac Newton in the 1600s. These laws describe effects of forces on objects' motions.

SIR ISSAC NEWTON

Sir Isaac Newton (1642–1727) published his ideas about motion in his 1687 book *Philosophiæ Naturalis Principia Mathematica*, and he also developed practical telescopes and calculus. How does his work allow us to predict how objects will move?

Newton's Law of Universal Gravitation

Additionally, Newton developed an elegant explanation for the way **gravity** works. In Newton's law of universal gravitation, he showed that the **force**, due to gravity, between two bodies is **directly proportional** to their masses. Therefore, it is stronger between more massive objects. At the same time, gravity is also **inversely proportional** to the square of the **distance** between the bodies. So, it is stronger between objects that are closer together.

As an example, suppose a student stands on Earth. The distance between the student's and Earth's centers of **mass** is very nearly the radius of Earth. The student's (relatively small) mass and Earth's (relatively large) mass pull on each other with substantial **gravitational force**.

The measure of this force is the student's weight on Earth. It is important to remember the difference between mass and weight. Mass is the amount of material that makes up an object. An object's weight is the force that mass exerts in a gravitational field. Scientists use units of kilograms when discussing mass and units of newtons when describing weight.

If the same student were standing on the moon, his mass would be the same as it would be anywhere, but his weight on the moon would be only one-sixth of his weight on Earth. Although he would be closer to the center of the moon than he would be to the center of Earth, the moon's mass is much less than Earth's.

The section on gravity gives more details of **Newton's law of universal gravitation**.

CURIOSITY ROVER

NASA engineers attached 80 kg of scientific equipment to the Curiosity rover before it was sent to Mars. Would the mass or weight of this equipment be different on Mars?

Newton's Law of Universal Gravitation: Sample Problem

Newton's second law of motion says that any force exerted on an object will cause that object to accelerate. Any two objects with mass will exert a gravitational force on each other. This force will then create an acceleration that can be used to describe the motion of the two objects. Before the motion can be described, the force of gravity between the two objects must be found. Newton's law of universal gravitation says that the force of gravity can be described by the following equation:

$$F_g = \frac{Gm_1m_2}{r^2}$$

where G is Newton's gravitational constant, 6.67×10^{-11} N $\times$ m²/kg², m_1 and m_2 are the masses of the two objects, and r is the distance between them.

The moon and Earth have masses of 7.35×10^{22} kg and 5.98×10^{24} kg, respectively. The distance between these bodies is about 3.84×10^8 m. To calculate the force of gravity between them, use Newton's law of universal gravitation:

$$F_g = \frac{(6.67 \times 10^{-11} \, \text{N} \times \text{m}^2/\text{kg}^2)(7.35 \times 10^{22} \, \text{kg})(5.98 \times 10^{24} \, \text{kg})}{(3.84 \times 10^8 \, \text{m})^2}$$

$$F_g = 1.99 \times 10^{20} \, \text{N}$$

The force of gravity that Earth exerts on the moon is about 2×10^{20} N.

Validity and Usefulness of Newton's Laws

Newton's laws are most useful only within inertial frames of reference. They can be carefully modified for use in non-inertial frames.

They work best in everyday situations, with everyday-sized objects traveling at everyday speeds. When objects are very tiny, such as atoms and molecules, they do not follow Newton's laws of motion. Another set of physics laws, quantum mechanics, works better at that scale. When objects travel very fast, more than about one-tenth of the **speed** of light, Newton's laws do not work well either. The theory of relativity better describes objects' behavior at those speeds.

Even with these restrictions, Newton's laws have many applications. If physicists know what forces act on everyday objects, the laws allow practical predictions of their motions.

Consider the Explain Question

| How can we describe the motion of glaciers and the forces that cause the movement of glaciers?

Go online to complete the scientific explanation.

dlc.com/ca11010s

Check Your Understanding

| What type and axes of a reference frame would be used in a high school physics classroom for the motion of an object in three dimensions?

dlc.com/ca11011s

STEM in Action

Applying Understanding and Describing Motion

Acceleration can result in a change in an object's **speed**, but it can also result in a change in the object's direction of **motion**. Revolving objects experience a constant change in direction. The acceleration due to this motion places these objects in a non-**inertial frame of reference**.

For example, consider an observer on a balcony overlooking a child on a merry-go-round. A child sitting on the spinning merry-go-round tries to toss a ball to the other child nearby on the ground. The observer and the stationary child are in an inertial **frame of reference**. As seen by the observer from above, the ball's path would be a straight line after leaving the thrower's hand. This is what would be expected in accordance with Newton's first law.

The child on the moving merry-go-round is in a non-inertial reference frame. To her, the merry-go-round is stationary and the world moves around it. She sees the ball leave her hand and take a curved path through the air even though the only **force** acting on the ball once it leaves her hand is the downward force of **gravity**. This apparent violation of Newton's laws is due to the fact that Newton's first law does not apply in the girl's frame of reference.

ROBOTS WELDING CAR PARTS

Robots are used extensively at many manufacturing facilities. How is frame of reference important when programming the robots?

Robotics engineers must consider the effects of rotational motion and frame of reference effects such as this when designing robots for industrial applications. If a robot rotates with respect to its surroundings, in the frame of reference of the robot, the robot is stationary but the surroundings are accelerating around the robot. Any action of the robot, such as an arm of the robot working on a manufacturing part, must be programmed by the engineers from the robot's frame of reference.

When we attempt to understand or describe the motion of objects here on Earth, the obvious frame of reference is a stationary point, such as the ground. But what if we want to observe the motion of Earth itself? What reference frame do we choose then? It all depends on which aspect of Earth's motion we want to analyze. Earth rotates on its axis as it revolves around the sun. From this perspective, the sun might be a good reference point.

However, even the sun is not stationary. Our sun is only one of 200 billion stars that make up the Milky Way galaxy. All of these stars, including our sun, orbit the galactic core, the center of the Milky Way galaxy. Not even the galactic core is standing still. The entire galaxy is moving through space! So what is the best frame of reference? The answer depends on what motion we want to analyze. It would not make sense to place the origin at the galactic core if we wanted to analyze the rotational motion of Earth about its axis. However, this choice would be practical if we were investigating the rotation of the sun.

STEM and Understanding and Describing Motion

When scientists launch rockets from Earth, they carefully set up the launch conditions to make sure that the rocket travels along a prescribed trajectory that avoids unwanted collisions with planetary bodies and space debris. From a frame of reference based out in space, Earth is traveling along its orbital path around the sun, and its direction in relationship to the other planets varies depending on the date. Because Earth makes one full rotation about its axis every 24 hours, locations on the surface of Earth face in different directions throughout the day. Also, objects near Earth's equator travel through space faster than those at its poles. Scientists must carefully choose the launch time and date to ensure the spacecraft travels an exact trajectory.

Many of the scientists who calculate the launch times and trajectories needed for space flight work for the National Aeronautics and Space Administration (NASA), the federal agency that oversees this country's space program. Its mission is the peaceful exploration of space in order to advance human understanding of science. In addition to scientists, NASA employs engineers, pilots, technicians, mathematicians, and engineering designers.

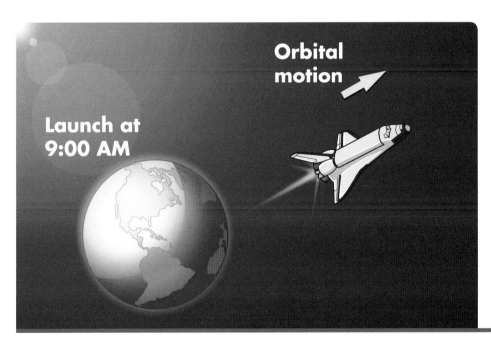

Orbital motion

Launch at 9:00 AM

TIMING OF SPACECRAFT LAUNCHES

Earth rotates about its axis as it orbits the sun. How does this rotational motion affect the location and timing of spacecraft launches?

Newton's Laws

dlc.com/ca11012s

LESSON OVERVIEW

Lesson Questions

■ What causes objects to start, stay, and stop moving?

■ How do forces affect the motion of objects?

■ What are action and reaction forces?

■ Do action and reaction forces cancel out?

Lesson Objectives

By the end of the lesson, you should be able to:

■ Analyze data and construct evidence of Newton's first law of motion.

■ Analyze data and construct evidence of Newton's second law of motion.

Key Vocabulary

Which terms do you already know?

☐ acceleration
☐ acceleration due to gravity
☐ center of gravity
☐ center of mass
☐ distance
☐ equilibrium
☐ force
☐ free body diagram
☐ gravitational force
☐ gravity
☐ inertia
☐ mass
☐ net force
☐ observation
☐ speed
☐ velocity

Newton's Laws in Action

In the winter Olympics, bobsledders compete in teams to see who can get a bobsled down an icy track the fastest. The initial push the riders give the sled before they jump inside is critical to the sport. What exactly is the relationship between the force that the bobsledders apply to the bobsled and the motion of the bobsled when the bobsledders jump in?

dlc.com/ca11013s

EXPLAIN QUESTION

> What causes a resting object to move and a moving object to change its speed or direction?

BOBSLED TEAM AT THE STARTING GATE

Bobsled teams push their sleds to get them started, and this push provides force. How does that initial force affect the acceleration, velocity, and position of the bobsled over time?

What Causes Objects to Start, Stay, and Stop Moving?

What causes motion? We know that if we set a book on a table, it will stay there unless something, an external **force**, causes it to move. For example, someone could pick up the book or bump the table, causing it to move. Why does the book not move if we press straight down on it? What causes objects to stop moving or change the way they are moving? If you push a ball across a gym floor hard enough, it continues to roll across the floor until it hits the wall, but if you push the ball gently, it seems to stop on its own before it hits the wall.

How do the rocks in the photo stay stacked so precariously, and what would cause them to tumble? These questions can be answered by describing how objects interact with each other.

BALANCING ROCKS
Stone stacks often serve as trail markers. What are the interactions between objects that keep these rocks from falling?

Using Inclined Planes to Study Motion

In the 1600s, the Italian scientist and astronomer Galileo Galilei was studying the motion of objects. He performed experiments that led to an improved way of viewing the nature of motion. One set of Galileo's experiments involved inclined planes. An inclined plane is a flat surface placed at an angle to the direction of the force of **gravity**. A ramp is an example of an inclined plane. Many physics motion experiments involve objects sliding or rolling up or down inclined planes. In his experiments, Galileo observed that balls rolling from rest down inclined planes accelerate, or increase, in **velocity**, and that balls rolling up such planes decelerate until they come to a stop.

Next, Galileo put two inclined planes together and saw that balls released from rest at the top of one slope rolled down it and up to a stop on the other one. He noticed that a ball would roll up the second plane almost to the same height as its starting point on the first plane.

Galileo noticed that the smoother the surfaces, the closer the ball could come to its starting height, and he also observed that this was true regardless of the angles of the planes, although the distances the balls traveled along them varied. If the second plane was at a steep angle, the ball lost its **speed** quickly and came to a stop before it had traveled very far, and, if the second plane was at a shallow angle, the ball lost its speed slowly as it climbed and rolled a long **distance** before stopping. The flatter the angle of the second board, the more slowly the ball lost its speed. Galileo reasoned that if there were no friction, a rolling ball would lose no speed at all, and it would continue rolling along in a straight line forever, so his motion experiments showed that it is not the absence of a force that causes moving objects to slow and stop, but the presence of the force of friction.

Newton's First Law

In 1642, Galileo died, and Isaac Newton was born. In the late 1600s, Newton further developed ideas about motion and wrote about these ideas in one of the most important scientific books ever published, the *Philosophiæ Naturalis Principia Mathematica*. In this book, sometimes simply called the *Principia*, Newton explained his ideas about gravity and defined three "laws" governing the motion of objects. These three laws are now known as Newton's laws of motion. The first of these three laws clarified the concept of **inertia**, which says: "An object will remain at rest or continue moving in a straight line with a constant speed unless acted on by an unbalanced force." In other words, an object that is not moving will tend to stay motionless while an object that is moving will tend to continue moving with the same speed and in the same direction. Objects tend to continue doing whatever they are already doing, and only an unbalanced force will change that.

DIRECTION AND MAGNITUDE OF FORCES

Three forces are acting on this box, with different newtons (N) of force at different directions. Are the forces on this box balanced?

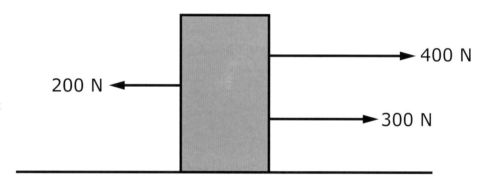

Usually several forces act on an object at the same time. A force is a push or a pull that acts on objects. For example, a **gravitational force** may pull a book down toward Earth's center, while a table surface may exert a normal force on the same book, pushing it upward so that it remains at the same height. A student might push the book along the table to the left while a frictional force to the right might resist the book's sliding motion. How the book moves depends on how the forces add up in magnitude and in direction such that the student will only be able to move the book across the table if his or her pushing force overcomes the opposing frictional force, which is only possible if he or she applies an unbalanced force. On the other hand, the vertical forces might become unbalanced if the weight of the book overcomes the table's ability to provide upward support. If that happens, the gravitational force between the book and Earth would break the table, and the book would fall downward.

If all the forces acting on an object exactly cancel out, they are said to be balanced, and the system is said to be in **equilibrium**. An object will not change its motion if the forces on it are balanced. However, an unbalanced force on an object will cause it to accelerate. Newton's first law also applies to objects that already are moving. An object that is already in motion at a constant velocity is also in a state of equilibrium; the forces on it are balanced. An unbalanced force will be needed to cause a change in its motion, as well.

BASIC PRINCIPLES OF FORCE

Think about sports you watch or play, like football, soccer, or billiards. How do unbalanced forces lead to winning or losing a game?

This is most clearly demonstrated in space where there is no friction. A spacecraft in motion does not need to keep its engine firing to keep it moving. Once in motion, it will stay in motion unless a force stops it. We say it has inertia, which is a property of matter. We can observe this on Earth in low-friction systems—a puck on ice, for example, will continue moving without a force being applied to it (although friction with the ice will eventually bring it to a stop). Objects in motion will only move faster if a force is applied to them. To use our spacecraft example, if the engine is switched on, it will accelerate. Newton's first law is sometimes referred to as Newton's law of inertia.

Newton's First Law of Motion Sample Problem

A car is traveling along a flat, straight highway with a speed of 25 meters per second. If the car's engine provides a forward force of 2,250 newtons, calculate the force of friction acting on the car.

Solution:

Because the car is moving with a constant velocity (speed and direction are unchanged), according to Newton's first law, all forces acting on it must be balanced. The force of friction acting opposite to the direction of motion must therefore be equal to the force of the engine acting in the direction of motion, so the force of friction on the car also must be 2,250 newtons.

How Do Forces Affect the Motion of Objects?

Forces, specifically unbalanced forces, cause a change in an object's motion. For instance, if someone wanted to pick up a backpack that is initially at rest, he would apply a force with his hand, and that **force** would cause the backpack to begin moving.

Newton discovered an important relationship between force and motion—that force causes **acceleration**. He discovered that the more force that is applied, the greater the acceleration, and the direction of the acceleration is always the same as the direction of the **net force**. Remember that acceleration is a change in an object's **velocity** over time, which is a change in the object's motion.

MOTORBOAT ON THE MOVE

This boat is moving at a constant speed and direction. What unbalanced forces cause the boat to accelerate or decelerate?

Keep in mind that many forces are often acting on objects. The acceleration of an object therefore depends not on a single force but on the combination of all forces acting on the object, called the net force.

Acceleration increases as the applied force increases, and an object's acceleration is directly proportional to the net force acting on it. That means that if the force doubles, the acceleration doubles; if the force triples, the acceleration triples; and so on. Newton discovered that acceleration depends not only on the net force applied, but also on the object's **mass**. In the World's Strongest Man competition, competitors sometimes pull massive 18-wheel trucks by themselves, with nothing more than a harness. While they are able to move these trucks, the acceleration they produce is very small. If a mass doubles but the force applied remains constant, the acceleration is halved. If a mass were tripled, the acceleration would be cut by a factor of 3 (to one-third of the original acceleration). When the force is constant, the acceleration is inversely proportional to the mass of the object.

HOW DOES MASS AFFECT ACCELERATION?

Because of the truck's large mass, the strongman's force is able to produce only a very small acceleration. How is the truck's acceleration related to its physical properties?

The mathematical expression of this is $\vec{F}_{Net} = m\vec{a}$, where $\vec{F}_{Net}$ is the net force, m is the mass, and $\vec{a}$ is the acceleration. The metric unit for force is a newton (N). Mass is measured in kilograms (kg), and acceleration is measured in meters per second squared (m/s^2). This is Newton's second law and can also be written as $a = \dfrac{\vec{F}_{Net}}{m}$.

Newton's Second Law of Motion: Sample Problems

Problem #1

Two men push a bobsled with a total force of 250 newtons. The combined mass of the men and the bobsled is 230 kilograms. Ignoring friction, what is the acceleration of the bobsled?

Solution:

Apply Newton's second law. The mass and the force are known, and the acceleration is the unknown. The magnitude of the acceleration is:

$$a = \frac{F_{Net}}{m}$$

$$= \frac{250\,N}{230\,kg}$$

$$= 1.1\,m/s^2$$

The acceleration is in the direction of the force.

Problem #2

Two men push a bobsled with a total force of 250 newtons. The combined mass of the men and the bobsled is 230 kilograms. Suppose that there is a constant 30-newton force due to friction. What is the acceleration of the bobsled?

Solution:

Remember that it is the net force that is important when calculating the acceleration. The force of friction opposes motion and therefore acts against the pushing of the sled. Thus, the net force will be the difference of the forces. The magnitude of the acceleration is therefore:

$$a = \frac{F_{Net}}{m}$$

$$= \frac{250\,N - 30\,N}{230\,kg}$$

$$= 0.96\,m/s^2$$

It makes sense that the acceleration is slightly smaller when there is an opposing force due to friction.

What Are Action and Reaction Forces?

If you have ever gone rafting and tried to push someone else's raft away from your own, you may have noticed that not only does the other person's raft move in the direction of your push, but also your own raft moves backward away from the raft you pushed. Why does your push cause both objects to move rather than just one? If the raft you are in is secured to a boat dock as you pull the other raft, you may notice that your raft will not move closer to the other raft as you pull it. How has tying the raft to the dock influenced the forces involved in this interaction? The answers to these questions lie in Newton's third law of motion.

One of Newton's most important observations is that a **force** cannot exist by itself. Rather, forces always come in pairs known as an action and reaction pair of forces. For example, when a hammer strikes a nail, the hammer exerts a large force on the nail, and the nail also exerts a force back onto the hammer. We know this has to be the case because the hammer stops moving, and the only thing that can cause a change in an object's motion is a force. Put another way, if there was no force, then the hammer would continue moving by Newton's first law of motion.

WHITEWATER RAFTING
What happens if someone from one of the rafts reaches over and pushes on the other raft?

This idea brought Newton to his third and final law of motion: For every action force, there is a reaction force that is equal in magnitude and opposite in direction. Examples of Newton's third law of motion are everywhere. When a book is placed on a desk, the weight of the book exerts a force down on the desk, and in response, the desk exerts a force back upward on the book that prevents the book from falling through the desk. If someone leans against a wall, he or she exerts a force on the wall. However, the wall also exerts a force back on the person. Without the response force, the person would go crashing through the wall.

Newton's third law of motion can also explain why birds fly and how rockets take off. When a bird flaps its wings in the air, the wings exert a downward force against the air. In return, the air exerts an upward reaction force (or "lift") on the bird, which is what allows the bird to stay in the air. Rockets rely on a similar principle such that a rocket pushes downward on the gases that exit it, and in return, the gases push upward on the rocket, causing it to launch.

Identifying the Action and Reaction Forces

One of the easiest ways to identify the action and reaction forces is to identify one of the forces, and then switch the language in the sentence to identify the other. For instance, in the case of a bird flapping its wings, we could say the action is "the bird's wings pushing down on the air," and to identify the reaction force, we would simply switch the order of the objects in the sentence, reverse the direction of the force, and say that the reaction force is "the air pushing upward on the bird's wings."

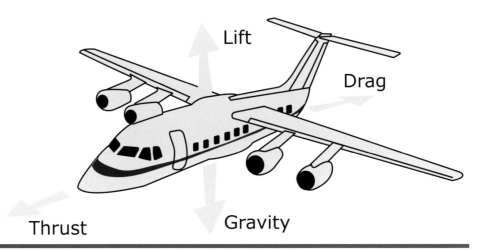

FORCES IN FLIGHT

Since accomplishing flight meant finding ways to fight the forces of gravity and drag, what forces were used to balance these and allow human flight?

Newton's second law states that forces affect the motion of objects. It would make sense to think that since action and reaction forces are equal in magnitude, they must affect the motion of the two objects involved in the same way. However, this is not always true because force is not the only factor involved. **Mass** is important, too.

The Importance of Mass: Sample Problem

A 40.0-kilogram boy is lying in an inner tube in a swimming pool when a larger boy with a mass of 80.0 kilograms floats by in his own inner tube. The first boy pushes the second with a force of 60.0 newtons. Assuming that the mass of each inner tube can be ignored, what is the **acceleration** of each boy and his inner tube?

ACTION AND REACTION

Two boys are floating in a swimming pool on their own inner tubes. What will happen when the lighter boy pushes the heavier boy away?

Solution:

If the first boy pushes the other boy's inner tube (the action force), then the reaction force is the other boy's inner tube pushing back on the first boy's hand. We know these forces are equal in magnitude but opposite in direction. Thus:

$$F_{action} = -F_{reaction}$$

$$F_{action} = 60\,N$$

$$F_{reaction} = -60\,N$$

Note that the negative sign for the reaction force indicates that the direction is opposite. We also know that the action force causes the second boy's inner tube to accelerate in the water, and the reaction force causes the first boy's inner tube to accelerate in the opposite direction (since the reaction force is in the opposite direction). From Newton's second law, $a = \dfrac{F}{m}$, use the forces and masses to determine the accelerations:

$$a_{1stBoy} = \frac{F_{1stBoy}}{m_{1stBoy}}$$

$$= \frac{-60\,N}{40.0\,kg}$$

$$= -1.50\ m/s^2$$

$$a_{2ndBoy} = \frac{F_{2ndBoy}}{m_{2ndBoy}}$$

$$= \frac{60\,N}{80.0\,kg}$$

$$= 0.750\ m/s^2$$

Note that the first boy accelerates away at twice the rate of the second boy. Newton's second law, $F = ma$, indicates that if the force is constant, then mass and acceleration are inversely proportional, and if the mass is doubled, the acceleration must be halved. The accelerations have opposite signs because they are in opposite directions.

Do Action and Reaction Forces Cancel Out?

Since action and reaction forces are equal in magnitude and opposite in direction, it is tempting to think that they cancel out; however, they do not. Consider the diagram, and note which objects the action and reaction forces act on. The action **force** acts on the nail, while the reaction force acts on the hammer. Because action and reaction forces act on different objects, they do not cancel out. Equal and opposite forces cancel out only when they are both acting on the same object, but this never happens with an action and reaction pair.

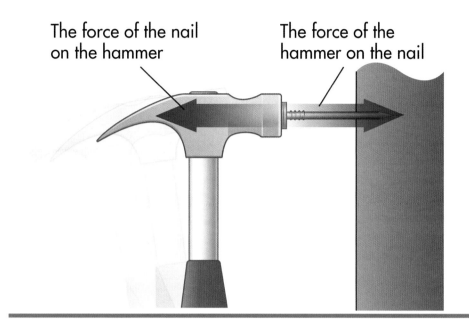

The force of the nail on the hammer

The force of the hammer on the nail

ACTION AND REACTION FORCES DO NOT CANCEL

The action and reaction forces between a hammer and a nail do not cancel out because the forces act on different objects. What is the action force, and what is the reaction force?

Newton's Third Law at Work

Newton's third law of motion is universally true for all forces and in all circumstances. For example, **gravity** is an attractive force between any two objects that have **mass**. Objects on Earth tend to fall toward the ground because the objects experience an attractive **gravitational force** toward the center of Earth. When a person drops a pen, Earth exerts a gravitational force on the pen. Because of Newton's third law of motion, we know that there must also be a force equal in magnitude but opposite in direction. What is this force? It is the gravitational force that the pen has on Earth. Just as the pen accelerates toward the center of Earth, the center of Earth accelerates toward the pen; however, we do not notice the **acceleration** of Earth because it is extremely small compared to that of the falling pen.

Newton's third law of motion also explains why the pen stops moving when it reaches the ground. If gravity exerts a force between any two objects, why does the pen not accelerate all the way to the center of Earth? That is due to the normal force exerted by the ground on the pen, which is equal in magnitude but opposite in direction to the weight of the object. Because of the normal force, the pen stops accelerating toward Earth, and Earth stops accelerating toward the pen when the pen is resting on the ground.

Just as Newton's third law of motion applies to gravity, it is also applicable to electrostatic forces. When two point charges are placed by each other, they experience an attractive or repulsive force that is proportional to the magnitude of their charges, depending on whether they bear the same charge or opposite charge. If two positive charges or two negative charges are placed by each other, they each will repel the other so that both point charges accelerate away from each other. If a positive and a negative charge are placed by each other, they both will accelerate toward each other. In all these cases, both point charges experience forces of the same magnitude but opposite in direction.

Newton's third law of motion can also explain why dragging objects across the floor leaves scratches. Friction is the force that opposes the momentum of an object as it moves; it is proportional to the normal force, and it is exerted in the direction opposite to the direction of motion. Friction is caused by the rubbing of two surfaces—as in the cases of when a heavy box is dragged across the floor, and the floor exerts a frictional force on the box. Because the floor exerts a frictional force on the box, the box must also exert a force on the floor. This force on the floor can sometimes displace the surface of the floor, leaving scratches.

Consider the Explain Question

What causes a resting object to move and a moving object to change its speed or direction?

dlc.com/ca11014s

Go online to complete the scientific explanation.

Check for Understanding

Can you describe an example of Newton's first law?

dlc.com/ca11015s

STEM in Action

Applying Newton's Laws

Have you ever seen a car used for drag racing? It has not been engineered to look like any car that you might see driving down the road or parked in a parking lot. A drag racer is engineered to accelerate down a racetrack rapidly by using large back tires that are able to generate a high level of traction with the track. This allows the wheels to push the car forward with a minimum amount of skidding. Thus, little **force** produced by the car is wasted; almost all of it is used to accelerate the car.

A typical drag racer has a **mass** of 1,020 kg and is capable of producing a force of 33,000 N. What will be the magnitude of the **acceleration** of a typical drag racer during its first few seconds of motion?

$$a = \frac{F_{Net}}{m} = \frac{33,000 \text{ N}}{1,020 \text{ kg}} = 32 \text{ m/s}^2$$

The acceleration will be about 32 m/s² in the direction of the **net force**.

DRAGSTER STARTING A RACE

When a dragster starts from rest, it accelerates rapidly to high speed. What forces are involved in allowing the dragster to reach high speeds?

Maybe you have never seen a drag racer, but it is likely that at some time, you had to move something heavy, such as a box of books or a piece of furniture. If the item was really heavy, perhaps you used a dolly. Basically, a dolly is a rolling platform that can be used to lift and move heavy objects. Suppose you have to move a large box of books and a refrigerator using identical dollies. If you move them at the same acceleration, which one requires the most force? How do you know?

Now consider a trip to a junkyard, where the technology used in a crane allows easy movement of a junked car from one place to another. Suppose one crane with a hook and another crane with a large magnet are lifting identical cars. How do you know which crane achieves greater acceleration of the car? How do you know which crane applies greater net force in an upward direction?

CRANE LIFTING A SHIPPING CONTAINER

When a crane lifts a heavy object such as a car or this shipping container, when does the crane have to apply a net force in a horizontal direction? In a vertical direction?

STEM and Newton's Laws

Newton's third law of motion states that for each force acting on a body, the body exerts another force that is equal in magnitude and opposite in direction. Engineers use their understanding of this law to design machines, infrastructures for our communities, and processes for the production of goods that apply concepts of action and reaction forces.

Aerospace engineers design rockets based on Newton's laws. All rocket engines apply force that produces reaction force. This reaction force is greater than the force of **gravity**, so the craft rises from the ground. A rocket must maintain this force against gravity for several minutes, using a limited amount of fuel in the process. Rockets also use small quantities of fuel to move in space, where **gravitational force** is small. Because the fuel makes up a part of the rocket's overall mass, the rocket's design must take the mass of the fuel into account. Here again, engineers use Newton's third law of motion as the guiding principle for the spacecraft's design.

Aerospace engineering is just one of many careers where forces are manipulated using Newton's third law of motion. This type of engineering specifically involves the design of rockets and spacecraft, with particular attention to the propulsion systems, so they can exert the necessary forces for motion with the most efficient use of fuel. Aerospace engineers also work on jet engines for airplanes flying close to Earth.

Understanding Newton's First Law of Motion

Use your knowledge of Newton's First Law of Motion to answer the following questions.

1. Why is Newton's First Law of Motion sometimes referred to as the Law of Inertia?

2. As a student is sitting in her chair she is not moving, but there are forces that are acting upon her. What must be true about the forces acting upon the girl?

3. An airplane is traveling at a cruising speed of 217 m/s. If the airplane's engines provide a forward force of 19,530 N, calculate the force of the air resistance (friction) that is acting on the plane.

4. As a skydiver with a mass of 54 kg falls toward the Earth, she accelerates at 9.8 m/s^2. What is the force of gravity acting upon the skydiver? What must be true about the force of air resistance working on the skydiver?

Using Vectors and Scalars to Describe Motion

dlc.com/ca11016s

LESSON OVERVIEW

Lesson Questions

- What are the differences between vector and scalar quantities?
- How may problems involving two-dimensional vectors and their components be solved?
- When a force is applied to an object in a direction perpendicular to its motion, what are the effects on its speed and direction?

Lesson Objectives

By the end of the lesson, you should be able to:

- Distinguish between vector and scalar quantities and cite examples.
- Construct solutions to problems involving two-dimensional vectors and their components.
- Predict the result of applying a force to an object perpendicular to its direction of motion.
- Show how physical concepts can be applied to design a device that minimizes the force on an object resulting from a collision.

Key Vocabulary

Which terms do you already know?

- [ ] acceleration
- [ ] acceleration due to gravity
- [ ] average speed
- [ ] centripetal force
- [ ] displacement (vector)
- [ ] distance
- [ ] energy
- [ ] force
- [ ] free body diagram
- [ ] gravitational force
- [ ] gravity
- [ ] mass
- [ ] measurement
- [ ] momentum
- [ ] power
- [ ] scalar
- [ ] speed
- [ ] uniform circular motion
- [ ] vector
- [ ] velocity
- [ ] work

Using Vectors and Scalars to Predict Locations

A family camping in the Santa Cruz Mountains was preparing dinner and setting up tents at a site near a nature trail and creek. The busy parents didn't realize that their 3-year-old son Aidan had wandered off about twenty minutes earlier. What information about Aidan's motion did the searchers use to help find him?

dlc.com/ca11017s

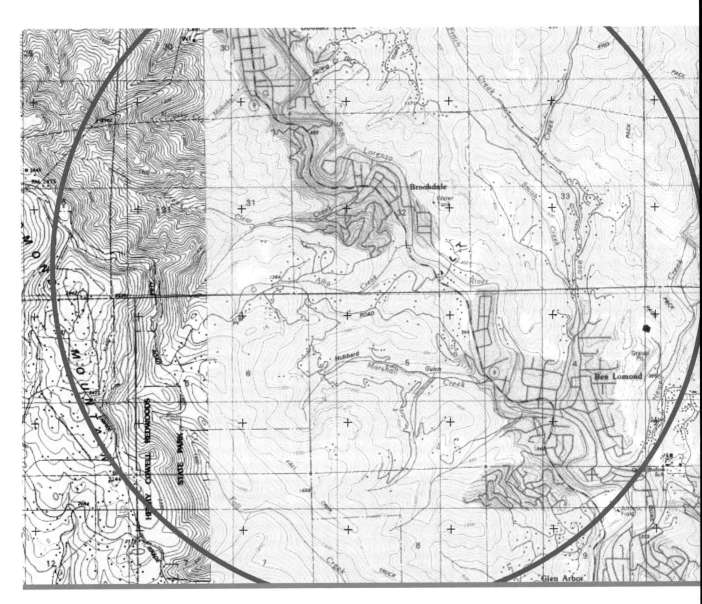

EXPLAIN QUESTION

Why is the total velocity of a roller coaster zero at the end of the ride? How does its speed vary with its location?

TOPOGRAPHY MAP
The likely speed of a lost child can provide information about the area to search, but what other information would make the search more effective?

What Are the Differences between Vector and Scalar Quantities?

Scalar Quantities

In physics, **speed** is one of many **scalar** quantities. A scalar quantity is a value or **measurement** that has magnitude, or size, only. It has units but does not include information about direction. Other examples of scalar quantities include

- **mass**
- time
- **distance**
- electric charge
- length
- area
- volume
- density
- pressure
- temperature
- **energy**
- **work**
- **power**

Scalar quantities are expressed with a number and the relevant units, for example:

- 31 kg
- 52 s
- −24°C

Vector Quantities

Many other quantities in physics are vectors. These quantities have magnitude and direction. The direction information can be just as important as the magnitude information.

Physicists use the **vector** term *velocity* more often than they use the scalar term *speed*. A **velocity** has both a magnitude and a direction. For physicists, speed and velocity are not the same thing, and they cannot be used interchangeably.

Other common **vector** quantities in physics include

- **displacement**
- **acceleration**
- **momentum**
- **force**

© Discovery Education | www.discoveryeducation.com

HOLD ON TO YOUR HAT!
The velocity of the roller coaster changes as its direction of motion changes. What is the total velocity of a roller coaster ride?

Sometimes vectors are indicated in text in boldface or italic type, and often written with an arrow along the top. The direction and units are included. Here are some examples of vectors:

$$\vec{v} = 67 \text{ m/s east}$$
$$\vec{F} = 13 \text{ N downward}$$
$$\vec{a} = 45 \text{ m/s}^2 \text{ to the right}$$

It is often useful to draw vectors as part of a diagram of an object that is moving or that is subject to forces. The vectors are shown as arrows. The length of the arrow indicates the magnitude of the vector, and the direction of the arrow shows the direction of the vector.

Vector quantities from the real world can point in any direction in any of the three dimensions, so their arrows can point in any direction. Physics problems often show simpler situations, with vector quantities acting in only two dimensions.

Two or more vectors of the same type can be combined. Vectors pointing in the same direction are added. If the vectors point in opposite directions, one is subtracted from the other.

A vector cannot, however, be added to a different type of vector. For example, an object's velocity cannot be added to its acceleration in a meaningful way.

Vector quantities cannot be added to scalar quantities. For example, the acceleration of an object cannot be added to its mass in a meaningful way.

How May Problems Involving Two-Dimensional Vectors and Their Components Be Solved?

Manipulating Vectors

The first step in solving problems involving **vector** quantities is usually to make a diagram. Sometimes the arrows representing vectors are drawn so that their lengths are proportional to the magnitude of the vectors they represent. In the diagram, a scale is chosen such that the vectors can be drawn with lengths directly proportional to their magnitudes.

For example, in **Illustration 1**, Car 1 has **velocity** to the right of 10 m/s. Car 2 has velocity to the right of 20 m/s, so its arrow is twice as long. A person making the drawing might draw Car 1's arrow 10 cm long and Car 2's arrow 20 cm long.

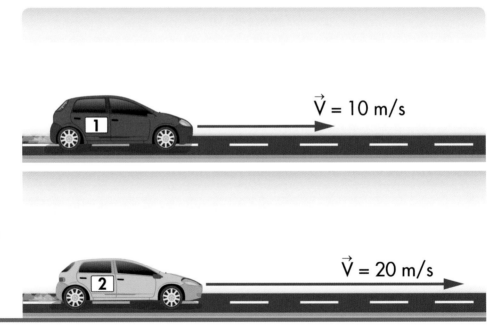

ILLUSTRATION 1

Vectors are drawn with lengths proportional to their magnitudes. What is the relationship between the velocities and vectors for the yellow car and the red car?

$\vec{V} = 10$ m/s

$\vec{V} = 20$ m/s

Vectors can be combined when they represent the same units and they act on the same object. If they act in the same direction, they are added. If they act in opposite directions, they are subtracted.

Suppose that two forces of 10 newtons act on the same object in the same direction. The two vectors of 10 newtons each would be added as in **Illustration 2** by using the head-to-tail method to form a combined resultant **vector** of 20 newtons.

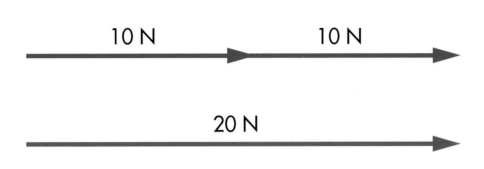

© Discovery Education | www.discoveryeducation.com

ILLUSTRATION 2

Vectors that point in the same direction can be added using the head-to-tail method. How does the force represented by two vectors of 10 newtons pointed to the right compare to a single vector of 20 newtons pointed to the right?

Illustration 3 shows the subtraction of **force** vectors applied to the same box on a level, frictionless surface. The force of 20 newtons acting to the right can be combined with the force of 5 newtons acting to the left to form a resultant vector of 15 newtons acting to the right.

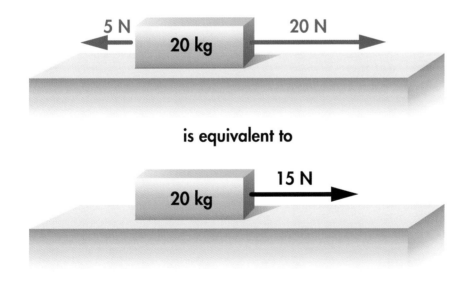

ILLUSTRATION 3

Vectors that act in opposite directions can be subtracted from each other. What is the relationship between the initial vectors and the resultant vector?

Drawing a diagram of the forces acting on an object can be very useful in analyzing motion problems. The Concept *Free Body Diagrams* has more information about showing force vectors.

When two-dimensional vectors of any type are to be added, they might not act in the same or exactly opposite directions. In this case, they can be combined using a diagram of a parallelogram, as shown in the example in **Illustration 4**. The two vectors are drawn as adjacent sides of a parallelogram, with their lengths proportional to their magnitudes. Sides added parallel to these vectors complete the parallelogram shape. Finally, drawing the diagonal of the parallelogram that starts at the base of the two original vectors gives the resultant vector. Its length gives the combined vector's magnitude, and its direction gives the combined direction.

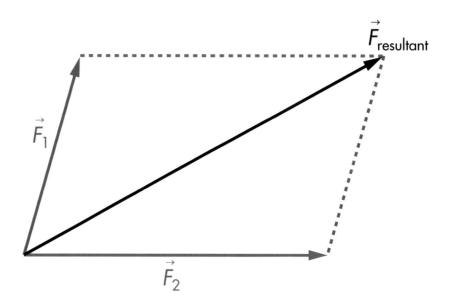

ILLUSTRATION 4

Forces acting in different directions can be depicted as vectors in a parallelogram, using the diagonal to find the resultant force. How does the resultant vector compare with the two initial vectors?

In the special case of the two vectors being at right angles to each other, the Pythagorean theorem can be used to find the length of the resultant vector.

If there are more than two vectors to add, draw the vectors in a chain by linking them head to tail in sequence. The resultant vector can then be drawn from the first vector's tail to the last vector's head, as in the example of **Illustration 5**. The order of the combinations does not matter.

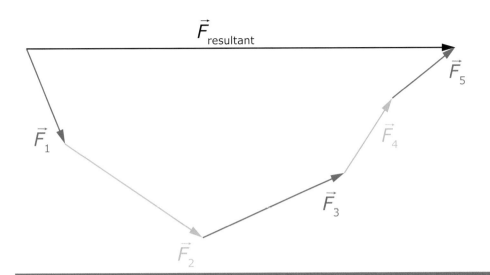

$\vec{F}_{\text{resultant}}$

$\vec{F}_1$

$\vec{F}_2$

$\vec{F}_3$

$\vec{F}_4$

$\vec{F}_5$

ILLUSTRATION 5

Vectors are placed head to tail in any order, and the resultant goes from the tail of the first vector to the head of the last. What is the resultant vector if all of the vectors combine so that the head of the final vector is at the same point as the tail of the first vector?

The process works the other way, too. Instead of combining vectors into a single resultant, a vector can be separated into two or more components. There are many ways to do this. **Illustration 6** shows three of the ways $\vec{F}_{\text{resultant}}$ could be broken down into two component vectors $\vec{F}_1$ and $\vec{F}_2$.

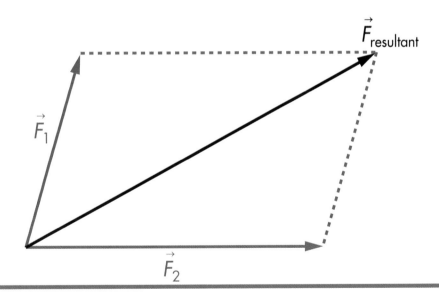

$\vec{F}_{\text{resultant}}$

$\vec{F}_1$

$\vec{F}_2$

ILLUSTRATION 6

A given vector may be resolved into any number of different sets of components. Why would you want to use the simplest way to resolve a vector on a diagonal?

In physics, when a vector quantity is in two dimensions, it is often useful to break it into two components that are at right angles to each other. This results in a parallelogram that is a rectangle. Often the alignment of the component vectors is chosen in a way that is convenient for analysis. For example, one component might be parallel to the angled surface of an inclined plane. The most common choice is to choose components so that they are parallel to the horizontal x-axis and vertical y-axis. **Illustration 7** shows an example.

ILLUSTRATION 7

A vector may be resolved into component vectors that are at right angles to each other and can be aligned with the x- and y-axes of a diagram. What is the advantage of aligning the vector components along the x- and y-axes?

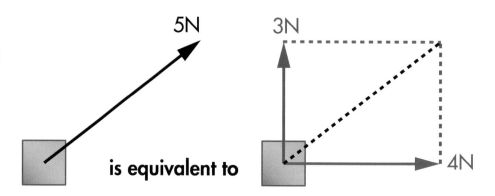

Instead of a drawing, trigonometry can be used to determine the components of a vector in two perpendicular directions.

Manipulating Vectors Sample Problem

A force of 5 newtons acts on a box at an angle to the horizontal. Use trigonometry to find the horizontal and vertical components of this force.

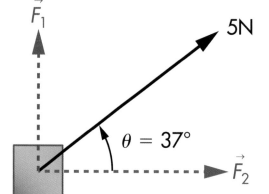

SAMPLE PROBLEM

A force of 5 newtons acts on a box at a 37° angle. What are the vertical and horizontal components of this vector?

Solution:

The lengths of all the vectors are proportional to their magnitudes, so trigonometric definitions can be used, just as if the force diagram were a plane figure of a triangle. Redrawing the diagram makes this clearer.

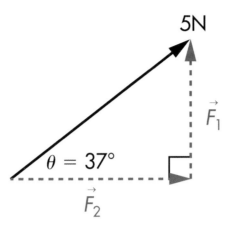

SAMPLE PROBLEM SOLUTION

The vector can be represented in the form of a right triangle. How does this representation enable the vertical and horizontal components of this vector to be determined?

Also, using the sine function to find $\vec{F}_2$ because it is opposite to the known angle:

$$\sin(37°) = \frac{\vec{F}_1}{5\ N}$$

Rearranging,

$$\vec{F} = (5\ N)\sin(37°)$$

$$= 3\ N$$

Also, using the cosine function to find $\vec{F}_2$ because it is adjacent to the known angle:

$$\cos(37°) = \frac{\vec{F}_2}{5\ N}$$

Rearranging,

$$\vec{F}_2 = (5\ N)\cos(37°)$$

$$= 4\ N$$

The horizontal component vector is 4 N, and the vertical component vector is 3 N.

When a Force Is Applied to an Object in a Direction Perpendicular to Its Motion, What Are the Effects on Its Speed and Direction?

Effects of Forces on Magnitude and Direction

An object may be subject to forces. If the forces are unbalanced, they will cause a change in the object's **velocity**. These changes in velocity may occur as changes in the magnitude, direction, or both. A change in an object's velocity is an **acceleration**.

An object that is already moving has a velocity **vector** with a direction and a nonzero magnitude. If a **force** acts on the object in a direction parallel to the velocity, the velocity's magnitude changes. The direction of the velocity stays the same.

For example, if a person walks along at constant velocity and then receives a push from behind, he will walk faster. Here, the acceleration is in the same direction as the motion. The result is an increase in the magnitude of the velocity without a change in direction.

Next, think about a ball rolling in a straight line experiencing friction along the surface. The friction acts parallel and opposite to the ball's velocity. The magnitude of the ball's velocity changes by slowing down, and the direction does not change.

What happens if two billiard balls, both in motion, collide with each other at an angle? The likely result is that each ball will have a change in both the magnitudes and the directions of their respective velocities.

On the other hand, if the force on the moving object acts in a direction perpendicular to the velocity, the velocity's direction changes, and the magnitude of the velocity stays the same. A common example is **uniform circular motion**. Objects travel along circular paths at constant **speed**. Their direction is always changing, and thus their velocity is always changing, and therefore they are accelerating. Whenever there is an acceleration, there must be an unbalanced force acting on the object. In uniform circular motion, this is the **centripetal force**, which acts to accelerate the object toward the center of the circle of its motion. In the case of orbiting objects, the centripetal force is provided by the force of **gravity** between the orbiting object and a massive object in the center.

Image: Pixabay • www.discoveryeducation.com • © Discovery Education

Consider the Explain Question

Why is the total velocity of a roller coaster zero at the end of the ride? How does its speed vary with its location?

Go online to complete the scientific explanation.

dlc.com/ca11018s

Check for Understanding

Using specific examples, what is the difference between a vector and scalar quantity?

dlc.com/ca11019s

POCKET BILLIARDS

Pocket billiards, also called pool, is a game based on understanding vectors. How can a player use knowledge of vectors to ensure that a ball ends up in the pocket?

STEM in Action

Applying Vectors and Scalars to Describe Motion

Like the distinction between **speed** and **velocity**, one a **scalar** quantity and the other a **vector**, an important distinction in physics exists between **distance** and displacement.

Distance is a scalar quantity that indicates how far something has traveled. Another way to think of it is the ground that was covered. An airplane takes off from Dublin, Ireland, and travels to Boston, Massachusetts. After a brief stop, the plane flies to Atlanta, Georgia, then on to Austin, Texas, and finally to Chicago, Illinois. The distance the plane traveled includes the distances from Dublin to Boston, Boston to Atlanta, Atlanta to Austin, and Austin to Chicago.

Displacement, on the other hand, is a **vector** quantity that indicates the net distance and direction a moving object is from its starting point. The airplane's displacement is calculated from Dublin to Chicago, the plane's starting and ending points.

The magnitude of the plane's average velocity is related to its displacement. The plane was moving for about 16 hours. The magnitude of its average velocity is the plane's displacement in miles (or kilometers) divided by the travel time in miles (or kilometers) per hour.

DISTANCE VS. DISPLACEMENT

The distance traveled by one airplane in a 24-hour period may be much greater than the plane's displacement. What would the plane's displacement be if it returns to the airport it started from? How would you calculate its average velocity?

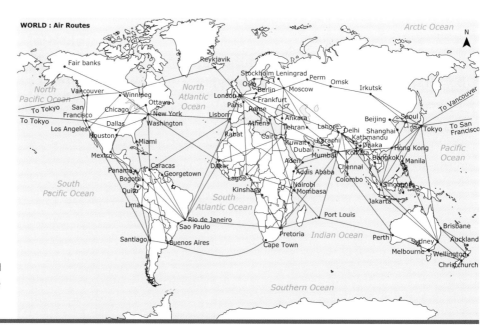

Airplane routes enable calculation of both displacement and distance traveled, using the airplane's flight paths and velocities. If an airplane's flight between two airports is a vector, how do you combine vectors going in different directions? How do you calculate the displacement of an airplane that has changed direction during a period of travel?

STEM and Using Vectors and Scalars to Describe Motion

Aeronautics engineers analyze aircraft flight by separating it into **four force** vectors: lift, **gravity**, thrust, and drag. Because they are vectors, each of the four forces has both magnitude and direction. And, these aircraft flight force vectors act in opposing pairs: lift versus gravity and thrust versus drag. In order for the airplane to fly, lift must equal or exceed gravity and thrust must exceed drag.

When the force of gravity is greater than the force of lift created by air moving over the wings, then the aircraft will not rise from the ground. If the drag force is greater than the thrust provided by the engines, the aircraft cannot move forward. To reduce drag, airplane wings are designed and shaped to let air flow easily and smoothly over them with a minimum of resistance. Wings are also designed to maximize the lift created by air flowing over the wings as the plane moves forward.

Aloft, when the airplane is in what engineers and pilots call "straight and level flight," the thrust vector, which is the vector propelling the plane forward, exceeds the drag vector and the airplane maintains a constant velocity. Meanwhile, all the upward lift force is balanced by the downward weight of the airplane due to gravity and the plane remains at a steady altitude. The plane and its wings are also engineered so that the lift acts perpendicular to the wings.

When the airplane turns, the lift force vector continues to act perpendicularly to the wings. The lift force now has both a vertical and a horizontal component. The horizontal component causes the plane to turn. This is similar to a ball whirling on the end of a string that turns in a circle when the string provides a force toward the circle's center.

In turning the plane, however, less of the original lift vector is available to offset gravity's weight vector. To remain at the same altitude, the pilot takes action to increase the wings' lift during a turn. The pilot may achieve this by pointing the nose slightly upward or by lowering wing flaps to increase the wings' surface area parallel to the ground.

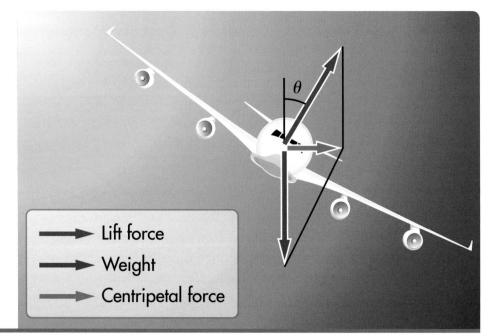

θ

Lift force
Weight
Centripetal force

FORCES AFFECTING LIFT

This diagram shows the vector forces acting on a banking airplane. How are vectors used to model airplane flight?

Manipulating Vectors

Use vector operations and a scientific or graphing calculator to solve the problems below.

1. A rope exerts a 35 N force on an object at an angle of 12° above the horizontal. What are the horizontal and vertical components of this force?

2. A boat pulls an inner tube behind it using a rope. The rope exerts a force 155 N on the inner tube at an angle of 5.88° above the horizontal. What are the horizontal and vertical components of this force?

3. A cannonball is fired at an angle of 18.2° above the horizontal at a velocity of 74.3 m/s. What are the horizontal and vertical components of the velocity of the cannonball?

4. A boy rows a rowboat across a river. The boat moves at 4.3 m/s at a direction of 25° south of east. Find the east and south components of the rowboat's velocity.

Solving Motion Problems

dlc.com/ca11020s

LESSON OVERVIEW

Lesson Questions

- How does an object's speed affect the distance it travels in time?
- How can position, velocity, and acceleration be used to describe the motion of an object?
- How can motion be represented graphically?
- How do objects, such as a basketball, move in the air?
- How can motion sensors be used to record and describe the motion of an object?
- How does friction affect the motion of an object?

Key Vocabulary

Which terms do you already know?

- [ ] acceleration
- [ ] acceleration due to gravity
- [ ] average speed
- [ ] average velocity
- [ ] center of gravity
- [ ] center of mass
- [ ] displacement (water)
- [ ] distance
- [ ] force
- [ ] instantaneous speed
- [ ] instantaneous velocity
- [ ] kinetic friction
- [ ] scalar
- [ ] speed
- [ ] static friction

Lesson Objectives

By the end of the lesson, you should be able to:

- Solve problems that involve both average and constant velocity.
- Distinguish between equations that use acceleration, average velocity, instantaneous velocity, velocity, distance, and displacement to describe motion in one dimension.
- Create graphs to illustrate and analyze motion.
- Apply an equation to describe the motion of a projectile in two dimensions.
- Demonstrate use of technology, such as photogates or motion detectors, to measure motion.
- Distinguish between kinetic friction and static friction, and differentiate their effects on motion.

Fast and Slow

dlc.com/ca11021s

In nature, the cheetah is one of the most dramatic illustrations of the role that motion has played in the evolution of a species. Researchers have recorded top speeds for this animal of approximately 65 miles per hour. What do you think is the difference between speed and acceleration, and why would these two parameters be important for a predator such as a cheetah?

© Discovery Education | www.discoveryeducation.com • Image: Werner Bollmann / Oxford Scientific / Getty Images

A CHEETAH IN MOTION
The cheetah is the world's fastest land mammal and can reach very high speeds. What physical attributes does the cheetah possess that enable it to run at such high speeds?

EXPLAIN QUESTION

How does the displacement, velocity, and acceleration of an object in motion change over time?

How Does an Object's Speed Affect the Distance It Travels in Time?

What Is Speed?

Speed is a measure of how fast an object is moving. Faster moving objects cover a greater **distance** than do slower moving objects in the same amount of time. Speed is the rate at which distance is traveled.

SPEEDOMETER

A speedometer measures only the instantaneous speed of an object and cannot measure average speed because it has no record of speed over time. What features would a speedometer need to measure the average speed?

What Are Average Speed and Constant Speed?

A car driving down a road does not usually maintain the same speed as it travels. It may travel faster at certain times but then slow down because of a slower moving vehicle in front. It may even come to a stop for a stoplight. The car's actual speed is likely to change over time. The speed at a particular instant in time is the car's **instantaneous speed**. A more accurate picture of how fast the car is going over a period of time can be found using the **average speed** during that period of time.

Sometimes objects travel at the same speed over a period of time. In this case, the speed is constant. For instance, on the highway, drivers often set the cruise control of their cars in an attempt to maintain a constant speed. Then the car maintains that speed for a certain period of time. Spacecraft speed up as they leave Earth but then maintain a constant speed as they escape Earth's orbit in space.

When an object is moving at a constant speed, its **instantaneous speed** at any moment is the same as its constant speed. Likewise, its average speed is equal to the constant speed and therefore the instantaneous speed at any moment.

BULLET TRAIN

A bullet train gets its name because it travels so fast. What factors can be used to describe the motion of the train?

How Is Average Speed Calculated?

Speed is simply the rate at which an object is covering distance. Therefore, the average speed of an object can be determined by finding the total distance traveled in a particular amount of time. For instance, if a car traveled 200.0 km in 8.0 h, then the average speed of the car is

$$S = \frac{d}{t} = \frac{200.0 \text{ km}}{8.0 \text{ h}} = 25 \text{ km/h}$$

In physics, SI units are typically used. The SI unit for distance is meters, and the SI unit for time is seconds. It would be typical to express a speed in meters per second (m/s). For instance, if a sprinter in the Olympics travels 100.0 m in 10.4 s, then his or her average speed is

$$S = \frac{d}{t} = \frac{100.0 \text{ km}}{10.4 \text{ s}} = 9.61 \text{ m/s}$$

Distance Traveled for an Object Moving at Constant Speed

To find the distance traveled by an object moving at constant speed, rearrange the equation for speed and solve for the distance. Multiplying both sides by t gives the equation $d = st$.

If both the speed of an object and the distance it traveled are known, the time can be found by solving the equation for time algebraically. Multiplying both sides by t and dividing both sides by s gives the equation $t = d/s$.

Distance Traveled for an Object Moving at Constant Speed Sample Problem

How long would it take a long-distance runner to run a distance of 1,100 m at a constant speed of 6.0 m/s?

Solution:

The distance traveled and the speed are known, so use the equation for speed that has been rearranged and solved for time.

$$t = \frac{d}{s} = \frac{(1100 \text{ m})}{(6.0 \text{ m/s})} = 183 \text{ s}$$

How Can Position, Velocity, and Acceleration Be Used to Describe the Motion of an Object?

How Is the Displacement of an Object Determined?

The displacement of an object is defined as the vector between an object's starting point and ending point. The starting point is called the initial position, and the ending point is called the final position.

For instance, the movement of an ant can be measured with a one-dimensional number line. Suppose an ant starts at $x = 4$ m and walks to $x = 8$ m on the number line.

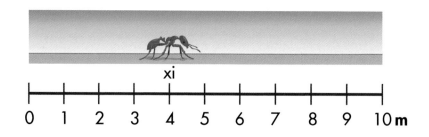

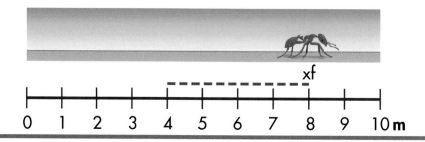

NUMBER LINE

The ant moves from its starting position of x_i to its final position x_f. How far did it travel?

The displacement is calculated as follows:

$$\Delta x = x_f - x_i$$
$$= 8 \text{ m} - 4 \text{ m}$$
$$= 4 \text{ m}$$

This equation describes motion in one dimension with the concept of displacement. The change in position or displacement of the ant is 4 m. However, what if the ant started walking backward from where it came? Suppose that after reaching 8 m, the ant walked backward 6 m and arrived at a position of 2 m on the number line.

What is the new displacement of the ant?

$$\Delta x = x_f - x_i$$
$$\Delta x = 2 \text{ m} - 4 \text{ m}$$
$$= -2 \text{ m}$$

Note that only the final position of 2 m and the initial position of 4 m matter. The fact that the ant walked all the way to the 8-m mark and back does not factor into the calculation. Displacement considers only the starting and ending points of the motion. The negative sign indicates the direction of overall motion. The displacement is negative because the net effect of this motion was that the ant walked in the negative direction (from 4 m back to 2 m).

What Is the Difference between Displacement and Distance Traveled?

In the previous example, the displacement did not take into account the ant's total movement from 4 m to 8 m and back to 2 m. It only took into account the change in position from a starting point to an ending point. In contrast, the **distance** traveled measures the total movement. In the previous example of the ant, the ant moved from 4 to 8 m, covering a distance of 4 m. Then, it moved from 8 to 2 m, covering a distance of 6 m. The total distance traveled is just the sum of the absolute values of these distances:

$$\text{Distance traveled} = 4 \text{ m} + 6 \text{ m} = 10 \text{ m}$$

Note that, unlike the displacement, the distance traveled ignores the direction of motion. Moving from the 8-m mark to the 2-m mark is just considered moving 6 m. The fact that the ant was moving in the negative direction is irrelevant.

Distance traveled is a **scalar** quantity, since the direction of each individual motion is not considered in the summation.

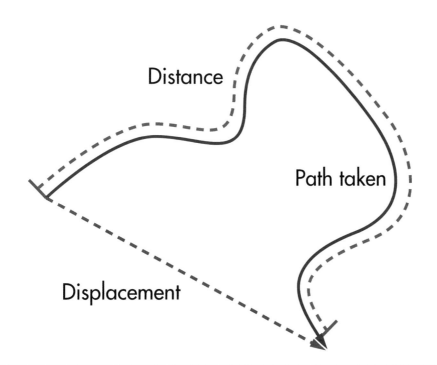

DISPLACEMENT VS. DISTANCE

Displacement takes only an object's starting (initial) point and ending (final) point into consideration, while distance measures the total distance an object travels along its path. Are there any situations in which the displacement will be greater than the distance traveled?

What Is the Difference between Speed and Velocity?

In everyday life, the words *speed* and *velocity* are sometimes used interchangeably. However, in physics, there is a difference. Velocity is displacement over time, and **speed** is distance over time. To specify the velocity of an object, one needs to state both how fast it is going (its speed) and the direction in which it is moving. For instance, the speed of a car might be 45 mph, but the velocity of the same car might be 45 mph south.

Velocity requires a direction, and therefore it is a vector quantity. Speed takes into account only the magnitude and not the direction of the object, and therefore it is a scalar quantity. For the velocity of an object to change, either the speed of the object will change, or the direction the object is traveling will change.

Speed is determined by dividing the distance traveled by the time it took the object to travel that distance.

$$s = \frac{d}{t}$$

This makes sense since speed and distance traveled are scalars. However, velocity is a vector, so instead of using the distance traveled to determine the **average velocity**, displacement in one dimension is used. The equation for average velocity is

$$v = \frac{\Delta \vec{x}}{\Delta t} = \frac{\vec{x}_f - \vec{x}_i}{t_f - t_i}$$

The velocity of the object at any particular moment during this time interval is known as the **instantaneous velocity**, and it may be different from the average velocity. To understand **instantaneous velocity**

$$\vec{v}_{inst}$$

from a mathematical viewpoint, think about how displacement in average velocity changes as the difference between t_f and t_i becomes smaller. At some very small difference in time, the displacement likewise becomes smaller, so that the ratio of $\Delta \vec{x}$ to Δt is still a finite value. This change to an infinitesimally small time interval is indicated by the expression

$$\lim_{\Delta t \to 0}$$

which stands for "in the limit as the difference in time approaches zero." The concept of instantaneous velocity for motion in one dimension is described by the following equation:

$$\vec{v}_{inst} = \lim_{\Delta t \to 0} \vec{v} = \lim_{\Delta t \to 0} \frac{\Delta \vec{x}}{\Delta t}$$

Just as **average speed** "v" is the scalar of average velocity, so the scalar "v_{inst}" indicates "**instantaneous speed**," or the magnitude of instantaneous velocity.

In motion that takes place in more than one dimension, the difference between velocity and speed becomes more evident. Objects can have a constant speed but a varying velocity if their direction is changing. Distance increases for all motion because distance is the sum of displacement magnitudes. If this increase is uniform with the change in time, the speed will be constant.

However, if the direction of motion changes, the velocity is not constant, even if the speed is. For instance, a car traveling around a bend in the road may keep its speed constant but as it turns, its velocity is continuously changing since its direction is changing. Similarly, a satellite might have a nearly constant speed in orbit, but since it travels in a circle around Earth, its direction of motion is constantly changing and therefore its velocity is changing.

Speed and velocity can also differ if the motion is not in a straight line. Since velocity is displacement over time, there can be a dramatic difference between the speed and velocity of an object. For example, suppose a jogger runs 400.0 m around an oval track in 72.2 s, returning precisely to her starting point. Her average speed is (400.0 m)/(72.2 s) = 5.54 m/s. However, since her displacement is zero, her average velocity is zero.

What Is the Difference between Speed and Velocity? Sample Problem

A driver travels 6,240 m north on a straight stretch of road for 4.0 minutes. Analyzing the motion in one dimension, what is his average velocity?

Solution:

First, convert 4.0 minutes to seconds, using the conversion factor of 60 seconds per minute.

$$4.0 \text{ minutes} = 4.0 \text{ minutes} \times \frac{60 \text{ s}}{1 \text{ minute}} = 240 \text{ s}$$

Next, use the equation for average velocity, substituting 6,240 m north as the change in displacement, and 240 s for the change in time.

$$\vec{v} = \frac{\vec{\Delta x}}{\Delta t} = \frac{6240 \text{ m, north}}{240 \text{ s}} = 26 \text{ m/s, north}$$

The Average Acceleration of an Object

Acceleration is defined as the rate of change in the velocity of an object per unit time. For instance, when a stoplight turns green, the cars waiting at the intersection begin to accelerate to increase their speed in a particular direction. The equation used for determining acceleration is

$$\vec{a} = \frac{\Delta \vec{v}}{t} = \frac{\vec{v}_f - \vec{v}_i}{t}$$

This equation describes motion in one dimension with the concept of acceleration. Suppose an electric car that is initially traveling at a velocity of 12 m/s forward increases its speed to 34 m/s in 5.0 s without changing its direction. What is the acceleration?

$$\vec{a} = \frac{\vec{v}_f - \vec{v}_i}{t}$$

$$= \frac{34 \text{ m/s} - 12 \text{ m/s}}{5.0 \text{ s}}$$

$$= \frac{22 \text{ m/s}}{5.0 \text{ s}}$$

$$= 4.4 \text{ m/s}^2$$

The acceleration, in this case, is in the direction of motion. An acceleration of 4.4 m/s² means that for every second, the electric car gained 4.4 m/s of velocity. The velocity of the car increased by 4.4 m/s each second. Phrasing the acceleration in this manner helps one to understand why the unit has seconds squared in the denominator.

ATHLETES RACING

As athletes run a race, their motion can be described in terms of their displacement, velocity, and acceleration. How can these quantities be used to determine who will cross the finish line first?

The Average Acceleration of an Object Sample Problem

A race car traveling forward at a velocity of $+75$ m/s crosses the finish line. After 9.0 s, the car has a velocity of $+23$ m/s. Analyzing the motion in one dimension, what is the car's acceleration?

Solution:

Note that

$$\vec{v}_f = +23 \text{ m/s}$$
$$\vec{v}_i = +75 \text{ m/s}$$
$$\text{and } t = 9.0 \text{ s}$$

Substituting these values into the equation for average acceleration,

$$\vec{a} = \frac{\vec{v}_f - \vec{v}_i}{\Delta t} = \frac{(+23 \text{ m/s}) - (+75 \text{ m/s})}{9.0 \text{ s}} = \frac{-52 \text{ m/s}}{9.0 \text{ s}} = -5.8 \text{ m/s}^2$$

The negative sign indicates that the acceleration is in the opposite direction to the motion of the car, and therefore the car is slowing down.

Distance Traveled under Uniform Acceleration

When people speak of "uniform acceleration," they mean that the acceleration is constant. When the acceleration of an object is uniform, the velocity of an object changes at a constant rate. The equation used to determine the distance, or magnitude of the total displacement traveled, Δx, by an object starting at rest that is accelerating uniformly with acceleration a is

$$\Delta x = (1/2)at^2$$

Consider the previous case, but now suppose the object was not initially at rest. If the magnitude of the object's initial velocity is vi, the total distance traveled will increase. In this situation, the equation for the distance traveled is

$$\Delta x = v_i t + (1/2)at^2$$

How Can Motion Be Represented Graphically?

Graphing Position vs. Time

The one-dimensional motion of an object can be described by a graph of its position over time, where position is plotted as the dependent, *y*-axis variable and time is plotted as the independent, *x*-axis variable. For instance, consider the graph:

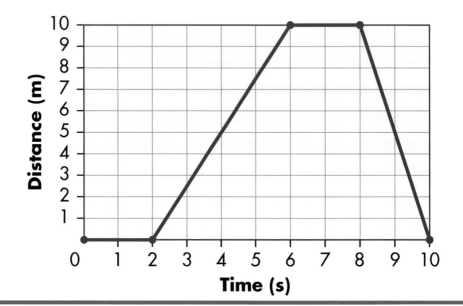

POSITION VS. TIME

In this graph, an object's position is graphed versus time. How does the object's position change over time?

In the first 2 s, the object's position is not changing. This means that the object is not moving, or as physicists often say, the object is "at rest." After 2 s, the object begins moving since the position begins changing in one dimension over time. The **speed** of the object can be determined by using the data available on the graph. The object starts at a position of 0 m at the 2 s mark and travels to a position of 10 m at the 6 s mark. Using this information about position and time, the magnitude of the object's **average velocity** is

$$v = \frac{\Delta x}{\Delta t} = \frac{x_f - x_i}{t_f - t_i} = \frac{10 \text{ m} - 2 \text{ m}}{6 \text{ s} - 2 \text{ s}} = \frac{8 \text{ m}}{4 \text{ s}} = 2 \text{ m/s}$$

Note that because the change in position is equal to the rise of the line between 2 s and 6 s and the time is equal to the run of the line, the velocity is the slope of the line during that time period. Remember that the slope of a line is the rise divided by the run. This is true at every moment in time along the position-time graph and is a useful insight that allows physicists to calculate the average velocities of objects given information about their positions over time. After 6 s, the object stops moving since the position is not changing in the 6 s to 8 s interval. Then, at the 8 s mark the position begins to decrease. The change in position is negative, so the object is moving backward toward its starting position.

Graphing Position vs. Time Sample Problem

Use the preceding graph to answer the following:

(a) What is the object's average velocity in the time interval between 8 s and 10 s?

(b) What is the object's **instantaneous velocity** at 9 s?

(c) Do the answers for a) and b) differ? Why or why not?

Solution:

(a) The average velocity of the object is equal to the slope of the position-time graph.

$$v = \frac{x_f - x_i}{t_f - t_i}$$

$$= \frac{0 \text{ m} - 10 \text{ m}}{10 \text{ s} - 8 \text{ s}}$$

$$= -5 \text{ m/s}$$

Note that the average velocity during this time interval equals the slope, which is –5 m/s. The minus sign indicates that the object is moving backward, not that it is slowing down. In physics, the negative sign for displacement or velocity in one dimension indicates direction.

(b) The **instantaneous velocity** at 9 s is equal to the slope of the line at $t = 9$ s. This is the same as the slope over the interval between 8 s and 10 s, so the instantaneous velocity is -5 m/s.

(c) The instantaneous velocity is the same as the average velocity in this case. This is because there is no change in the slope of the line in the interval between 8 s and 10 s. The slope at the instant of 9 s is no different from the overall slope during the 2 s interval.

Graphing Velocity vs. Time

The motion of an object can also be described by a graph of its velocity over time. The velocity is plotted as the dependent, *y*-axis variable and time is plotted as the independent, *x*-axis variable. For instance, consider the velocity vs. time graph below for the same motion described in the preceding position vs. time graph:

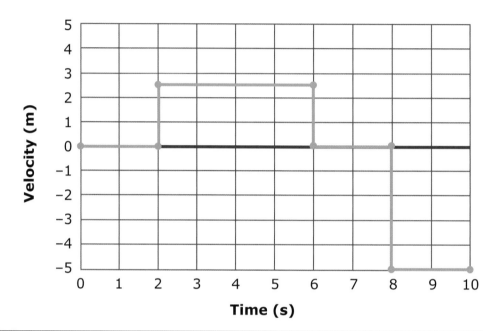

VELOCITY VS. TIME

This graph shows changes in velocity over time. How does this graph differ from one that shows position vs. time?

In the first 2 s, the object's velocity is zero. This means that the object is not moving. From 2 s to 6 s, the object's velocity is 2.5 m/s. From 6 s to 8 s, the velocity is 0 m/s, indicating that the object is again at rest. Finally, the object moves backward with a negative velocity of −5 m/s in the time interval 8 s to 10 s.

Consider a different situation now. In the following velocity vs. time graph, the velocity increases gradually from 0 m/s to 20 m/s over 5 s.

Just as the slope of the position vs. time graph has significance (it represents the velocity), so has the slope of the velocity vs. time graph. The slope of the velocity vs. time graph is the **acceleration**. Remember that acceleration is

$$\vec{a} = \frac{\Delta \vec{v}}{t} = \frac{\vec{v}_f - \vec{v}_i}{t}$$

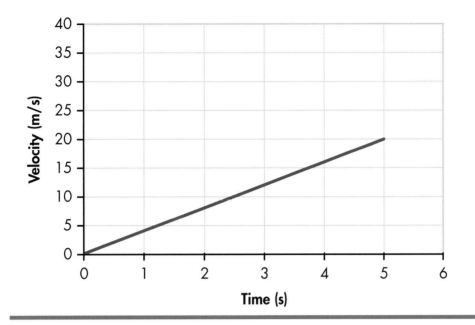

VELOCITY VS. TIME

This graph shows changes in velocity over time. How does this graph differ from one that shows distance vs. time?

On the velocity vs. time graph, the change in velocity represents the rise of the line, and the change in time represents the run of the line. Thus, the acceleration is the slope of the velocity vs. time graph.

The area between the curve and the horizontal axis on a velocity vs. time graph also has significance. Consider the time interval of 2 s to 6 s on the first velocity vs. time graph above. The area under the curve is the width of the time interval multiplied by the height of the graph during that time. Since the height is 2 m/s and the width of the time interval is 4 s, the area is 8 (m/s)s. The seconds cancel, leaving 8 m. Note that this is equal to the displacement of the object during that time. Review the position vs. time graph and observe that it moved from a starting position of 2 m to an ending position of 10 m during the time interval of 2 s to 6 s. This example demonstrates that the area under a velocity vs. time graph between two moments in time is the displacement of the object during that time. In fact, this is always true for every time interval on a velocity vs. time graph.

How Do Objects, Such as a Basketball, Move in the Air?

Introduction to Projectile Motion

When a basketball player lines up at the free throw line and shoots, the basketball has what in physics is known as projectile motion. In fact, any object that is launched into the air is known as a projectile and has projectile motion. A projectile is any object launched into the air, with gravity being the only **force** acting on it. Air resistance is typically ignored because it greatly simplifies the system, and it has only a very small impact on the path of the projectile.

BASKETBALL TRAJECTORY

When the player throws the basketball, it follows a trajectory. How can mathematics describe the ball's motions?

As a basketball travels toward the hoop, it follows a curved trajectory. The trajectory is parabolic. It is the same shape that is traced out by a function like $y = -x^2$.

What are the laws of physics that cause projectiles to follow a parabolic path? To understand this, it is important to distinguish between an object's motion in the horizontal (or left–right) direction and the vertical (or up–down) direction. In the horizontal direction, there are no forces pulling on an object once it is in the air (if air resistance is ignored). When there are no forces acting on an object, Newton's second law says that there is no **acceleration**. When there is no acceleration, the velocity is constant. Therefore, the horizontal component of a projectile's velocity is constant.

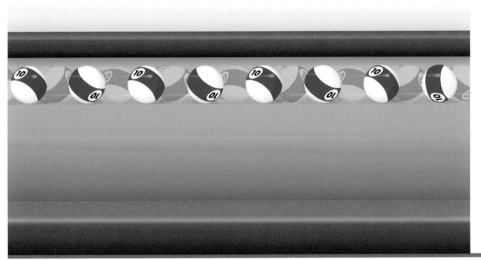

HORIZONTAL MOTION

For an object moving at constant speed in the horizontal direction, the velocity is constant. How does the velocity of a projectile compare with an object like this rolling ball?

In the vertical direction, the story is different. The force of gravity pulls the object downward, and therefore in accordance with Newton's second law, the object experiences an acceleration that is directed downward. Furthermore, since the force of gravity is constant, so is the acceleration. This causes the object to accelerate in the vertical direction.

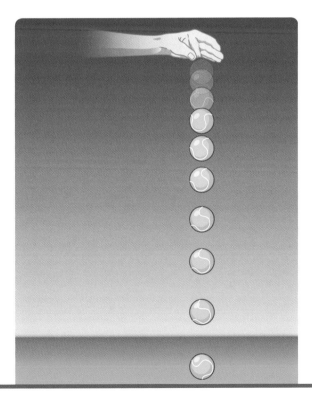

VERTICAL MOTION

Projectiles experience acceleration in the vertical direction and therefore fall a greater and greater distance in each time interval. How could measurement using this time-lapse image demonstrate that?

The parabolic or curved shape of projectile motion is caused by the combination of horizontal and vertical motion. Because the object is traveling at a constant velocity in the horizontal direction but is accelerating in the vertical direction, the **distance** traveled for each successive time interval is different in the two directions.

Would an object launched sideways (horizontally) fall faster or slower than an object dropped straight down from the same height? (Assume that neither object is given any downward velocity to start with.) The answer is neither. Both objects would hit the ground at exactly the same time. The reason is that the horizontal and vertical components of a projectile's motion are independent of each other. What determines how long an object takes to hit the ground is the rate of **acceleration due to gravity**, the object's vertical velocity, and its height above the ground. Giving an object a horizontal velocity does not in any way affect the time needed to hit the ground.

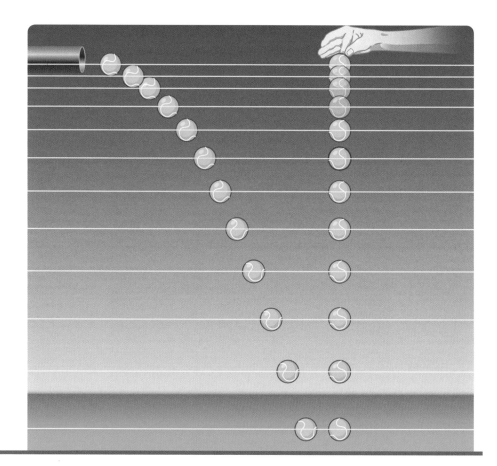

PROJECTILE MOTION

The initial horizontal velocity given to the yellow ball affects the direction of the ball. What explains why both balls hit the ground at the same time?

Equations of Projectile Motion

To describe projectile motion, apply the existing equations of motion for velocity and position to a two-dimensional situation. As a reminder, these equations are

$$\Delta x = x_0 + v_i t + \frac{1}{2}at^2$$
$$v_f = v_i + at$$

In the horizontal direction, the velocity of the projectile is constant, and therefore the acceleration in the horizontal direction is zero. Any terms with acceleration are therefore zero. The variable x is used to emphasize that the displacement being referenced is only in the horizontal direction. All the horizontal velocities are labeled with a subscript x to show that only the horizontal x-direction is being considered. Since there is no acceleration, the velocity v_x at any time in the motion is always equal to the initial velocity v_{ix}. This gives the equation $v_x = v_{ix}$. Since the velocity is constant, the distance in the horizontal direction is just $x = v_x t$.

In the vertical direction, there is an acceleration. That acceleration is caused by the force of gravity and is therefore denoted as g. It is vital to use -9.8 m/s^2, a negative value, for the acceleration due to gravity. The direction of the acceleration must be included. The subscript y is used to show that the equations are considered only for the vertical direction. Displacement is now y, to emphasize that the direction being referenced is only in the vertical direction.

$$y = y_0 + v_{iy} t + \frac{1}{2}gt^2$$
$$v_y = v_{iy} + gt$$

When you encounter projectile problems within this course, assume the motion starts from the origin of the coordinate system ($x_0 = 0, y_0 = 0$).

Equations of Projectile Motion Sample Problem

A ball rolls off a 30-m high cliff with a horizontal velocity of 3 m/s. (a) How long does it take to reach the ground below? (b) How far has the ball traveled horizontally when it reaches the base of the cliff?

Solution:

(a) To determine how long the ball takes to reach the ground below, use the equations for vertical motion. The height of the cliff is known and can be used for the vertical distance y that the ball must travel to reach the ground.

The equation $y = y_0 + v_{iy}t + \frac{1}{2}gt^2$ can be simplified in this case because the initial velocity in the y-direction is zero. The resulting equation is

$$y = \frac{1}{2}gt^2$$

Rearrange this equation and solve for time:

$$t = \sqrt{\frac{2y}{g}}$$

When the ball hits the ground, it will have a vertical displacement of -30.0 m. Plugging in the known values yields

$$t = \sqrt{\frac{2(-30.0 \text{ m})}{-9.8 \text{ m/s}^2}}$$

$$= 2.5 \text{ s}$$

(b) To determine how far the ball traveled horizontally before reaching the ground, use the equations for motion in the horizontal direction. The time is known so apply the equation for horizontal position:

$$x = x_0 + v_x t = (3.0 \text{ m/s})(2.5 \text{ s}) = 7.5 \text{ m}$$

How Can Motion Sensors Be Used to Record and Describe the Motion of an Object?

Measuring Motion

The human eye in combination with the visual cortex (the part of the human brain responsible for vision) has evolved to detect motion in the environment. It is an important survival mechanism. This ability relies on the use of sophisticated biological sensors in our eyes.

Electronics can also play the role of observing and recording motion. In a physics laboratory, stopwatches are used to record how long it takes for something to happen. However, a far more accurate way to measure the motion of an object is to use a device called a photogate or a motion sensor.

A photogate measures the time at which an object passes between two probes on the photogate. When an object blocks an optical or ultrasonic signal being sent between these two probes, the photogate senses that an object is present. This technology can be used to very accurately determine the time at which something happens, such as when a lab cart reaches a certain position on a track.

A motion sensor can record the position of an object over time. A sequence of motion sensors can be used to determine exactly how far away an object is at any point in time by sending ultrasonic sound pulses. The sensor records how long it takes for these pulses to bounce off an object and return to the sensor. Then, a computer interprets the information and determines the **distance** of the object from the sensor.

Motion sensors and photogates are very useful to students and scientists in the laboratory. They provide much more accurate data about the position of objects over time than more primitive methods such as a stopwatch.

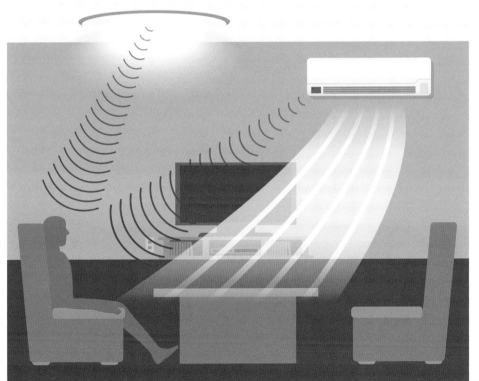

SEEING MOTION

Motion sensors are used in a variety of commercial applications. How might these sensors be used as part of computerized security systems to prevent theft?

How Does Friction Affect the Motion of an Object?

What Is Friction?

Friction is a **force** that resists motion. Friction can be felt all around. For instance, when a person slides his or her foot against a rough carpet, the friction created between shoes and carpet requires effort to overcome. Ice, for example, has very low levels of friction and so is very slippery. However, even ice has some friction.

Friction is caused by the microscopic roughness between two surfaces. Even surfaces that look very smooth to the naked eye are actually quite rough when seen through a microscope. It is this roughness that makes it hard for two objects to slide past one another when a force is applied.

What Is the Difference between Static and Kinetic Friction?

Static friction is the name given to the type of friction that exists between two objects when the objects are at rest with respect to one another. (*Static* means "stationary.") For instance, if a person tries to push a sofa that is at rest across a carpeted floor, the person is trying to overcome static friction. However, once the sofa is moving, the force of friction that is opposing motion is called **kinetic friction**. (*Kinetic* means "in motion.")

FRICTION

Static friction keeps objects from moving, whereas kinetic friction is the force of friction experienced by objects in motion. How is the motion of an object determined by the two kinds of friction?

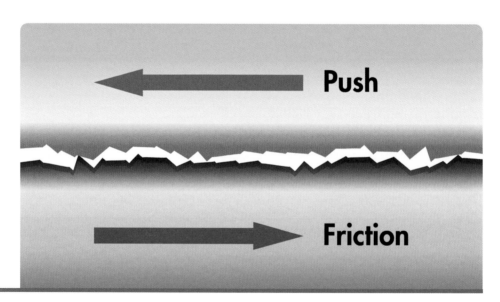

Friction Occurs in Fluids

Friction exists not only between solid objects but between objects in liquid or gaseous states, including between a fluid and a solid. For instance, boats moving through the water experience a frictional force known as drag, which is caused by the boat bumping into the water molecules and trying to move past them.

Skydivers experience another type of friction known as air resistance. Skydivers accelerate rapidly, and once they reach high velocities, they experience a significant amount of air resistance caused by the interaction between their bodies and the air molecules around them. It is this type of drag that allows skydivers to slow down enough for a safe landing after their parachute has opened.

The magnitude of the force due to air resistance experienced by a skydiver increases as his or her **speed** increases. If a skydiver is falling fast enough, air resistance will balance the force of gravity. When this happens, skydivers stop accelerating and they reach what is called "terminal velocity."

Consider the Explain Question

How does the displacement, velocity, and acceleration of an object in motion change over time?

dlc.com/ca11022s

Go online to complete the scientific explanation.

Check for Understanding

A woman pushes a couch, from rest position, across a carpeted floor. How does this example illustrate static and kinetic friction?

dlc.com/ca11023s

STEM in Action

Applying Methods of Solving Motion Problems

Projectiles are an excellent application of the principles of motion. Have you ever thrown a baseball or lobbed a volleyball over a net? The resulting action is called projectile motion. During projectile motion, the object in motion is only subject to the downward **force** of gravity (for practical purposes, we can ignore friction from the air). The motion can be broken down into horizontal and vertical motion. In the vertical direction, the object experiences a constant downward **acceleration** and is governed by the same equations that govern an object in free fall. However, in the horizontal direction there is no acceleration. Therefore, the object travels with a constant horizontal velocity equal to its initial horizontal velocity in this direction. In order to solve projectile motion problems, both the horizontal and vertical motion must be solved independently and then combined. The result is a parabolic trajectory. Solving problems involving projectile motion is a good way to test your understanding of the principles of motion.

The game of paintball is one application of projectile motion. Almost like real bullets, paintball pellets travel with extremely large speeds as they leave the muzzle of the paintball gun. Some paintball pellets can reach speeds of up to 220 miles per hour. At such speeds it is tempting to think that the paintballs do not follow the curved path of a projectile in the way that a basketball or a football does.

However, paintballs experience projectile motion every bit as much as a basketball or softball does. Like all projectiles, their path is parabolic in shape even though the curves are often too slight to notice with the naked eye. In fact, since the horizontal and vertical motions of a projectile are independent of one another, a paintball shot horizontally out of a paintball gun falls to the ground in the same amount of time as if someone had dropped a paintball from the same height. The only difference is that the paintball shot out of a paintball gun might travel a very large horizontal **distance**. When aiming at a target over a long distance, what would the shooter need to do to compensate for this drop? What calculations would the shooter need to do?

PAINTBALL

Once a paintball pellet leaves the nozzle of the paintball gun, it follows the same path as any projectile. What would a graph of the horizontal and vertical components of the position, velocity, and acceleration look like?

STEM and Solving Motion Problems

Think about the last time you took a trip on an airplane. How long did it take you to travel from your starting point to your destination? Imagine cutting that time down by half, three-quarters, or even more. This is what engineers and researchers are attempting to do. They hope that one day, airplanes will be able to travel at significantly higher speeds than today's commercial aircraft. In 2004, NASA set a record by flying the hypersonic, rocket-powered X-43 A at almost 7,000 miles per hour. That is just over nine times the **speed** of sound!

How would the use of superfast commercial aircrafts change our world? Imagine flying from New York to Tokyo in about two hours; that is better than the 15–17 hours currently required for a flight on today's commercial aircraft. This ability would revolutionize the air travel industry!

However, traveling at extremely fast speeds presents many engineering design challenges. An engineer who designs and builds these types of vehicles is called an aerospace engineer. The drag, or air resistance, that acts on an aircraft increases with increasing speed. Therefore, a superfast aircraft would experience an enormous drag force, which would generate a lot of heat. When designing these aircrafts, engineers must develop a mechanism for dissipating this thermal energy quickly and efficiently. In spite of these and other design challenges, aerospace engineers are working hard to solve these problems.

Calculating Acceleration in One Dimension

Use the equations for acceleration in one-dimension to solve the problems below.

1. A car moving with a velocity of 6.4 m/s, forward, accelerates to a velocity of 10.6 m/s, forward, in 16 s. What is the car's acceleration?

2. A train changes velocity from +64 km/h to +25 km/h in a period of 10.0 minutes. What is the train's acceleration?

3. If a runner starts from rest to run a distance of 50.0 m in 16.5 s, what is the runner's acceleration?

4. A ship travels 2200 m, east in 425 s. If the ship's initial velocity is 5.7 m/s, east, what is the ship's acceleration?

5. A driver travels +2170 m in 35.0 s. If the driver's initial velocity is +62.0 m/s, what is her acceleration?

Calculating Accelerated Motion in Two Dimensions

Use the equations for motion in one-dimension to solve the problems for two-dimensional motion below.

1. A rock is kicked off the edge of a cliff that is 127 m high. If its initial velocity is 4.2 m/s in the horizontal direction, how far from the base of the cliff will the rock land?

2. How long will it take the rock described in the previous question to land below the cliff?

3. A football player kicks a football upward at an angle of 45°, so that the horizontal and vertical components of velocity are equal. If it takes 2.2 s for the ball to reach its maximum height, and another 2.2 s for the ball to return to the ground, what is the maximum height of the ball's trajectory?

4. What is the horizontal range of the football in the previous question?

5. After opening her parachute, a skydiver falls at a constant rate of 3.5 m/s. At the same time, a steady wind from the west moves her eastward with an acceleration of 1.7 m/s². If the skydiver is 275 m above the ground, how far to the east will she land?

6. In the previous question, how long will it take the skydiver to reach the ground?

Distance Traveled by an Object at Constant Speed

Use mechanics equations to solve the problems below.

1. If a swimmer is traveling at a constant speed of 0.85 m/s, how long would it take to swim the length of a 50-meter Olympic sized pool?

2. A motorcycle is traveling along a highway at 26 m/s. How far does the motorcycle travel in 15 s?

3. A model railroad train travels at a constant speed of 8 cm/s. How far would the train travel in one minute?

4. If a commercial airplane traveled at a constant speed of 775 km/h, how long would it take to travel from New York to Johannesburg, South Africa if the distance separating these cities is 12,830 km?

5. A person jogged for 6.0 minutes at a speed of 5.0 km/h. How far did they jog?

Calculating Speed and Velocity in One Dimension

Use the equations for average velocity in one-dimension to solve the problems below.

1. A train travels 55 km, south along a straight track in 34 minutes. What is the train's average velocity in kilometers per hour?

2. A student walks 144 m west, then turns around and walks 89 m east. If this takes place in a 7.5 minute interval, what is the student's average velocity, in meters per second? What is the student's average speed?

3. A plane travels 204 km, northeast in 15.0 minutes. It also increases elevation by 1.6 km, upward in the same amount of time. What are the average velocities in the two separate directions?

4. A driver travels 135 km, east in 1.5 h, stops for 45 minutes for lunch, and then resumes driving for the next 2.0 h through a displacement of 215 km, east. What is the driver's average velocity?

5. An athlete runs 5.4 laps around a circular track that is 400.0 m long. If this takes 540 s, what is the average velocity of the athlete? What is the average speed of the athlete over the complete distance of the run?

6. A bus travels north on some busy city streets for 2.5 km, and a trip that takes 9 minutes. At one point in the trip, the bus is stopped at a red light. What is its instantaneous velocity in m/s? At another point, the bus travels at a constant speed of 18 m/s. What is its instantaneous velocity?

Graphing Displacement vs. Time

Use principles of motion to solve the problems below.

1. Consider the displacement vs. time graph below for a woman's movement in a hallway:

   a. What is the woman's velocity from 0 to 2 seconds?

   b. What is the woman's velocity from 4 to 5 seconds?

   c. What is the woman's velocity from 5 to 7 seconds?

   d. What does the negative slope from 7 to 8 seconds indicate the woman is doing?

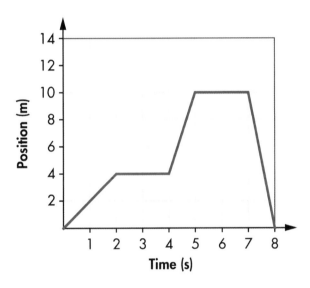

2. Create a displacement vs. time graph for an object that is moving at a constantvelocity of 4 m/s for 4 seconds and then comes to rest for the next 4 seconds.

3. Create a displacement vs. time graph for an object that starts at a position of 10 meters and moves to a position of 2 meters after 2 seconds.

4. Consider the velocity vs. time graph below for a car's movement down the street:

a. What is the car's acceleration from 0 to 10 seconds?

b. What is the car's acceleration from 10 to 20 seconds?

c. What is the car's acceleration from 40 to 50 seconds?

d. What does the negative slope from 20 to 35 seconds indicate the car is doing?

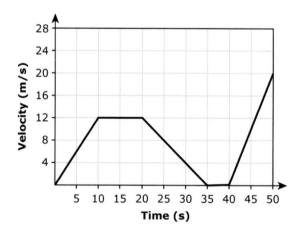

Equations of Projectile Motion

Use principles of projectile motion to solve the problems below.

1. A motorcycle stunt driver rides his motorcycle off a small ledge that is 8.4 meters high. His initial velocity as he rides off the cliff is 24 m/s in the horizontal direction.

   a. How long does it take before he lands on the ground below?

   b. How far away from the base of the cliff does he travel while in the air?

2. A man accidentally kicks a pebble off a cliff that is 18 meters high with a horizontal velocity of 2.3 m/s. How long does it take to hit the ground below?

3. A quarter rolls off a table with an initial horizontal velocity of 0.24 m/s. If the quarter lands 0.42 seconds later on the ground:

   a. How far from the table did it land?

   b. How high is the table?

4. A diver dives off a 32-meter high diving board into the water below. If the diver pushes off with an initial horizontal velocity of 1.2 m/s, how far from the base of the board does she land?

Conservation of Momentum

dlc.com/ca11024s

LESSON OVERVIEW

Lesson Questions

- How are kinetic energy and momentum similar to and different from one another?
- What is the law of conservation of momentum, and how can it be used to solve problems of motion?
- How do the laws of conservation of momentum and conservation of energy describe the motion of objects during elastic and inelastic collisions?
- What demonstrations can be performed that obey the law of conservation of momentum?
- How do net external forces affect the momentum of a system?

Key Vocabulary

Which terms do you already know?

- ☐ closed system
- ☐ conservation of energy
- ☐ conservation of momentum
- ☐ distance
- ☐ elastic collision
- ☐ inelastic collision
- ☐ kinetic energy
- ☐ momentum
- ☐ physical property

Lesson Objectives

By the end of the lesson, you should be able to:

- Explain the difference between energy and momentum.
- Apply the law of conservation of momentum to solve problems.
- Describe and predict the behavior of objects using the laws of conservation of momentum and conservation of energy.
- Demonstrate the law of conservation of momentum.
- Generate evidence that unbalanced forces cause a change in momentum.

Driving with Friends

dlc.com/ca11025s

You are in the passenger seat of your friend's car as she drives down the highway. Are you at an increased chance of more serious injury if your feet are placed on the dashboard?

AIR BAGS

Airbags are designed to save lives during a collision. How can the concept of momentum be applied to explain why air bags are such an important safety feature?

EXPLAIN QUESTION

▌ **How can momentum be transferred during a car collision?**

How Are Kinetic Energy and Momentum Similar to and Different from One Another?

Definition of Momentum

Think of the important physical quantities. Think about mass, position, velocity, acceleration, force, or energy. Here is another fundamental physical quantity: **momentum**. All objects in motion have momentum. You know that a small car is easier to stop than a large truck traveling at the same speed. This is because the truck has more mass. It is more difficult to stop because it has more momentum:

$$\text{momentum} = \text{mass} \times \text{velocity}$$

Similar to energy, momentum can be transferred between objects or systems. Because of this, momentum helps describe the motion of objects or systems, especially systems in which objects collide with one another.

The momentum, $\vec{p}$ of a mass m traveling at velocity $\vec{v}$ is a vector quantity defined as

$$\vec{p} = m\vec{v}$$

The direction of the momentum of an object is the same as the direction of the object's velocity.

Mass is given in units of kilograms. Velocity is given in units of meters per second. This means that momentum has units of kilogram meters per second (kg$\times$m/s).

SPEED SKATING

These speed skaters have momentum as they race around a track. If the skaters increase their velocity, what happens to their momentum?

Comparing Momentum and Kinetic Energy

Recall that **kinetic energy** is the energy associated with the motion of an object. Recall that the kinetic energy, *KE*, of a mass *m* traveling at a velocity $\vec{v}$ is defined as

$$KE = \frac{1}{2}mv^2$$

Compare this to the equation for momentum, $\vec{p}$:

$$\vec{p} = m\vec{v}$$

There are some immediate similarities: Both momentum and kinetic energy are associated with moving objects, and they both depend on the mass and velocity of an object. However, one difference is that kinetic energy is a scalar quantity while momentum is a vector. Why? Momentum is about mass in motion, and there is a direction associated with motion. On the other hand, kinetic energy is the energy of the mass in motion. Energy is a system's ability to do work, which does not require a direction. Kinetic energy has magnitude but no direction. Conversely, momentum is a vector, meaning it has both magnitude and direction.

One additional distinction is that the units for the quantities are different. Kinetic energy has units of joules (J), which are equivalent to newton-meters (N×m), or kilogram-meters squared per second squared (kg×m²/s²). Note that the units of momentum are simply kilogram-meters per second (kg×m/s).

What Is the Law of Conservation of Momentum, and How Can It Be Used to Solve Problems of Motion?

Conservation of Momentum

As discussed, moving objects have **momentum**, but an interesting property of momentum is that it can be transferred from one object to another. If a system is a **closed system** (meaning it does not experience any net external forces), momentum is conserved in that system. That is, the momentum in a system may shift from one object to another, but the total amount of momentum in the system remains constant.

HITTING A PUCK

A hockey player swings a hockey stick to hit a puck. What happens to momentum when the stick hits the puck?

Consider a system containing two objects on a frictionless surface, such as two different-sized pucks on an ice rink. The first puck has a mass m_1 and it is traveling at an initial velocity $\vec{v}_{i1}$. The first puck has a momentum $\vec{p}_{i1}$ given by the equation

$$\vec{p}_{i1} = m_1 \vec{v}_{i1}$$

A second puck has a mass m_2 and is traveling at an initial velocity $\vec{v}_{i2}$. The second puck has a momentum $\vec{p}_{i2}$ given by the equation

$$\vec{p}_{i2} = m_2 \vec{v}_{i2}$$

The total initial momentum of the system, $\vec{p}_i$, is the sum of the initial momentum of both pucks:

$$\vec{p}_i = \vec{p}_{i1} + \vec{p}_{i2}$$
$$= m_1 \vec{v}_{i1} + m_2 \vec{v}_{i2}$$

Assume that the two pucks collide with one another. After the collision, the first puck has a velocity $\vec{v}_{f1}$ and the second puck has a velocity $\vec{v}_{f2}$.

The final momentum of the system, $\vec{p}_f$ is the sum of the final momentum of both pucks after the collision:

$$\vec{p}_f = \vec{p}_{f1} + \vec{p}_{f2}$$
$$= m_1 \vec{v}_{f1} + m_2 \vec{v}_{f2}$$

The law of **conservation of momentum** states that the total momentum before the collision, $\vec{p}_i$, is equal to the total momentum after the collision, $\vec{p}_f$:

$$\vec{p}_i = \vec{p}_f$$

$$m_1 \vec{v}_{i1} + m_2 \vec{v}_{i2} = m_1 \vec{v}_{f1} + m_2 \vec{v}_{f2}$$

Use the law of conservation of momentum to solve problems in which moving objects collide with one another.

Conservation of Momentum Sample Problem

During the last shot of a billiards game, a cue ball is struck and travels toward an eight ball with a speed of 7.6 m/s. The cue ball has a mass of 0.17 kg, and the eight ball has a mass of 0.16 kg.

PLAYING BILLIARDS

Playing billiards is all about momentum. How will momentum be conserved when the cue ball strikes the other balls?

(a) What is the initial momentum of the system?

(b) The cue ball strikes the eight ball and comes to rest immediately. The eight ball begins traveling in the same direction that the cue ball had been traveling at a velocity of $\vec{v}_{f,eight}$. Write an expression in terms of $\vec{v}_{f,eight}$ for the final momentum of the system.

(c) Use the law of conservation of momentum to determine the velocity of the eight ball after the collision, $\vec{v}_{f,eight}$. Assume both balls slide rather than roll, and neglect any frictional forces from the table.

Solution:

(a) The initial momentum $\vec{p}_i$ of the system is the sum of the initial momentum of the cue ball and the eight ball. The cue ball has a mass of 0.17 kg and an initial forward velocity of 7.6 m/s. The eight ball has a mass of 0.16 kg and is at rest initially, so its initial velocity is 0 m/s:

$$m_{cue} = 0.17 \text{ kg}$$

$$\vec{v}_{i,\,cue} = 7.6 \text{ m/s}$$

$$m_{eight} = 0.16 \text{ kg}$$

$$\vec{v}_{i,\,eight} = 0 \text{ m/s}$$

Use the definition of momentum to solve for the total initial momentum of the system:

$$\vec{p}_i = \vec{p}_{i,\,cue} + \vec{p}_{i,\,eight}$$

$$= m_{cue}\vec{v}_{i,\,cue} + m_{eight}\vec{v}_{i,\,eight}$$

$$= (0.17 \text{ kg})(7.6 \text{ m/s}) + (0.16 \text{ kg})(0 \text{ m/s})$$

$$= 1.3 \text{ kg} \cdot \text{m/s}$$

The total initial momentum of the system is 1.3 kg×m/s in the same direction as the velocity of the cue ball.

(b) Calculate the final momentum of the system $\vec{p}_f$, by adding the final momenta of the cue ball and the eight ball. Since the cue ball comes to rest after the collision, its final velocity is zero. Thus,

$$m_{cue} = 0.17 \text{ kg}$$

$$\vec{v}_{f,\,cue} = 0 \text{ m/s}$$

$$m_{eight} = 0.16 \text{ kg}$$

$$\vec{v}_{f,\,eight} = ?$$

The final momentum of the system is given by

$$\vec{p}_f = \vec{p}_{f,\,cue} + \vec{p}_{f,\,eight}$$

$$= m_{cue}\vec{v}_{f,\,cue} + m_{eight}\vec{v}_{f,\,eight}$$

$$= (0.17 \text{ kg})(0 \text{ m/s}) + (0.16 \text{ kg})\vec{v}_{f,\,eight}$$

$$= (0.16 \text{ kg})\vec{v}_{f,\,eight}$$

(c) Use the law of conservation of momentum to determine the final velocity of the eight ball. The law of conservation of momentum states that the initial momentum of the system equals the final momentum of the system:

$$\vec{p}_i = \vec{p}_f$$

$$1.3 \text{ kg} \cdot \text{m/s} = (0.16 \text{ kg})\vec{v}_{f,\text{eight}}$$

$$\vec{v}_{f,\text{eight}} = \frac{1.3 \text{ kg} \cdot \text{m/s}}{0.16 \text{ kg}}$$

$$= 8.1 \text{ m/s}$$

The final velocity of the eight ball is 8.1 m/s in the same direction that the cue ball had been traveling initially.

How Do the Laws of Conservation of Momentum and Conservation of Energy Describe the Motion of Objects throughout Elastic and Inelastic Collisions?

Perfectly Elastic Collisions

The laws of **conservation of momentum** and **conservation of energy** can be used to describe the motion of objects during collisions. As mentioned earlier, these laws apply only when the system is closed, meaning no net external force acts on it. That is, the total **momentum** of the system will remain constant unless a net external force acts on any object in the system. Note that in the real world, all systems do experience some external forces, mostly due to friction. However, physicists consider these forces negligible when discussing the basic conservation laws.

One type of collision is a perfectly **elastic collision**. During this collision, two objects strike one another and perfectly transfer their momentum and kinetic energy. In other words, both momentum and **kinetic energy** are conserved, or constant, during these collisions.

In most elastic collisions, objects bounce away from one another (as opposed to sticking together). In general, the harder the objects, the more elastic the collision. When thinking of elastic collisions, think of the way steel marbles and billiard balls bounce apart when they strike one another. These objects undergo extremely little compression during the collision, meaning they transfer kinetic energy quite efficiently from one to the other.

COLLISIONS

When a cue ball bounces against another billiard ball, it transfers energy to that ball. What else does the cue ball transfer when it hits the other ball?

Inelastic Collisions and Explosions

In the real world, no collision is perfectly elastic because some energy usually is lost to sound or thermal energy during the collision. In particular, energy is lost when objects compress or stick together during a collision. Whenever energy is lost during a collision, the collision is called inelastic. Note, however, that momentum still is conserved during inelastic collisions.

When considering inelastic collisions, think about two objects that collide, stick together, and then travel as one unit after the collision. Examples include cars that crash into each other and then move as one unit, and football players who grab onto each other during the tackle and move as one unit as they fall to the ground.

Another situation in which conservation laws apply occurs when an object explodes or splits into two separate masses as it moves. For example, assume that a toy rocket is launched into the air. If an unexpected explosion causes the rocket to split into two pieces during its trajectory, the two pieces will travel away with different velocities. In this case, the sum of the momenta of each broken piece must equal the total initial momentum of the rocket. The conservation of momentum and the conservation of energy both apply to this situation.

Solving Problems Involving Elastic and Inelastic Collisions

When solving problems of motion involving elastic and inelastic collisions, it is very important to keep quantities or variables organized, because there are usually multiple masses and velocities (before and after a collision) involved in the problem. To stay organized, use subscripts to represent the different properties of objects in the problem.

If there are two masses, it is a good idea to use numbers or words as subscripts to distinguish the masses. For example, if there is a red ball and a blue ball, represent their masses as m_{red} and m_{blue}. Another good idea is to represent the initial and final velocities of each mass with the subscripts i for *initial* and f for *final*. For example, the initial velocity of the red ball would be $\vec{v}_{i,red}$, and the final velocity of the blue ball would be $\vec{v}_{f,blue}$. When you become more proficient in solving problems, you can use a system of abbreviations for the quantities, such as m_{rr} for the mass of the red ball.

The following steps outline a general prolem-solving method for momentum in one dimension:

1. Identify the objects involved in the system. Then, make sure that no net external forces act on the system. This ensures that momentum is conserved in the collision.

2. List all the known information. Be sure to define the positive direction of motion. Thus, if an object travels opposite to this direction, its velocity and momentum will be considered "negative."

3. Determine the total momentum before the collision and the total momentum after the collision. To determine the initial momentum, add up the momenta of each moving object before the collision. To determine the final momentum, add up the momenta of each moving object after the collision.

4. For inelastic collisions in which the masses stick together, treat the masses as one object after the collision. This final mass is the sum of the initial masses, and it moves with one final velocity.

5. Apply the law of conservation of momentum. To do this, set the initial momentum of the system equal to the final momentum of the system.

6. Solve for any unknown variables. Typically, this will mean solving for the initial or final velocities of objects in the system.

Solving Problems Involving Elastic and Inelastic Collisions: Sample Problem: Bumper Car Collisions

An adult and a child are riding bumper cars on a track in an amusement park. The combined mass of the adult and the car is 300.0 kg, while the combined mass of the child and the car is 200.0 kg. The adult travels at 1.00 m/s to the right across the track. The child travels at 0.50 m/s to the right. The adult's car strikes the child's car and bounces backward at 0.25 m/s. At what speed does the child bounce away after the collision? Assume that there is negligible friction between the bumper cars and the track.

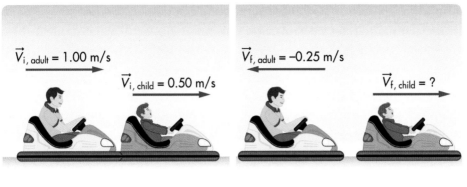

$\vec{V}_{i,\,adult} = 1.00$ m/s

$\vec{V}_{i,\,child} = 0.50$ m/s

$\vec{V}_{f,\,adult} = -0.25$ m/s

$\vec{V}_{f,\,child} = ?$

initial

final

BUMPER CAR COLLISIONS

Two bumper cars with different masses and velocities collide. At what speed does the child's car bounce away after the collision?

Solution:

The two objects in this system are the adult's bumper car and the child's bumper car. Because there is negligible friction between the cars and the track, there are no net external forces acting on this system. This means that the total momentum in the system is conserved.

Define the positive direction of velocity as "to the right." This means that any velocity "to the left" will be considered negative. Here are the values from the question:

$$m_{adult} = 300.0 \text{ kg}$$

$$m_{child} = 200.0 \text{ kg}$$

$$\vec{v}_{i,\,adult} = 1.00 \text{ m/s}$$

$$\vec{v}_{i,\,child} = 0.50 \text{ m/s}$$

$$\vec{v}_{f,\,adult} = -0.25 \text{ m/s}$$

(Since the adult travels to the left after the collision, the last value is negative.)

Determine the initial and final momenta of the system.

Initial:

$$\vec{p}_i = \vec{p}_{i,\,child} + \vec{p}_{i,\,adult} = m_{child}\,\vec{v}_{i,child} + m_{adult}\,\vec{v}_{i,adult}$$

Final:

$$\vec{p}_f = \vec{p}_{f,\,child} + \vec{p}_{f,\,adult} = m_{child}\,\vec{v}_{f,child} + m_{adult}\,\vec{v}_{f,adult}$$

Apply the law of conservation of momentum, setting the initial momentum equal to the final momentum:

$$\vec{p}_i = \vec{p}_f = m_{child}\,\vec{v}_{i,child} + m_{adult}\,\vec{v}_{i,adult} = m_{child}\,\vec{v}_{f,child} + m_{adult}\,\vec{v}_{f,adult}$$

Solve for the final velocity of the child, $\vec{v}_{f,child}$. (Do not be put off by the amount of text in this calculation. The subscripts make the calculation look far more complicated than it actually is.)

$$m_{child}\,\vec{v}_{f,child} + m_{adult}\,\vec{v}_{i,adult} = m_{child}\,\vec{v}_{f,child} + m_{adult}\,\vec{v}_{f,adult}$$

$$m_{child}\,\vec{v}_{f,child} + m_{adult}\,\vec{v}_{i,adult} - m_{adult}\,\vec{v}_{f,adult} = m_{child}\,\vec{v}_{f,child}$$

$$\vec{v}_{f,child} = \frac{m_{child}\,\vec{v}_{f,child} + m_{adult}(\vec{v}_{i,adult} - \vec{v}_{f,adult})}{m_{child}}$$

Now, plugging in the known quantities yields

$$\vec{v}_{f,child} = \frac{m_{child}\,\vec{v}_{i,child} + m_{adult}(\vec{v}_{i,adult} - \vec{v}_{f,adult})}{m_{child}}$$

$$= \frac{(200.0\ kg)(0.50\ m/s) + (300.0\ kg)(1.00\ m/s - (-0.25\ m/s))}{200.0\ kg}$$

$$= \frac{(200.0\ kg)(0.50\ m/s) + (300.0\ kg)(1.25\ m/s)}{200.0\ kg}$$

$$= \frac{(1.0 \times 10^2\ kg \cdot m/s) + (3.75 \times 10^2\ kg \cdot m/s)}{200.0\ kg}$$

$$= \frac{4.8 \times 10^2\ kg \cdot m/s}{200.0\ kg}$$

Solving Problems for Elastic and Inelastic Collisions: Sample Problem: Football Tackle Collisions

Two football players are charging toward one another. The offensive player has a mass of 95.0 kg and is running at a velocity of 6.0 m/s to the right down the field. The defensive player has a mass of 120.0 kg and is running at a velocity of 2.0 m/s to the left down the field. After the players collide, the defensive player grabs onto the offensive player and the two move as one unit as they fall to the ground. Ignore any frictional forces from the air or field.

(a) At what velocity do they move after the collision? Express the velocity in terms of m/s and mi/h.

(b) How much does the kinetic energy of the offensive player change during this collision?

FOOTBALL TACKLE

Two football players collide during a game. How can kinetic energy and momentum be used to analyze this collision?

Solution:

(a) The two objects in this system are the two football players. Any frictional forces from the air or track can be ignored, so there are no net external forces acting on this system. Thus, the law of conservation of momentum can be applied.

Define the positive direction of velocity as "to the right." This means that any velocity "to the left" will be considered negative. Use the subscript "off" for offensive and "def" for defensive. From the problem statement,

$$m_{off} = 95.0 \text{ kg}$$

$$m_{def} = 120.0 \text{ kg}$$

$$\vec{v}_{i,off} = 6.0 \text{ m/s}$$

$$\vec{v}_{i,def} = -2.0 \text{ m/s}$$

(Since the defensive player travels to the left, his initial velocity is negative.)

The final velocity $\vec{v}_f$ is the velocity at which the two players move after the collisions. Determine the initial momentum of the system.

Initial:

$$\vec{p}_i = \vec{p}_{i,\text{off}} + \vec{p}_{i,\text{def}}$$

$$= m_{\text{off}}\,\vec{v}_{i,\text{off}} + m_{\text{def}}\,\vec{v}_{i,\text{def}}$$

To determine the final momentum of the system, note that the two players move as one single mass after the collision. The final momentum is equal to the momentum of this combined mass moving at the velocity $\vec{v}_f$.

Final:

$$\vec{p}_f = \vec{p}_{f,\text{off}} + \vec{p}_{f,\text{def}}$$

$$= m_{\text{off}}\vec{v}_f + m_{\text{def}}\vec{v}_f$$

Apply the law of conservation of momentum, setting the initial momentum equal to the final momentum:

$$\vec{p}_f = \vec{p}_i$$

$$m_{\text{off}}\vec{v}_{i,\text{off}} + m_{\text{def}}\vec{v}_{i,\text{def}} = (m_{\text{off}} + m_{\text{def}})\vec{v}_f$$

Solve for the final velocity of the players, $\vec{v}_f$

$$m_{\text{off}}\vec{v}_{i,\text{off}} + m_{\text{def}}\vec{v}_{i,\text{def}} = (m_{\text{off}} + m_{\text{def}})\vec{v}_f$$

$$\vec{v}_f = \frac{m_{\text{off}}\vec{v}_{i,\text{off}} + m_{\text{def}}\vec{v}_{i,\text{def}}}{m_{\text{off}} + m_{\text{def}}}$$

Now, plugging in the known quantities yields

$$= \frac{(95.0\ \text{kg})(6.0\ \text{m/s}) + (120.0\ \text{kg})(-2.0\ \text{m/s})}{(95.0\ \text{kg}) + (120.0\ \text{kg})}$$

$$= 1.5\ \text{m/s}$$

Thus, the two players will travel at a velocity of 1.5 m/s after the collision. Because this is a positive value and "to the right" has been defined as positive, the players move toward the right.

Second part of the first question is resolved as follows:

In miles per hour, the final velocity is:

$$1.5 = \frac{\text{m}}{\text{s}} \times 3600\ \frac{\text{s}}{\text{h}} \times \frac{1\ \text{km}}{1000\ \text{m}} \times \frac{1\ \text{mi}}{1.6\ \text{km}} =$$

$$1.5 = \frac{\cancel{\text{m}}}{\cancel{\text{s}}} \times 3600\ \frac{\cancel{\text{s}}}{\text{h}} \times \frac{1\ \cancel{\text{km}}}{1000\ \cancel{\text{m}}} \times \frac{1\ \text{mi}}{1.6\ \cancel{\text{km}}} = 3.4\ \frac{\text{mi}}{\text{h}}$$

(b) To determine the change in the kinetic energy of the offensive player, calculate the initial kinetic energy of the player and compare that to his final kinetic energy.

The initial kinetic energy of the offensive player, KE_i, is given by

$$KE_i = \frac{1}{2}m_{off}v_{i,off}^2$$

From the question,

$$m_{off} = 95.0 \text{ kg}$$

$$v_{i,off} = 6.0 \text{ m/s}$$

Plugging in the known quantities yields

$$KE_i = \frac{1}{2}(95.0 \text{ kg}) (6.0 \text{ m/s})^2$$

$$KE_i = 1700 \text{ J}$$

The final kinetic energy of the offensive player, KE_f, is given by

$$KE_f = \frac{1}{2}m_{off}v_f^2$$

From the question and solution to (a),

$$m_{off} = 95.0 \text{ kg}$$

$$v_f = 1.5 \text{ m/s}$$

Plugging in the known quantities yields

$$KE_i = \frac{1}{2}(95.0 \text{ kg}) (1.5 \text{ m/s})^2$$

$$= 110 \text{ J}$$

Thus, the change in kinetic energy is

$$\Delta KE = KE_i - KE_f$$

$$= 1700 \text{j} - 110 \text{ J}$$

$$= 1600 \text{ J}$$

The offensive player gives up 1,600 J of kinetic energy during the collision.

What Demonstrations Can Be Performed That Obey the Law of Conservation of Momentum?

Demonstrating Conservation of Momentum

There are various ways in which **conservation of momentum** can be demonstrated in a classroom. In each demonstration, the key idea is to collide different masses with each other and measure the initial and final velocities of each mass. Then, compare the initial and final momenta of the system.

One demonstration involves the use of an air track. An air track is a rail with "gliding" masses. The masses are said to "glide" on the track because the track supplies small jets of air below each mass, therein reducing the friction between the mass and the track. This is similar to how an air-hockey table works.

Why is it important to reduce the friction between the masses and the track? Recall that **momentum** is conserved only in systems that do not experience a net external force. Systems subject to frictional forces will not exhibit conservation of momentum. To demonstrate conservation of momentum, the frictional forces must be removed.

To use the air track, place different masses on the track and have them collide at different velocities. Then, observe the final velocities of the masses to see how momentum is transferred and conserved in the system.

Another demonstration involves a device called Newton's Cradle. This apparatus consists of various heavy balls or marbles suspended by wires in a horizontal line. When one marble is lifted to the side and then released, it strikes the line of marbles and transfers its momentum through the marbles all the way to the last marble on the far side of the line. This last marble receives this transferred momentum and moves upward. It then falls back down, striking the line of marbles and transferring the momentum back to the original marble, which rises almost to its starting position. The cycle of "back-and-forth" momentum transfer then is repeated. When different combinations of marbles are lifted to different heights, they transfer different amounts of momentum to the line of marbles.

NEWTON'S CRADLE

When the ball at one end collides with the others, only the ball at the other end moves. Why do the other balls in a Newton's cradle not move during this collision?

How Do Net External Forces Affect the Momentum of a System?

External Forces and Momentum

As discussed earlier, **momentum** is conserved in a system only when no net external forces act on the system. In other words, if a force from outside the system acts, it can change the momentum of the system. This fact can be understood by observing Newton's second law of motion:

$$F_{net} = ma$$

If the external force is zero, then the average acceleration of an object in a system also must be zero.

$$a = \Delta v / \Delta t = 0$$

In turn, the change of velocity is zero and the change in momentum ($m\Delta v$) is also zero. Thus, momentum is conserved in a system in the absence of a net external force.

KICKING A BALL

A kick is an external force that acts on a soccer ball. How does a kick affect the ball's momentum?

In the case of an open system, external forces (such as friction) can act. If they do, they may change an object's momentum. Once again, this can be understood by applying Newton's second law of motion:

$$F_{net} = ma$$

Recall that average acceleration is defined as the change in velocity over a change in time.

$$a = \frac{\Delta v}{\Delta t}$$

$$\Delta v = v_f - v_i$$

Substituting this into Newton's second law yields

$$F_{net} = \frac{mv_f - mv_i}{\Delta t}$$

Recall that the initial and final momenta of a mass, m, are defined as

$$P_i = mv_i$$

$$P_f = mv_f$$

Substituting these into the equation yields

$$F_{net} = \frac{mv_f - mv_i}{\Delta t}$$

$$= \frac{p_f - p_i}{\Delta t}$$

$$= \frac{\Delta p}{\Delta t}$$

When the mass m of an object remains constant, a net force F_{net} on an object is equal to its change in momentum, Δp, divided by the change in time, Δt. Thus, any unbalanced forces ($F_{net} \neq 0$) acting on an object cause a change in momentum, $\Delta p = p_f - p_i \neq 0$. In these cases, momentum is not conserved.

This relationship between a change in momentum, change in time, and applied force has useful applications. Consider, for example, the use of air bags and seatbelts in cars. The change in the momentum of the car during a collision is very large. This large change occurs over a small interval of time. This means that the force bringing the car to a sudden stop is also large. In fact, it can injure seriously or kill unprotected passengers. Air bags and seatbelts change the momentum of the passengers over a longer time interval than for the change for the rest of the car. Because this time interval is longer, the force acting on the passengers is reduced greatly. That way, the passengers escape serious injury.

What happens in the case where an external force can and does act on a system? In such an instance, the system must be thought of as an open system so that external forces can act upon it. However, the way a system is defined is often a matter of choice. In such an open system, the change of the momentum within the system is balanced by an equal and opposite change in momentum from outside the system. In the end, all open systems are part of the universe, which is itself a **closed system**. As no external force can act from outside the universe, the total momentum in the universe must be conserved.

Consider the Explain Question

| **How can momentum be transferred during a car collision?**

Go online to complete the scientific explanation.

dlc.com/ca11026s

Check for Understanding

| **Go online to check your understanding of this concept's key ideas.**

dlc.com/ca11027s

STEM in Action

Applying Conservation of Momentum

Many sports, such as baseball, soccer, football, golf, tennis, billiards, bowling, and rugby, involve "throwing" a ball or transferring **momentum** to objects. Which of these sports do you enjoy playing the most? When you engage in these sports, have you ever thought about the amount of momentum you transfer to the ball each time you throw it? It is often desirable to transfer as much momentum as possible to the ball in order to make it travel as far as possible. Think about the last time you threw a ball. Can you think of things you might do to make the ball go faster and therefore have more momentum?

Athletes rarely stand still when throwing an object. Instead, they usually lunge forward to allow the mass of their body to help transfer additional momentum to the object being thrown. This makes objects travel farther at greater speeds. Try this tactic the next time you have to throw a ball as fast and as far as you can.

HOW FAST CAN THE BALL GO?

Why do athletes often lunge forward when they need to throw a ball as fast as possible?

Momentum is conserved in a system except when a net external force acts on the system. When a falling object, like a martial artist or a break-dancer, strikes the ground, the external force of the ground pushes back on the object. This changes the object's momentum, causing it to come to a stop. The amount of force that the ground supplies to the object is proportional to the change in momentum of the object. If a falling object has a lot of momentum, the ground will exert a strong force to stop it on impact. Skilled athletes know ways to reduce the impact of this force. One way is to transfer the downward "falling" momentum into "rolling" momentum when the object strikes the ground.

Dancers also need to utilize an understanding of momentum when carrying out intricate maneuvers, such as spinning. Skilled dancers know how to change the configuration of their bodies in order to increase or decrease their momentum. Changing the momentum of one dancer causes both dancers to either speed up or slow down.

STEM and Conservation of Momentum

A structural engineer is a type of civil engineer who specializes in making structures safe and secure. He or she evaluates the environmental demands that will be place on a structure and ensures that it can withstand these stresses. A structural engineer may be called upon to evaluate existing buildings, make observations of environmental conditions, perform calculations to determine structural integrity, and create new designs and models.

One environmental challenge facing many structures is the impact from flying shrapnel. When shrapnel breaks off during an explosion, it travels at high velocities. This means it has a very high momentum. When it collides with objects in the surrounding area, it transfers its high momentum to those objects. This can cause great damage to those objects. In order to reduce this damage, engineers have developed materials such as the Rhino liner. The liner causes shrapnel to come to a stop when it collides with the material. It is designed to deflect the shrapnel only slightly during the collision. This causes the liner to absorb most of the momentum of shrapnel. To manufacture this liner, scientists and engineers must analyze the momentum of shrapnel from an explosion. This helps them understand how momentum is transferred to the liner. This kind of material can prevent dangerous debris from striking a building or people during an explosion.

Fundamental Forces

dlc.com/ca11028s

LESSON OVERVIEW

Lesson Questions

- What are the ways in which matter and energy can interact?

- What is plasma, and how does it compare with other states of matter?

- How were the four fundamental forces discovered?

- What factors determine the magnitude of the gravitational force between two objects?

- How can atoms and molecules be identified by how they absorb and emit light?

Key Vocabulary

Which terms do you already know?

- ☐ absorption
- ☐ absorption spectra
- ☐ atomic nucleus
- ☐ atomic spectroscopy
- ☐ electron
- ☐ emission
- ☐ gravitational force
- ☐ gravity
- ☐ light
- ☐ mass-energy equivalence
- ☐ matter
- ☐ neutrino
- ☐ neutron
- ☐ Newton's laws
- ☐ nucleus (atom)

Lesson Objectives

By the end of the lesson, you should be able to:

- Demonstrate the various ways in which matter and energy can interact. Describe plasmas and compare them with other states of matter.

- Describe the discovery of the four fundamental forces: gravity electromagnetism, weak nuclear force, and strong nuclear force.

- Solve problems involving the gravitational force between two objects.

- Explain how atoms or molecules can be identified by how they absorb and emit light.

Key Vocabulary continued

- ☐ photoelectric effect
- ☐ quantum
- ☐ quantum mechanics
- ☐ quark
- ☐ solar system
- ☐ star
- ☐ state of matter
- ☐ strong nuclear force
- ☐ subatomic
- ☐ thermal energy

Recognizing the Fundamental Forces

dlc.com/ca11029s

Although you may not realize it, various types of forces are acting on you while you are reading this. What do these forces have in common, and how are they different?

SKYDIVERS

The same force that pulls skydivers toward Earth pulls stars together in galaxies. What other forces are important in the lives of these skydivers?

EXPLAIN QUESTION

How do electromagnetism and gravitation differ from the strong and weak nuclear forces?

What Are the Ways in Which Matter and Energy Can Interact?

Four Forces

Newton's laws describe the way objects react to forces. Many types of forces come up in physics problems. In physics, **matter** and energy interact through just four fundamental forces. The four fundamental forces are the **gravitational force**, the electromagnetic force, the **strong nuclear force**, and the weak nuclear force. All other forces and interactions can be explained in terms of these four fundamental forces.

For example, the friction between two objects, such as a helium-filled balloon resting against a ceiling, is actually caused by the electromagnetic forces between atoms in the balloon and the ceiling. Energy produced in a nuclear reactor is due to the weak nuclear force.

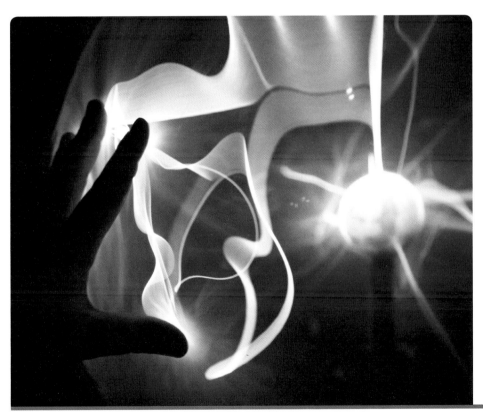

PLASMA BALL
The bright tendrils in a plasma ball move towards the hand because of electromagnetic forces. What other forces are involved in this effect?

Particles, Forces, and Quanta

The four fundamental forces explain how different types of matter interact. Matter makes up the physical world and includes solids such as sandstone, liquids such as water, and gases such as carbon dioxide. Matter also includes plasma in stars and the clouds of dust and gas out in space.

In the 1800s, many scientists thought that the smallest particles were atoms. Near the turn of the 20th century, atoms were discovered to have "**subatomic**" parts, which were named electrons, protons, and neutrons. Investigations of electromagnetic forces by Max Planck and others starting in 1900 showed that energy in **light** and other radiation is emitted in packets Planck called "quanta." In the mid-20th century, protons and neutrons were proven to consist of even smaller particles that were named quarks and neutrinos, identified in part by their quanta. These subatomic particles interact with each other through the fundamental forces.

Not all fundamental particles can interact through all of the fundamental forces. For example, only particles that have an electric charge will experience an electromagnetic force. However, all particles interact through the gravitational force. The study of the behavior and relationships of subatomic particles is called **quantum mechanics**, or **quantum** physics.

The standard model of particle physics is the theory that describes interactions of three of the four fundamental forces: electromagnetism, the strong nuclear force, and the weak nuclear force. **Gravity** is described by the theory of general relativity. Physicists today are working to find an expected, but currently unknown, connection between the standard model and the theory of general relativity.

What Is Plasma, and How Does It Compare to Other States of Matter?

Plasmas

Subatomic particles interact through the four fundamental forces. These forces allow particles to combine into atoms and molecules, and also to form larger objects such as desks and planets. The familiar **matter** surrounding us is made of combinations of countless subatomic particles.

Gases, liquids, and solids are familiar states of matter, but particles can also combine as a fourth **state of matter** called plasma. Plasma is a state of matter similar to a gas. Particles in plasma can move much more freely than in a solid or liquid. In a gas, particles form electrically neutral combinations of atoms or molecules. For example, gaseous carbon dioxide molecules do not have net electric charges.

The difference is that atoms in plasma do have a net electric charge. An atom can pick up an electric charge if it loses an **electron**. An ion is an electrically charged particle. Plasma is like a gas of charged particles: positively charged ions and negatively charged electrons.

Plasmas are not as common on Earth as the other matter states, but plasmas are by far the most common state of matter in the universe as a whole. In fact, the sun and other stars are giant balls of plasma.

PLASMAS

Stars are made of plasma. How is plasma different from a gas?

Creating Plasmas

Plasmas can be created by heating a gas, which gives **thermal energy** to the gas. The added energy allows electrons to escape from the atoms. The atoms become ionized when the atoms gain enough energy and lose electrons. This process means that the temperature of plasmas is often much higher than the temperatures of gases, liquids, or solids.

Lightning is plasma created by friction between moving particles within a cloud. Friction between ice particles and super-cooled liquid causes the ice to become positively charged and the liquid to become negatively charged. This is similar to the charge separation created when a person rubs their socks across a carpet in the wintertime. Plasmas are used inside neon lights and CFLs. "Plasma" TV screens and computer monitors also contain plasma.

PLASMA ON EARTH

During a storm, particles in a cloud become charged and produce a plasma we call lightning. What are some of the properties of lightning?

How Were the Four Fundamental Forces Discovered?

Gravitational Force

Gravity was the first fundamental force to be well understood. Physicist Sir Isaac Newton realized that the force that causes an apple to fall to the ground is the same force that keeps the planets in orbit around the sun. In fact, this force of gravity explains the motions of planets, stars, galaxies, and the universe as a whole. Newton's law of universal gravitation described this force. Gravity is a long-range force. Even objects that are very far apart still interact through gravity. Gravity is an attractive force. Masses, even separated by huge distances, feel a force pulling them towards each other. Earth feels a pull towards the sun, and it also feels a pull toward stars on the other side of the Milky Way galaxy. It even feels a pull toward stars across the universe.

Newton explained how objects can be attracted by gravity, but not fall into each other. As a free body, the moon would move in a straight line unless acted upon by a force. Earth's gravity pulls the moon toward Earth, and this changes the direction the moon moves. It doesn't change how fast the moon is moving. The moon is thus always falling toward Earth, but missing it and staying in its orbit.

Ancient thinkers believed the orbits of the moon and the planets were circular. The astronomer Johannes Kepler showed that they are slightly elliptical. Kepler introduced the first two of his laws of planetary motion in 1609, about eighty years before Newton presented his theory of universal gravitation in 1687. Newton showed how he could derive Kepler's laws by using this theory. This helped scientists of the time understand and accept it.

Physicists now describe gravity with the theory called general relativity. Albert Einstein developed general relativity in the early part of the 20th century. Newton's theory is still a useful approximation for many situations, like describing the orbit of Earth around the sun.

Electromagnetic Force

Researchers once thought electrical discharges and magnetic fields were separate. The theory of electromagnetism linked the two. Electric currents flow and magnetic fields arise because of this common cause.

The electromagnetic force is between particles that have an electric charge. Charged particles also interact with electromagnetic fields. The electromagnetic force explains electricity, magnetism, **light**, and other electromagnetic waves.

In 1795, Charles-Augustin de Coulomb studied the force between two charged objects. He noticed that the closer the charges are, the stronger the force. His measurements showed that the force is inversely proportional to the square of the distance between charges. Coulomb's law was an early statement about the electromagnetic force.

CHARLES-AUGUSTIN DE COULOMB

A French physicist named Charles-Augustin de Coulomb discovered Coulomb's law in the 18th century. How did he uncover this mathematical relationship?

In 1831, Michael Faraday showed an electric current can create a magnetic field. Also, a moving magnetic field can induce an electric current. This led to the invention of motors and generators. Both devices use the relationships between electricity and magnetism to transform energy of one type into another.

In 1864, Scottish physicist James Clerk Maxwell realized the connection between electricity, magnetism, and light. He drew upon the work of Coulomb, Faraday, and others to help him understand it. In 1873, he published a set of four equations that came to bear his name. These give a way to use math to think about and predict these forces.

Today, physicists think of electromagnetism as one of the forces explained by the standard model. This more general theory includes the strong and weak nuclear forces as well.

INDUSTRIAL MAGNET

This equipment uses magnetism to pick up heavy metal objects. How is a magnetic field induced in this equipment?

Nuclear Forces

The nucleus of an atom contains a mix of positively charged protons and uncharged neutrons. The protons in a nucleus repel each other due to the electromagnetic force and their positive charge. The neutrons do not have a charge, so they do not experience an electromagnetic force. The attractive force due to gravity between protons and neutrons is very weak because of their small masses. This fact means gravity cannot hold the nucleus together. What does hold the nucleus together?

The answer is a third fundamental force called the **strong nuclear force**. The strong nuclear force involves gluons that act to hold protons and neutrons together in an **atomic nucleus**. Gluons are thought to be massless particles that can bind quarks together.

FORCES IN ATOMS

Positively charged protons in an atom's nucleus repel each other. What force holds these particles together, along with neutrons, in a nucleus?

The fourth fundamental force is called the weak nuclear force. The weak nuclear force is an interaction between **subatomic** particles that is responsible for radioactivity. The weak force allows protons to transform into neutrons and neutrons to transform into protons. These changes allow an atom's nucleus to change its combination of protons and neutrons. The nucleus emits other types of subatomic particles when the protons and neutrons transform through the weak force. The generation of these emitted particles is called radioactive decay.

GEIGER COUNTER

A Geiger counter can be used to measure the radioactivity of objects. Radioactivity provides the main evidence for the weak nuclear force.

Standard Model

The strong, weak, and electromagnetic forces are described by the theory called the standard model. The standard model was developed during the 20th century after researchers had discovered **quantum mechanics**. The standard model and **quantum** mechanics describe the interactions of subatomic particles through three of the fundamental forces. The fourth force, gravity, does not yet fit into the standard model. Researchers are still searching for a theory that will unify the four fundamental forces.

What Factors Determine the Magnitude of the Gravitational Force between Two Objects?

Gravitational Forces

Researchers currently describe **gravity** using the theory of general relativity developed by Einstein. Newton's law of universal gravitation is still a useful rule though, particularly in typical day-to-day situations, where Newton's theory is often a very good approximation. The law of universal gravitation is useful for describing the **gravitational force** attracting two large, slow-moving objects such as Earth and the sun.

Newton's law gives the force F_g attracting two masses m_1 and m_2 separated by a distance r. The gravitational force between them has a magnitude of:

$$F_g = \frac{Gm_1m_2}{r^2}$$

The gravitational constant G is about 6.67×10^{-11} N $\times$ m^2/kg^2.

Each mass exerts a force on every other mass, meaning that the forces occur as pairs. The force on object 1 points toward object 2, and vice versa.

Gravitational Forces: Sample Problem

Earth has a mass of 6.0×10^{24} kg, and the sun has a mass of 2.0×10^{30} kg. Earth orbits the sun at an average distance of 1.5×10^8 km. Calculate the force of gravity on Earth due to the sun.

Solution:

The force of gravity F_g attracting two masses m_1 and m_2 separated by a distance r has a magnitude of:

$$F_g = \frac{Gm_1m_2}{r^2}$$

G has a value of 6.67×10^{-11} N $\times$ m²/kg². If m_1 is 6.0×10^{24} kg, m_2 is 2.0×10^{30} kg, and r is 1.5×10^8 km (or equivalently 1.5×10^{11} m), then F_g is:

$$F_g = \frac{Gm_1m_2}{r^2}$$

$$= \frac{\left(6.67 \times 10^{-11}\, \dfrac{\text{N} \times \text{m}^2}{\text{kg}^2}\right)(6.0 \times 10^{24}\,\text{kg})(2.0 \times 10^{30}\,\text{kg})}{(1.5 \times 10^{11}\,\text{m})^2}$$

$$= 3.6 \times 10^{22}\,\text{N}$$

The force of gravity on Earth due to the sun is 3.6×10^{22} N directed from Earth toward the sun.

How Can Atoms and Molecules Be Identified by How They Absorb and Emit Light?

Identifying Atoms

Subatomic particles combine into atoms, and atoms combine into molecules. Particles in atoms and molecules still interact through the fundamental forces. The interactions are very complicated and difficult to calculate. Fortunately, the complicated effects have at least one simple result. Each atom or molecule can only absorb and emit particular wavelengths of **light**.

The specific wavelengths depend on the type of atom or molecule. The particular pattern of wavelengths that an atom or molecule absorbs or emits can be used to identify the atom or molecule. This pattern is called the atom's spectrum. For example, carbon atoms absorb different wavelengths than oxygen atoms, and carbon dioxide molecules emit different wavelengths than methane molecules.

The standard model predicts that electrons in an atom can only have certain values of energy called energy levels. The particular values are different for different atoms. An **electron** in an atom can change energy level, but it can only change to one of the allowed energy levels. An electron raises its energy level by absorbing the energy of a photon. It lowers its energy level by emitting a photon that carries away energy.

Atoms only absorb or emit photons of light with energies that match the energy gap between their electron energy levels. The energy of a photon is directly linked to the wavelength of the photon. The result is that atoms can only absorb or emit photons with particular wavelengths.

Spectroscopy

Atomic spectroscopy is the technique that allows atoms to be identified by the light they absorb or emit. The pattern of wavelengths is called the atomic spectrum, so spectroscopy is the method of measuring the spectrum of an atom.

Researchers have developed many techniques for measuring atomic spectra. Researchers can, for instance, put a gas in a closed container and then shine white light on the gas. White light contains light of all visible wavelengths. The gas will absorb only the photons with the particular wavelengths associated with its spectrum. Researchers measure the light that passes through the gas and look for the spectrum of wavelengths that were absorbed and did not pass through. This technique is called **absorption** spectroscopy. The pattern produced is the absorption spectrum.

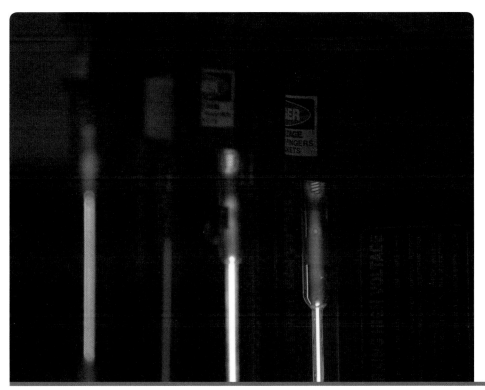

ATOMIC SPECTRA

Different gas elements glow with different colors of light when heated. How are colors of light related to wavelengths?

Another technique is called **emission** spectroscopy. Researchers excite the atoms in a gas, usually by heating them. The excited atoms release the energy they have absorbed by emitting photons. The emitted photons can only have energies equal to the differences in energy levels. By measuring the wavelengths of the emitted light, researchers measure the spectrum of the gas. The pattern is the emission spectrum.

Spectroscopy
Emission Spectrum - Hydrogen

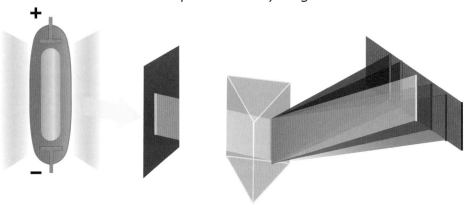

EMISSION SPECTRUM OF HYDROGEN

All elements, including hydrogen, have a unique emission spectrum. What wavelengths of light are part of hydrogen's emission spectrum?

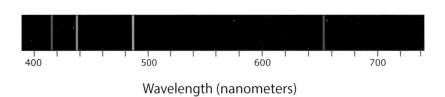

Wavelength (nanometers)

Consider the Explain Question

How do electromagnetism and gravitation differ from the strong and weak nuclear forces?

Go online to complete the scientific explanation.

dlc.com/ca11030s

Check Your Understanding

Can you give an example of a phenomenon that illustrates each fundamental force?

dlc.com/ca11031s

STEM in Action

Expanding Our Way of Thinking: Applying Fundamental Forces

In what ways do the four fundamental forces affect **matter** in the universe? One way that is very important to life on Earth is the role of these forces in the sun. The combined effects of the fundamental forces are more obvious in large, energetic objects such as stars, where atomic nuclei are able to interact more strongly with each other. Stars have a lot of mass, so the forces due to **gravity** are stronger. Because of the **gravitational force**, the material in stars becomes very hot and dense. At these high temperatures and densities, the atoms of matter in the stars are stripped of some or all of their electrons so that they take the form of plasma. In plasmas, the electromagnetic forces have a large effect on the charged particles. Most notably, they cause positively charged nuclei to repel each other. However, at high densities the nuclei still can be pushed close enough together for the **strong nuclear force** to cause the nuclei to fuse. The strong and weak nuclear forces cause the formation of heavier nuclei and radioactive processes that release energy, which powers the sun and gives Earth **thermal energy** and **light**.

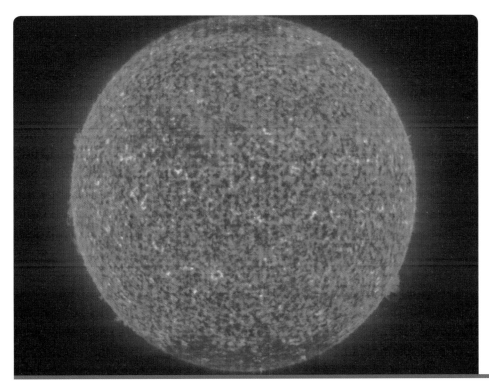

THE SUN

Forces among nuclei result in fusion that releases tremendous amounts of energy. What effects do forces among nuclei have on our everyday lives?

The nuclear forces have no effect between objects that are a large distance apart, and the charges in matter tend to balance each other, so the only fundamental force that significantly affects the objects is gravity. Isaac Newton's theory of universal gravitation is part of what we now call "classical mechanics." Newton's theory, along with the principles of conservation of linear momentum and conservation of angular momentum, describes the motions of planets and stars. Early scientists believed the universe does not change. By the end of the nineteenth century, new discoveries challenged both Newton's theory of gravitation and this static interpretation of the universe. Measurements showed that the speed of light was constant, even within and between moving systems. Newtonian mechanics did not predict this, but the theories of Albert Einstein did. In this way, Einstein expanded upon Newton's theory.

In his theory of special relativity, Einstein considered four dimensions. Along with the usual three dimensions of space, he included time. Because the speed of light is independent of the motion of either the source of light or an observer, both space and time as separate measured properties differ for observers in frames that are at rest or move with respect to the light source. That's because the motion of a reference frame with respect to an observer in another frame slows down time and shortens length within the first reference frame. Treating these dimensions as interrelated—a space-time continuum—replaced the constant, uniform, and separate "space" and "time" of Newton's model. Einstein's general theory of relativity reinterprets gravity, so that matter (noticeably for objects as massive as stars) locally warps the space-time continuum. Orbiting planets move in straight lines in the warped continuum. Even light is affected by gravity in this interpretation—something that does not happen in Newtonian mechanics.

Though he didn't say it in 1915, Einstein's theories also imply that the universe is expanding. Astronomer Edwin Hubble's findings supported the idea of an expanding universe. After the new science of radio astronomy noted a constant background microwave noise in the universe, scientists now had additional evidence to support the big bang theory. From this point of view, the universe started from a single point about 13 billion years ago and expanded into the universe of today. The radio noise is a "fingerprint" left over from the big bang.

Einstein's theories and Hubble's observations changed scientific thought and society. Before, the universe had been viewed as static and as predictable as a clock. Now, it is seen as much more complex. In addition, fields of **quantum mechanics** and cosmology, which have reinterpreted the physics at the atomic and **subatomic** levels and refined our understanding of the four fundamental forces, have also given society new innovations and perspectives in modern physics.

STEM and Fundamental Forces

Physicists use their knowledge of the fundamental forces to explain physical phenomena and solve applied problems. For example, plasmas can be found in stars, but they also exist on Earth in common devices, such as fluorescent lamps and some television monitors. Research into the behavior of plasmas involves advanced knowledge about the electromagnetic force, and in subjects like nuclear fusion physics, physicists study nuclear forces as well, so as to provide insights into the process that powers stars and may provide clean energy in the future.

Another pursuit in physics is to understand why the four fundamental forces are different, and under which conditions they become the same. This is part of an effort to unify the four forces so that all physics may be explained with just one theory. While advances in this field have been made (such as the unification of electromagnetism with the weak nuclear force), a complete unified theory will take a long time, advanced engineering, and a lot of hard work to realize. Researchers will have to be very creative to design experiments that will produce data linking the four fundamental forces.

FLUORESCENT LAMP

A fluorescent lamp contains a noble gas and a tiny amount of mercury vapor. When you turn the lamp on, plasma is produced. What is plasma?

Gravitational Force

Use mechanics equations to solve the problems below.

1. Earth has a mass of 5.98×10^{24} kg, and the moon has a mass of 7.35×10^{22} kg. The moon orbits Earth at an average distance of 3.84×10^8 m. Calculate the force of gravity between Earth and the moon.

2. Mars has a mass of 6.42×10^{23} kg and the sun has a mass of 1.99×10^{30} kg. Mars orbits the sun at an average distance of 2.28×10^{11} m. Calculate the force of gravity between Mars and the sun.

3. Venus has a mass of 4.87×10^{24} kg and the sun has a mass of 1.99×10^{30} kg. Venus orbits the sun at an average distance of 1.08×10^{11} m.

a. Calculate the force of gravity between Venus and the sun.

b. What is the ratio of the gravitational force between Venus and the sun and the gravitational force between Mars and the sun?

c. What factors contribute to such a high ratio?

4. When the mass of one object doubles, what happens to its gravitational attraction to another object of constant mass assuming the distance between the two objects remains constant?

5. When the distance between two objects doubles, what happens to the gravitational attraction between these two objects?

Nuclear Forces

LESSON OVERVIEW

Lesson Questions

■ What are the strong and weak nuclear forces, and how do they work?

■ How are nuclear fission and nuclear fusion related in terms of mass and energy?

■ What are some examples of technological applications of nuclear processes?

Lesson Objectives

By the end of the lesson, you should be able to:

■ Cite evidence that supports the concepts of the strong and weak nuclear forces.

■ Analyze a model of mass-energy equivalence in relation to nuclear fission and nuclear fusion.

■ Describe examples of technological applications of nuclear processes.

Key Vocabulary

Which terms do you already know?

☐ atomic spectroscopy
☐ mass-energy equivalence
☐ nuclear fission
☐ nuclear fusion
☐ strong nuclear force
☐ weak nuclear force

dlc.com/ca11032s

Thinking about Nuclear Forces

What do you think of when you think of nuclear energy? Do you think of a potentially unlimited power source that can supply our world's rapidly increasing needs? Or do you think of the potential damage that could be caused by an accidental nuclear reactor meltdown?

dlc.com/ca11033s

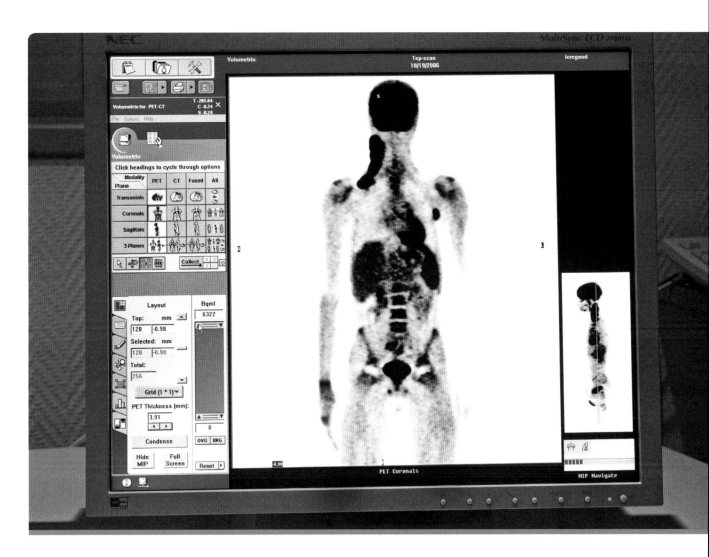

EXPLAIN QUESTION

How do the forces that hold an atom together produce enough energy to power large-scale systems?

POSITRON EMISSION TOMOGRAPHY
Today, we use nuclear reactions to meet energy needs and in applying sophisticated medical technology. What are some of the positive and negative consequences of using controlled nuclear reactions?

What Are the Strong and Weak Nuclear Forces, and How Do They Work?

Nuclear Forces

Four fundamental forces of nature exist in the universe. Before the 1930s, physicists knew of two fundamental forces: gravity and the electromagnetic force. Then they discovered the existence of two more fundamental forces: the **strong nuclear force** and the **weak nuclear force**. The nuclear forces involve the interactions among subatomic particles known as quarks. Quarks are elementary particles that have mass, spin, and electric charge. They combine in pairs and triplets to form composite particles known as hadrons. The most common examples of hadrons are protons and neutrons. Electrons are not known to be composed of any smaller particles.

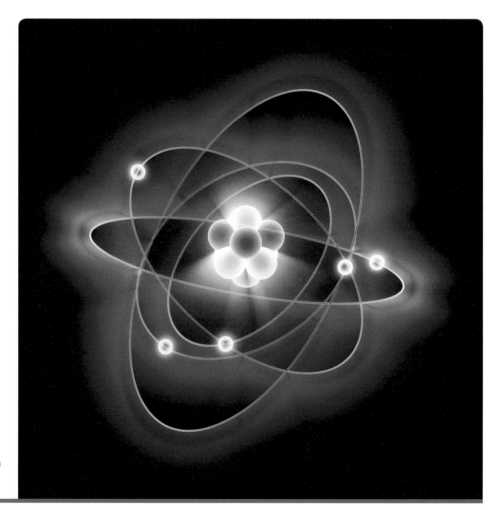

NUCLEAR FORCE

The nucleus of an atom contains positively charged protons and neutral neutrons. What holds protons together in the nucleus of an atom?

Neutrons have no charge, so it is not a surprise that they stay close together in the nuclei of atoms. Protons, however, have positive electrical charges, and thus the electromagnetic force causes them to naturally repel each other. This repulsion is very great because there are so many positively charged particles (protons) that are close together. Experiments in particle physics have established that protons are held in the nucleus of atoms by a force that overcomes the repulsive electromagnetic force. The strong nuclear force is this force that binds protons and neutrons together in atomic nuclei. The strong nuclear force is also what keeps the quarks together in hadrons.

By the middle of the 1930s, the Italian-born physicist Enrico Fermi developed the theory of beta decay. Beta decay happens in nuclei that have many neutrons. In beta decay, a neutron emits an electron to become a proton. Similarly, a proton can emit a positron (a positively charged electron) to become a neutron. Fermi realized that beta decay could not be explained by the strong nuclear force, which would be "too strong" to cause such a subtle decay process. He therefore postulated the existence of a weak nuclear force to explain what transforms neutrons into protons, and vice versa. In the current model for the weak nuclear force, beta decay occurs through the exchange of subatomic particles called W bosons.

To study the nature of subatomic particles, physicists use particle accelerators to "smash" atoms and break them down into their fundamental particles. Atom smashing allows researchers to study the behaviors of the subatomic particles and the forces acting among them. Physicists hope to discover the beginnings of the universe through this analysis.

How Are Nuclear Fission and Nuclear Fusion Related in Terms of Mass and Energy?

Fusion and Fission

Two different types of nuclear reactions exist: **nuclear fusion** reactions and **nuclear fission** reactions. A fusion reaction joins lighter atoms to form heavier atoms. This type of reaction results in loss of mass, which is converted into energy. The most common type of fusion reaction is from hydrogen to helium. Physicists have been unable to sustain fusion reactions in labs because of the extreme temperatures required.

A fission reaction splits apart atoms of heavier elements, such as uranium or plutonium, forming smaller atoms. Just as in nuclear fusion, the mass of the resulting atoms following the reaction is smaller because of released energy. The nuclear reactors in the world today are fission reactors. They produce enormous amounts of energy.

THE USS CALIFORNIA

The USS California is a nuclear-powered guided missile cruiser that was launched in 1971. What atomic reactions are responsible for powering this massive vessel?

Theory of Relativity

Even if they are not studying physics, most people have heard of Albert Einstein, the theory of relativity, and the famous mass–energy conversion equation, $E = 5\ mc^2$. Einstein discovered that energy is equivalent to the mass of an object times the square of the speed of light in a vacuum. In other words, mass is a property of energy and energy is a property of mass. They are linked by a constant (the speed of light). Under the equivalence, mass and energy are interchangeable. A small amount of mass can be converted into an enormous amount of energy. Using nuclear fusion or nuclear fission reactions to join or split atoms results in the release of huge amounts of energy, such as that produced by an atomic bomb.

NUCLEAR EXPLOSION

A nuclear explosion releases enormous amounts of energy. Where does that energy come from?

What Are Some Examples of Technological Applications of Nuclear Processes?

Electricity from Nuclear Power

Nuclear fusion is a "green" alternative to fossil-fuel sources of electricity, as it tends to be more environmentally friendly than traditional means of energy production, such as burning coal. However, physicists have not yet been able to devise ways for fusion reactions to be self-sustaining.

In contrast to nuclear fusion, **nuclear fission** has been used to generate electricity since the 1950s. A nuclear reactor was used to generate electricity for the first time in 1951. There are currently over 440 nuclear reactors in use, with over 60 more under construction. The nuclear reactors in use today produce over 368 GW (i.e., 3.68×10^{11} W) of electricity. The United States has the most nuclear reactors, with more than 100 in operation.

The thermal energy released from fission is used to heat liquid water into steam. The steam is used to drive turbines that produce electricity. While nuclear reactors are capable of producing vast amounts of energy, there also are great risks. Problems with the cooling systems can result in meltdowns. These can release harmful radioactivity into the atmosphere.

USES OF NUCLEAR FISSION

Nuclear fission powers both nuclear bombs and nuclear power plants. How is the energy dispersed differently in these two applications?

In the history of nuclear power, there have been only three major accidents:

- Three Mile Island, United States, 1979
- Chernobyl, Ukraine, 1986
- Fukushima, Japan, 2011

At Three Mile Island, there were no direct fatalities nor any death indirectly connected to the accident. Although the reactor itself was badly damaged, no adverse health or environmental consequences have ever been reported.

The explosion of the reactor at Chernobyl killed 31 people, while many more people suffered radiation poisoning, Contamination from the explosion also had a very adverse effect on the environment.

At Fukushima, three old reactors were destroyed by a tsunami, which disrupted the flow of coolant. After an earthquake, the nuclear reactors shut down automatically and emergency generators were triggered to run the coolant systems. The tsunami, which was a consequence of the quake, caused the emergency generators to flood and break down. This caused the pumps that circulated the coolant to stop. The reactors overheated without proper coolant. The meltdowns did not result in any immediate deaths, although the earthquake itself claimed many lives. A number of workers who came in to help with the cleanup efforts suffered extreme radiation poisoning.

Scientists consider properly maintained nuclear reactors to be very safe. When accidents do happen, they can have disastrous consequences. This underlines the importance of proper safety precautions.

Nuclear Weapons

Nuclear weapons, using nuclear fission, carry the possibilities of extreme destruction. Atomic bombs were used by the United States in 1945, when two separate nuclear bombs were dropped on Japan during World War II.

In the first of the two atomic bombs dropped on Japan, uranium-235 was split. In the other, plutonium-239 was used. In both, a series of nuclear fissions was produced that resulted in a chain reaction with a continuous release of energy. Thousands of people died instantly. Many more suffered the aftereffects of radiation sickness and cancer.

Nuclear bombs were originally carried in bombers, which are large aircraft designed especially for bombing missions. Now, missiles can be launched from the ground, air, or underwater.

AN ATOMIC BOMB EXPLODES OVER NAGASAKI, JAPAN

In 1945, two nuclear bombs were dropped on Japan. What types of reactions create the release of energy emitted by an atomic bomb?

Medical Use of Nuclear Energy

Nuclear energy has more positive applications than negative applications. It is used in medicine in both medical technology and cancer treatments. In nuclear medicine, small amounts of radioactive materials are used to help doctors gather information and treat disease.

In 1902, scientists Marie and Pierre Curie discovered radium, leading to the birth of nuclear medicine. Radiation therapy has been used since the discovery of artificial radiation in the 1920s. Physicians use radiation beams to reduce the size of tumors and prevent their recurrence. They also measure radiation emitted in PET scans to detect tumors, aneurysms, and blood-cell disorders.

Consider the Explain Question

> **How do the forces that hold an atom together produce enough energy to power large scale systems?**

dlc.com/ca11034s

Go online to complete the scientific explanation.

Check Your Understanding

> **Go online to check your understanding of this concept's key ideas.**

dlc.com/ca11035s

STEM in Action

Applying Nuclear Forces

Human understanding of nuclear forces has enabled us to harness the power stored in nuclear bonds. However, the question still remains: How should we use this power? The use of nuclear power as an energy source has the potential to meet the world's growing energy needs, but its use as a military weapon gives a country the capability of vast destruction. The United States used atomic bombs in Japan to end World War II. President John F. Kennedy was ready to use atomic weapons during the Cuban Missile Crisis in 1962. Fortunately these types of weapons have not been used since 1945.

NUCLEAR POWER PLANTS

Nuclear power plants produce large amounts of energy without emitting greenhouse gases. What are some issues with nuclear power?

After World War II, the United States established the Atomic Energy Commission (AEC), whose primary purpose was to control the use and proliferation of nuclear weapons. Its secondary purpose was to encourage the commercial use of nuclear power. The AEC was replaced by the Nuclear Regulatory Commission (NRC) in the mid-1970s. Today, the primary purpose of the NRC is to protect workers and the public from the effects of hazardous levels of radiation.

Learning from 20th-century accidents such as the meltdown at Three Mile Island in Pennsylvania and the disaster at Chernobyl in Ukraine, the NRC has focused on the safety of nuclear reactors in the 21st century. Most developed countries have their own nuclear regulatory agencies as well. When a serious nuclear accident occurred in Japan in the spring of 2011, relatively few injuries or deaths resulted, in part because of effective regulation by the Japanese government.

The benefits of **nuclear fission** power are significant. Nuclear fuel is abundant, and nuclear power plants are relatively cheap to run, although they are expensive to build. The average life cycle of a nuclear reactor is 40 years. Moreover, nuclear power does not emit "greenhouse" gases, although proper storage of radioactive waste products still poses environmental problems. It remains to be seen whether human society is capable of addressing the negative aspects of nuclear energy in order to successfully utilize its many benefits.

STEM and Nuclear Forces

Researchers all around the world are working on developing new and safer ways to harness nuclear energy. Engineers and physicists are attempting to develop self-sustaining **nuclear fusion** reactions. Nuclear fusion is theoretically one of the safest ways to produce clean, inexpensive electricity, certainly much safer than nuclear fission. However the amount of activation energy required to initiate nuclear fusion reactions compared to the amount of energy that we can obtain from those reactions makes their use impractical given the current limitations of our technology.

Right now, all nuclear power is derived from nuclear fission reactions. Nuclear fission reactors are regulated around the world. The goal of such regulation is to prevent nuclear accidents and ensure that reactors provide reliable, clean energy. Close to 4,000 individuals currently work for the Nuclear Regulatory Commission. They monitor the use of radioactive materials in academic, industrial, and medical settings; they regulate nuclear power plants; they oversee the transportation and disposal of radioactive materials; and they are responsible for the security of nuclear power. They have the authority to make rules, issue licenses, enforce rules, respond to incidents, and evaluate facilities. The people who work for the NRC come from a wide variety of educational backgrounds and prior work experiences, but they work together to ensure that this country's nuclear power is used safely and effectively.

NUCLEAR ENERGY GENERATION

An engineer uses special tools to handle fuel rods at a nuclear power plant. How much of the United States energy demands are being met by nuclear power?

Electric Forces

LESSON OVERVIEW

Lesson Questions

- How does the electric force relate to the common contact forces people experience each day?
- What determines the strength of the electric force?

Lesson Objectives

By the end of the lesson, you should be able to:

- Describe how most observable forces ultimately result from electric forces that act between atoms and molecules.
- Show how the strength of the electric force between two charged objects is proportional to the charges and inversely proportional to the square of the distance between them.

Key Vocabulary

Which terms do you already know?

- ☐ atom
- ☐ Coulomb's law
- ☐ electron
- ☐ force
- ☐ molecule
- ☐ negative charge
- ☐ nucleus (atom)
- ☐ positive charge
- ☐ proton

dlc.com/ca11036s

Force Fields

When watching a cartoon or a movie, have you ever observed someone deploy a force field to fend off an attack or harmful substances? Have you ever wondered how a force field really works?

dlc.com/ca11037s

EXPLAIN QUESTION

How can we calculate the strength of the electric force needed to generate a force field?

MAGNETIC FIELD
This depiction is an artist's rendering of a magnetic field shielding a space vehicle. In addition to protecting astronauts from radiation, what are other benefits of this technological solution?

How Does the Electric Force Relate to the Common Contact Forces People Experience Each Day?

The Electric Force

The ancient Greeks noticed that when a piece of amber is rubbed on the fur of an animal, it starts to exhibit strange properties. If brought near small objects such as bits of wool, it attracts the wool. It can also lift the wool off the ground. The Greeks were intrigued by this behavior and offered theories to explain it. They thought a mysterious fluid flowed from the fur into the amber, causing the unusual properties. Their theories were not completely accurate, but they did offer some interesting insights. Today, scientists know that the electric **force** is behind this phenomenon.

STATIC ELECTRICITY ATTRACTING WOOL FIBERS TO AMBER

An electrically charged piece of amber exerts an electric force on small bits of wool. How can amber become electrically charged?

Atoms are made of subatomic particles with different electric charges. The **electron** has a **negative charge** while the **proton**, which is inside the nucleus, has a **positive charge**. Therefore, people do not usually notice the electrical forces between objects. The fluid that the Greeks described is actually a flow of electrons from one object to another. Normally, molecules of a substance are electrically neutral because they contain the same number of electrons and protons.

However, this balance of positive and negative charges is sometimes thrown off. Electrons may flow away from certain atoms (leaving an excess of positive charge) and flow toward other atoms (creating an excess of negative charge). When this happens on a large scale, two objects can become oppositely charged. That produces an electric force that is attractive. It pulls the two charged objects or particles together. By contrast, two like charges such as two negative charges or two positive charges produce a repulsive force. Both are examples of the electric force.

STATIC ELECTRICITY ATTRACTING HAIR TO A COMB

Why does your hair stick up when you comb it on a winter's day?

Another interesting demonstration of the electric force arises when an acrylic rod is given a negative charge and brought near a stream of flowing water. The stream of water is attracted to the negatively charged rod. The electric force deflects it. Even a fast-moving stream of water can be deflected significantly by a moderate amount of electric charge, which shows that the electric force is quite strong.

Common Contact Forces

In the study of physics, common forces such as a person's push are often called applied forces. Applied forces and other common forces such as the normal force are often known as contact forces since two objects appear to be in contact with each other. However, when one examines what is happening on the atomic level between two objects that appear to be in contact, it might be surprising to know that there is never any contact at all. Instead, atoms of one object are simply coming very close to atoms of the other object. Once this happens, the strength of the electric force becomes very strong between the two objects. Therefore, they are repelled away from each other. The electric force can act at a distance and therefore does not require that the atoms ever make contact at all for this repulsive force to exist.

For example, when a person pushes on a wall, there is no actual contact between the person and the wall. The electrons in the person's hand and the electrons in the wall repel one another. The sensation of this repulsive force makes people feel like they are in contact with another object. However, the repulsion from the electric force is so strong that contact cannot happen.

What Determines the Strength of the Electric Force?

Coulomb's Law

It is clear that two charged objects exert forces on each other. Like charges repel one another, and unlike charges attract. How can the strength of these two charges be determined? Coulomb discovered this relationship in the late 1780s. He discovered that the strength of the electric **force**, F_e, between two charged objects depends on two factors: the amount of charge on the two objects and the distance between them. The equation for Coulomb's law is:

$$F_e = \frac{kq_1q_2}{r^2}$$

In this equation, q_1 and q_2 represent the amount of charge on objects 1 and 2, respectively. Charge is measured in units of coulombs (C). The lowercase r represents the distance between the two charges measured in meters. Finally, $k = 8.99 \times 10^9$ N $\times$ m^2/C^2 is a constant of proportionality.

COULOMB'S LAW

Coulomb's law states that the electric force between two objects increases as the charge on the two objects increases and it decreases as the distance between the objects increases. When does Coulomb's law apply?

Examining Coulomb's law, it should be clear that the greater the magnitudes of the two charges, the stronger the electric force. In other words, the magnitude of the electric force is directly proportional to the product of the magnitudes of the charges. However, the reverse is true of the distance between the two charges. As the distance increases, the magnitude of the electric force decreases. Therefore, the electric force is inversely proportional to the square of the distance between the two objects. The equation for Coulomb's law follows what is called an inverse square law. Because force is inversely proportional to the square of the distance rather than just the distance, the strength of the force decreases rapidly as the distance increases.

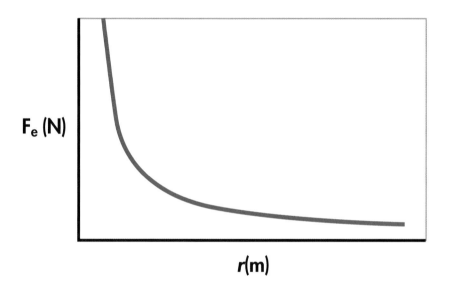

INVERSE SQUARE LAW

Because the electric force is inversely related to the square of distance, it decreases very rapidly as the distance between two charges increases. How could this relationship be represented mathematically?

Coulomb's Law: Sample Problem

Two large metal spheres are given charges. The first sphere has a charge of $q_1 = 2.0 \times 10^{-4}$ C. However, q_2 is unknown. A scientist measures that the distance between the two charges is 0.20 m and the force between the two spheres is 450 N. What is the charge on the second object?

Solution:

Apply Coulomb's law:

$$F_e = \frac{kq_1q_2}{r^2}$$

Every quantity in the law is known except for one of the charges. Thus, rearranging the equation and solving for the second charge yields:

$$q_2 = \frac{F_e r^2}{kq_1}$$

Substituting the known quantities leads to:

$$q_2 = \frac{F_e r^2}{kq_1}$$

$$= \frac{(450\ N)(0.20\ m)^2}{(8.99 \times 10^9\ N \times m^2/C^2)(2.0 \times 10^{-4}\ C)}$$

$$= 1.0 \times 10^{-5}\ C$$

Consider the Explain Question

How can we calculate the strength of the electric force needed to generate a force field?

Go online to complete the scientific explanation.

dlc.com/ca11038s

Check for Understanding

Without using an equation, how would you describe the magnitude of the electric force between two charges?

dlc.com/ca11039s

STEM in Action

Applying Electric Forces

Benjamin Franklin was fascinated by electricity. In addition to his famous kite experiments, Benjamin Franklin invented a set of bells that could detect when a storm was approaching. The apparatus was made with a metal ball that swung freely like a pendulum between two bells. The bells ring because of electric forces.

One bell is connected to a lightning rod that picks up a **negative charge** (electrons) from the surrounding atmosphere. The other bell is grounded to Earth, and therefore, can discharge electrons. Once the first bell picks up enough electrons from the atmosphere, it begins to attract the metal pendulum. The metal ball moves toward the first bell once the electric **force** between the bell and the metal ball becomes strong enough to overcome the force of gravity holding the ball in middle.

When the metal ball touches the first bell, electrons are transferred from the bell to the ball. Now both objects will be negatively charged. Since like charges repel, the ball is now pushed away from the first bell and toward the second. Then the ball makes contact with the second bell. When it touches, it transfers its electrons to the second bell and swings back toward the first. Since the ball no longer contains extra electrons, it is again attracted to the first bell, just as indicated by Coulomb's law, and the cycle repeats.

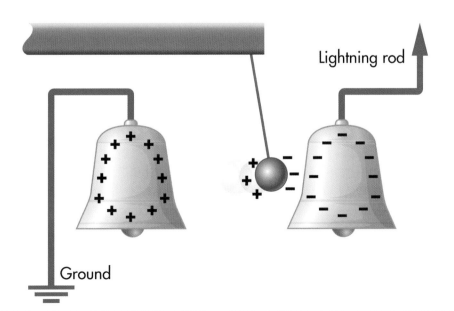

Lightning rod

Ground

BEN FRANKLIN'S LIGHTNING BELLS

Can you use the principles of electric force to explain how Franklin's lightning bells work?

Although Franklin's lightning bells are not used anymore, it doesn't mean there aren't many applications that work on the same principles of electric forces. For example, copy machines, certain air filters, food purification, and paint coating are some. Benjamin Franklin paved the way for many modern-day uses of this simple principle.

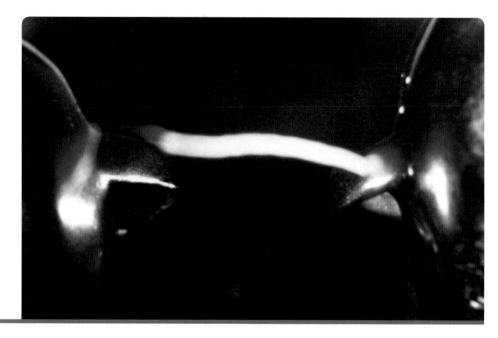

ELECTROSTATIC GENERATOR

How can the principles of electric forces create a spark in an electrostatic generator?

STEM and Electric Forces

When a net charge builds up on an object, it is known as an electrostatic charge. Static in this case means stationary, so the word *electrostatic* can be thought of as electric charge at rest. Like a comb on a dry winter day, a lot of objects can build up electric charge under the right circumstances. Too much built-up charge can lead to electric forces that could be dangerous to electronics and other technological equipment.

Engineers need to take this danger into account when designing systems. For instance, airplane designers must account for the varying amounts of charge that different materials on the outside surface of an airplane pick up from the air. Then they must figure out how to conduct any excess charge away from areas where they could be dangerous.

A computer repair technician is someone who is trained to fix and maintain computers and computer servers. The education required is normally a technical school, and a computer repair technician needs to know the ins and outs of all aspects related to computers.

Computer repair technicians also need to worry about electric charge. Too much static electricity can damage hard drives and other sensitive electronic equipment. Therefore, technicians often wear armbands that ground their hands to an object that can accept electric charge. In this way, they ensure that their hands never build up too much charge as they work on sensitive electronic equipment

COMPUTER MOTHERBOARD

How might static electricity damage a computer's motherboard?

Coulomb's Law

Use electricity and magnetism equations to solve the problems below.

1. Two copper spheres are currently 1.2 meters apart. One sphere has a charge of $+2.2 \times 10^{-4}$ C and the other has a charge of -8.9×10^{-4} C. What is the force between the charged spheres? Is the force attractive or repulsive?

2. Two metal rods in a factory are oppositely charged and placed 8.9 cm apart. One rod has a charge of $+7.5 \times 10^{-7}$ C and the other has a charge of -5.1×10^{-5} C. What is the force between the rods? Is it an attractive or repulsive force?

3. Two charged objects in a laboratory are brought to a distance of 0.22 meters away from each other. If the force between the spheres is 4,550 N and the charge on one object is 9.9×10^{-5} C, what is the charge on the other object?

4. What is the force between two protons that are separated by 1.0 mm? The charge of a proton is 1.6×10^{-19} C.

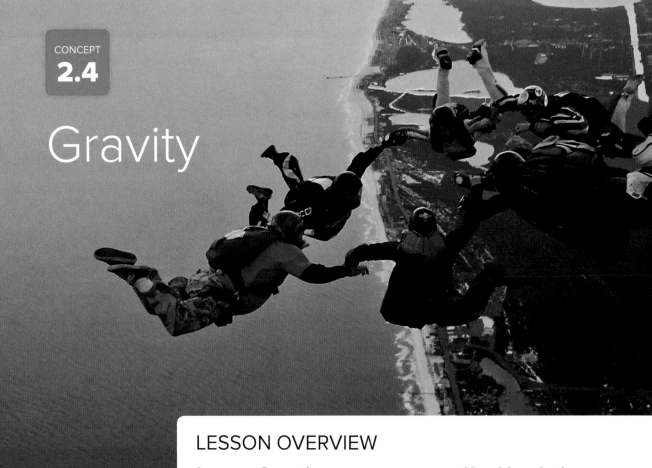

Gravity

dlc.com/ca11040s

LESSON OVERVIEW

Lesson Questions

■ How is the magnitude of the gravitational force between two objects related to their masses and the distance between them?

■ What is Newton's law of universal gravitation?

■ How does Newton's law of gravitation relate the distance between two objects, their masses, and the force of attraction between them?

■ What is the difference between center of mass and center of gravity?

■ How does the law of universal gravitation apply to objects near Earth's surface?

■ How do we solve problems that involve universal gravitation?

■ How do we use Newton's second law of motion and the law of universal gravitation to solve problems that involve the orbital motion of satellites?

Key Vocabulary

Which terms do you already know?

☐ distance
☐ force
☐ gravitational force
☐ gravitational potential energy
☐ gravity
☐ mass
☐ Newton's law of universal gravitation
☐ Newton's laws
☐ orbit

Lesson Objectives

By the end of the lesson, you should be able to:

- Show how the magnitude of gravitational force between two objects is proportional to their masses and inversely proportional to the square of the distance between them

- Identify each term in the equation for Newton's law of universal gravitation and summarize what they mean

- Cite evidence that relates Newton's law of gravitation to the distance between two objects, their masses, and the force of attraction between them

- Differentiate between center of mass and center of gravity

- Interpret how the law of universal gravitation applies to objects near Earth's surface

- Construct solutions to problems that involve universal gravitation

- Construct solutions to problems involving the orbital motion of satellites using the equations for Newton's second law of motion and the law of universal gravitation

Thinking about Gravity

dlc.com/ca11041s

What happens when you jump up into the air? You reach a maximum height and then fall back toward the ground. What happens if you drop a basketball? It falls to the ground because the force of gravity pulls it toward the center of Earth.

THE SUNRISE FROM SPACE
Even though the sun and Earth are far apart, they are very massive. Therefore, they exert a significant gravitational pull on each other. What is the result of this attractive force?

EXPLAIN QUESTION

❚ **What evidence is there that gravity affects Earth and the sun?**

How Is the Magnitude of the Gravitational Force between Two Objects Related to Their Masses and the Distance between Them?

Gravitational Force

There is a **force** that pulls the moon toward the center of planet Earth. This force acts on the moon during every part of its **orbit**. The force is proportional to the masses of both the moon and Earth. This force is **gravity**.

The **gravitational force** is an interaction between any two objects in the universe that have **mass**. The magnitude of the force of gravity is directly proportional to the masses of the two objects. Therefore, the force increases as the mass of either object increases. The magnitude of the force of gravity between Earth and the moon is large, because the masses of the two objects are large.

The force of gravity is smaller when two objects are far apart. Earth is fairly close to the moon, so the force of gravity between them is strong. The moon Io, which orbits Jupiter, has a mass roughly similar to that of the moon. Io is far from Earth, however, so the force of gravity between Io and Earth is weaker.

Gravitational force is inversely proportional to the square of the **distance** between the two objects. As the distance increases, the force becomes weaker. As the distance decreases, the force becomes stronger.

CLOSE PROXIMITY

The moon is so close to Earth that its craters are visible from Earth even without a telescope. How does their close distance affect the gravitational force between these two objects?

What Is Newton's Law of Universal Gravitation?

Newton's Law of Universal Gravitation

The sun exerts a **gravitational force** on Earth. Earth exerts an equal but opposite **force** on the sun. **Gravity** and Earth's momentum keep Earth and the sun in **orbit** around each other. The gravitational force from Earth also holds you to the ground and causes baseballs, rocks, and apples to fall downward.

The English physicist Isaac Newton discovered a simple law that describes the force of gravity between any two objects.

Newton's law of universal gravitation states that the gravitational force between two objects has a magnitude of:

$$F_g = \frac{Gm_1m_2}{r^2}$$

where F_g is the magnitude of the force, m_1 and m_2 are the objects' masses, and r is the **distance** between the two objects. The constant G is the universal gravitational constant:

$$G = 6.67 \times 10^{-11} \, N \times m^2/kg^2$$

SIR ISAAC NEWTON

Sir Isaac Newton discovered the law of universal gravitation. How did he represent gravitation mathematically?

Gravitational Fields

The law of universal gravitation describes the gravitational field of every object. The gravitational field of an object, like Earth, represents the force that another object, like the moon or a rock, will feel due to Earth, divided by that object's **mass**:

$$g_{Earth} = \frac{F_g}{m_{Moon}}$$

$$g_{Earth} = \frac{1}{m_{Moon}} \frac{Gm_{Earth}m_{Moon}}{r^2}$$

$$g_{Earth} = \frac{Gm_{Earth}}{r^2}$$

If another object, like the moon, is at a distance r from Earth, it feels a force equal to the moon's mass times Earth's gravitational field:

$$F_g = m_{Moon}g_{Earth}$$

$$F_g = \frac{Gm_{Earth}m_{Moon}}{r^2}$$

If another object, like the moon, is at a distance r from Earth, it feels a force equal to the moon's mass times Earth's gravitational field at that distance.

Gravitational Fields: Sample Problem

A sphere that has a mass of 1,400 kg sits at one location. At another location 130 km due south, sits a sphere with a mass of 5,800 kg.

How strong is the force of gravity exerted by the second sphere on the first one? Compare this to the force exerted by the first sphere on the second.

Solution:

The law of universal gravitation states that the magnitude of the force is:

$$F_g = \frac{Gm_1m_2}{r^2}$$

We know the mass of the first sphere, m_1, is 1,400 kg. The mass of the second sphere, m_2, is 5,800 kg. The distance, r, is 130 km, or 1.3×10^5 m. Newton's constant, G, is 6.67×10^{-11} N $\times$ m^2/kg^2.

Insert these values and calculate:

$$F_g = \frac{Gm_1m_2}{r^2}$$

$$= \frac{(6.67 \times 10^{-11}\,\text{N} \times \text{m}^2/\text{kg}^2)(1{,}400\ \text{kg})(5{,}800\ \text{kg})}{(1.3 \times 10^5\,\text{m})^2}$$

$$F_g = 3.2 \times 10^{-14}\,\text{N}$$

The first sphere exerts a force of magnitude $3.2 \times 10^{-14}\,\text{N}$ on the second sphere.

The second sphere exerts a force of magnitude $3.2 \times 10^{-14}\,\text{N}$ on the first sphere.

How Does Newton's Law of Gravitation Relate the Distance between Two Objects, Their Masses, and the Force of Attraction between Them?

Forces between Objects

It is important to remember that the **gravitational force** is an interaction between the two objects. The same amount of **force** is acting on both of them. Earth exerts a force on the moon, but the moon also exerts a force on Earth. The strengths of these forces are the same in both directions. We can describe these forces as "equal but opposite."

Newton's law of universal gravitation describes the force between any two objects: Mars and the sun, two distant galaxies, or even you and Earth. The law states that the gravitational force between two objects has a magnitude of:

$$F_g = \frac{Gm_1m_2}{r^2}$$

We can also say that:

$$F_{g1} = F_{g2}$$

The magnitude of the force is the same between the two objects.

The force of **gravity** is always attractive. This means that the direction of the force on each object points toward the other object. The gravitational force on Earth due to the sun points from Earth's center toward the sun's center. The gravitational force on the sun due to Earth has the same magnitude but the opposite direction.

The force of gravity is considered to come from the center of each object. When drawing force diagrams related to gravity, the force vector points from the center of one object to the center of the other.

The gravitational field of an object is represented by a vector at every point in space. This vector points in the same direction as the gravitational force experienced by a second object at that point. The field of Earth points toward Earth's center, since an astronaut at any point in space feels a force due to Earth that points toward Earth's center.

Forces between Objects: Sample Problem

A 1,600 kg object is subject to a gravitational force of 24 N due to a 2,300 kilogram object. What is the **distance** between the two objects?

Solution:

The law of universal gravitation states:

$$F_g = \frac{Gm_1 m_2}{r^2}$$

This equation can be solved for the distance r:

$$r^2 = \frac{Gm_1 m_2}{F_g}$$

$$r = \sqrt{\frac{Gm_1 m_2}{F_g}}$$

The **mass** m_1 has the value 1,600 kg, and m_2 has the value 2,300 kg. The force has a magnitude F_g of 24 N. Newton's constant G has the value $6.67 \times 10^{-11}\ N \times m_2/kg^2$. Inserting these values gives the distance:

$$r = \sqrt{\frac{Gm_1 m_2}{F_g}}$$

$$= \sqrt{\frac{(6.67 \times 10^{-11}\ N \times m^2/kg^2)(1{,}600\ kg)(2{,}300\ kg)}{24\ N}}$$

$$r = 3.2 \times 10^{-2}\ m$$

The two objects are separated by a distance of 3.2×10^{-2} m.

What Is the Difference between Center of Mass and Center of Gravity?

Center of Mass

The sun, eight planets, and other orbiting bodies make up the solar system. Any two bodies in the system attract each other according to the law of universal gravitation. The sun and all orbiting bodies have **mass**.

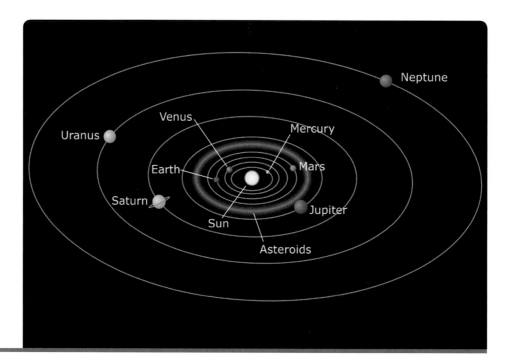

THE SOLAR SYSTEM

The center of mass in the solar system is very close to the center of the sun. How can we mathematically compute this?

The center of mass of a system like the solar system is the average location of the mass in the system. The location of the center of mass is described by a vector that is defined by the equation:

$$\vec{r}_c = \frac{\Sigma_i\, m_i \vec{r}_i}{\Sigma_i\, m_i}$$

where the sum is the number of individual objects of the system, the m_i are the masses, and the $\vec{r}_i$ are the location vectors of the objects.

You can calculate the center of mass of the solar system by taking the sum of the values for the sun and each planet. In fact, the sun has much more mass than the rest of the solar system combined. This means that:

$$\Sigma_i \, m_i \approx m_{sun}$$

and

$$\Sigma_i \, m_i \vec{r_i} \approx m_{sun} \, \vec{r}_{sun}$$

Putting these facts together gives:

$$\vec{r_c} = \frac{\Sigma_i m_i \vec{r_i}}{\Sigma_i m_i}$$

$$\approx \frac{m_{sun} \, r_{sun}}{m_{sun}}$$

$$\vec{r_c} \approx \vec{r}_{sun}$$

The center of mass of the solar system is very close to the center of the sun.

Center of Gravity

The center of **gravity** of a system, like the solar system, is the average location of the **gravitational force** on the system. Physicists use different ways to define the center of gravity. The center of gravity does not always equal the center of mass.

One definition of center of gravity uses the average of the weights of the objects. The weight of an object is simply the magnitude of gravitational **force** on the object. A book's weight on Earth is equal to Earth's gravitational pull on the book. The weight of the book on Mars would equal Mars' gravitational pull on the book.

Imagine a system of objects like the solar system. Object 1 (the sun) has a location vector $\vec{r_i}$. A gravitational force of magnitude w_1 acts on it. This is also true for object 2, object 3, and so on. The center of gravity is:

$$\vec{r_g} = \frac{\Sigma_i w_i \vec{r_i}}{\Sigma_i w_i}$$

Just like the center of mass, the center of gravity of the solar system is very close to the center of the sun.

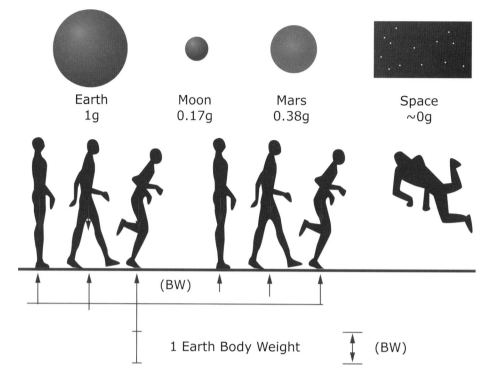

Earth
1g

Moon
0.17g

Mars
0.38g

Space
~0g

(BW)

1 Earth Body Weight

(BW)

YOUR WEIGHT CHANGES

At any given time, an astronaut's mass, like your mass, is constant. Why does an astronaut's weight change when visiting the moon or Mars, or floating in space?

Center of Gravity: Sample Problem

What is the acceleration due to gravity for the International Space Station? The ISS has a mass of 4.5×10^5 kg and is in an **orbit** of about 380 km. Earth has a mass of 6.0×10^{24} kg and a radius of 6,400 km.

Solution:

The **distance** between the ISS and the center of Earth is the sum of Earth's radius and the altitude of the ISS:

$$380 + 6400 = 6780 \text{ km} = 6.78 \times 10^6 \text{ m}$$

Earth has a mass of 6.0×10^{24} kg. Newton's constant, G, has the value 6.67×10^{-11} N $\times$ m²/kg².

The acceleration's magnitude is:

$$\frac{(6.0 \times 10^{24}) \times (6 \times 10^{-11})}{(6.78 \times 10^6) \times (6.78 \times 10^6)} = 8.7 \text{ ms}^{-2}$$

The ISS has an acceleration of 8.7 m/s² downward toward the center of Earth.

Comparing Center of Mass and Center of Gravity

The center of mass of a system and the center of gravity are not always equal. This is because mass and weight are different quantities.

The center of mass and the center of gravity are equal when the gravitational field is uniform. In this case, the gravitational field acts in the same direction and with the same magnitude throughout a system. The weight of an object is its mass times the magnitude of the gravitational field. When the field is uniform

$$\vec{r}_c = \frac{\Sigma_i w_i \vec{r}_i}{\Sigma_i w_i}$$

$$= \frac{\Sigma_i m_i g \vec{r}_i}{\Sigma_i m_i g}$$

$$= \frac{\Sigma_i m_i \vec{r}_i}{\Sigma_i m_i}$$

$$\vec{r}_g = \vec{r}_c$$

In this case of a uniform gravitational field, the center of mass equals the center of gravity.

The center of mass and the center of gravity of a body may actually lie outside the body. These locations depend on the body's shape and the way that the mass is distributed throughout the body. The center of mass and the center of gravity of the solar system are inside the sun. In many systems, however, these points are not inside any of the bodies present.

Comparing Center of Mass and Center of Gravity: Sample Problem

A 6.0 kg object sits at 2.0 m west of a 3.0 kg object. A 4.0 kg object sits at 1.5 m east of the 3.0 kg object. Find the center of mass of this system.

Solution:

The position of the center of mass is a convenient choice for the origin of the frame of reference. The line connecting the three objects is a convenient choice for the x-axis. The direction east is a convenient choice for the positive-x direction.

The center of mass $\vec{r}_c$ is given by:

$$\vec{r}_c = \frac{\Sigma_i m_i \vec{r}_i}{\Sigma_i m_i}$$

The position vectors of the three objects only have x-components, so $\vec{r_c}$ will lie along the *x*-axis.

The sum of the masses is

$$\Sigma_i\, m_i = 6.0 \text{ kg} + 3.0 \text{ kg} + 4.0 \text{ kg} = 13 \text{ kg}$$

The center of mass location is given by:

$$r_c = \frac{\Sigma_i\, m_i r_i}{\Sigma_i\, m_i}$$

$$= \frac{1}{(13 \text{ kg})}\,((6.0 \text{ kg})(-2.0 \text{ m}) + (3.0 \text{ kg})(0.0 \text{ m}) + (4.0 \text{ kg})(1.5 \text{ m}))$$

$$= \frac{-6.0 \text{ m} \times \text{kg}}{13 \text{ kg}}$$

$$r_c = -0.46 \text{ m}$$

The negative sign in the answer indicates that the center of mass sits 0.46 m west of the origin.

How Does the Law of Universal Gravitation Apply to Objects Near Earth's Surface?

Objects Near Earth's Surface

The law of universal gravitation states that spherical objects act as though their masses are concentrated at the center. Since Earth is spherical, objects on its surface are pulled by **gravity** toward its center.

Remember that the strength of gravity is lower when objects are far apart. The change in **distance** must be relatively large to see this effect. If you ride an elevator, your distance from Earth's center does not change much. Even if you climb a high mountain or ride in an airplane, the change in gravity is not significant enough to affect everyday life.

For objects near Earth's surface,

$$F_g = mg$$

Here, *m* is the object's **mass**, and *g* is the acceleration due to gravity. For objects near Earth's surface, *g* is a constant with approximate value

$$g = 9.8 \text{ m/s}^2$$

The value of g does decrease with increasing altitude, so there is, in fact, a small change in **gravitational force** between Denver, Colorado, and New Orleans, Louisiana, for example.

Newton's second law of motion states that the acceleration of an object is proportional to the force on it:

$$F = ma$$

Objects near Earth's surface that experience only the force of gravity have an acceleration equal to g:

$$F = F_g$$
$$ma = mg$$
$$a = g$$

Because of this connection, g is the acceleration due to gravity near Earth's surface.

Objects near Earth's Surface: Sample Problem

What is the force of gravity due to Earth on a 65 kg student standing on Earth's surface? Compare this to the force of gravity on the student due to an 18,000 kg house that is 2.5 m away.

Solution:

The force of gravity on the student due to Earth has a magnitude of

$$F_g = m_{student} g$$

The student has a mass of 65 kg, and g has the value 9.8 m/s². Inserting these values into the equation gives the force magnitude:

$$F_g = m_{student} g$$
$$= (65 \text{ kg})(9.8 \text{ m/s}^2)$$
$$F_g = 640 \text{ N}$$

The force of gravity on the student has a magnitude of 640 N and is directed downward toward Earth's center.

The law of universal gravitation says that the force of gravity on the student due to the house is

$$F_g = \frac{G m_{student} m_{house}}{r^2}$$

The student has a mass of 65 kg, and the house has a mass of 18,000 kg. The distance r between them is 2.5 m. Newton's constant G has the value 6.67×10^{-11} N $\times$ m²/kg². Inserting these values gives the magnitude of force:

$$F_g = \frac{Gm_{student}m_{house}}{r^2}$$

$$= \frac{(6.67 \times 10^{-11} \text{ N} \times \text{m}^2/\text{kg}^2)(65 \text{ kg})(18,000 \text{ kg})}{(2.5 \text{ m})^2}$$

$$F_g = 1.2 \times 10^{-5} \text{ N}$$

The force of gravity on the student due to the house has a magnitude of 1.2×10^{-5} N. This force is more than 10^{-8} times smaller than the force due to Earth.

How Do We Solve Problems That Involve Universal Gravitation?

Using Newton's Law

Newton's law of universal gravitation describes the effect of **gravity** on all objects in the universe. This law, when used together with **Newton's laws** of motion, can describe the motions of all objects: from pebbles to people to galaxies.

GALAXY 4414

The laws of gravity affect the motion of entire galaxies as well as objects on Earth. How does the Milky Way galaxy's gravity affect the sun?

Problems involving gravitation can be solved using Newton's law of universal gravitation.

$$F_g = \frac{Gm_1m_2}{r^2}$$

The law can be used to find the **force** between two objects. For a given force, Newton's law of universal gravitation can be combined with Newton's laws of motion to describe the motion of an object.

Newton's second law states that the force F on an object is proportional to the object's acceleration a:

$$F = ma$$

where m is the object's **mass**.

Using the law of universal gravitation, the acceleration of an object due to the gravitational attraction of a second object of mass m_2 is

$$a = \frac{1}{m}F$$

$$= \frac{1}{m}F_g$$

$$= \frac{1}{m}\frac{Gmm_2}{r^2}$$

$$a = \frac{Gm_2}{r^2}$$

The direction of acceleration is toward the center of the second object.

Using Newton's Law: Sample Problem

A spacecraft is orbiting Mars at an altitude of 110 km above the surface. The spacecraft releases a probe that falls from rest toward the surface. Mars has a mass of 6.4×10^{23} kg and a radius of 3,400 km. What is the acceleration of the spacecraft when the probe is released?

MAVEN ORBITING MARS

In 2013, NASA launched MAVEN, a satellite that orbits Mars, to study the planet's atmosphere. How would releasing a probe affect MAVEN's acceleration?

Solution:

First, find the **distance** between the satellite and the center of Mars. This distance equals the sum of the radius of Mars and the altitude of the satellite:

$$r = r_{Mars} + r_{altitude}$$

$$= 3.4 \times 10^6 \, m + 1.1 \times 10^5 \, m$$

$$r = 3.5 \times 10^6 \, m$$

Mars has a mass of 6.4×10^{23} kg. Newton's constant G has the value $6.67 \times 10^{-11} \, N \times m^2/kg^{-2}$.

The acceleration's magnitude is

$$a = \frac{Gm_{Mars}}{r^2}$$

$$= \frac{(6.67 \times 10^{-11} \, N \times m^2/kg^2)(6.4 \times 10^{23} \, kg)}{(3.5 \times 10^6 \, m)^2}$$

$$a = 3.5 \, m/s^2$$

The spacecraft has an acceleration of 3.5 m/s² downward toward the center of Mars.

How Do We Use Newton's Second Law of Motion and the Law of Universal Gravitation to Solve Problems That Involve the Orbital Motion of Satellites?

Satellites

The **gravitational force** between a satellite and Earth keeps the satellite in **orbit** around Earth. If a satellite were moving around Earth and the **force** of **gravity** suddenly stopped, Newton's first law of motion states that the satellite would continue in a straight line toward the outer reaches of the solar system. Satellites remain in orbit because the force of gravity pulls them toward Earth.

The momentum of satellites keeps them from crashing to Earth's surface. Gravity exerts just enough force to change the direction of a satellite's velocity. This keeps the satellite on its circular path.

If the gravitational force around any planet, star, or other object is known, Newton's second law can be used to describe the satellite's orbit.

SATELLITES

Many satellites orbit Earth to monitor the path of severe weather, such as hurricanes. How do momentum and gravity keep satellites in orbit?

Satellites: Sample Problem

What is the acceleration due to gravity felt by the International Space Station? The ISS has a **mass** of 4.5×10^5 kg and is in an orbit of about 380 km. Earth has a mass of 6.0×10^{24} kg and a radius of 6,400 km.

Solution:

The distance between the ISS and the center of Earth is the sum of Earth's radius and the altitude of the ISS:

$$r = r_{Earth} + r_{altitude}$$

$$= 6.4 \times 10^6 \, m + 3.8 \times 10^5 \, m$$

$$r = 6.8 \times 10^6 \, m$$

Earth has a mass of 6.0×10^{24} kg. The universal gravitational constant has the value 6.67×10^{-11} N $\times$ m²/kg².

The acceleration's magnitude is

$$a = \frac{Gm_{Earth}}{r^2}$$

$$= \frac{(6.67 \times 10^{-11} \, N \times m^2/kg^2)(6.0 \times 10^{24} \, kg)}{(6.8 \times 10^6 \, m)^2}$$

$$a = 8.7 \, m/s^2$$

The ISS has an acceleration of 8.7 m/s² downward toward the center of Earth.

Consider the Explain Question

| **What evidence is there that gravity affects Earth and the sun?**

Go online to complete the scientific explanation.

dlc.com/ca11042s

Check for Understanding

| **Can you describe how the law of universal gravitation can be seen at work during a baseball game?**

dlc.com/ca11043s

S T E M in Action

Applying Gravity

Our current understanding of classical mechanics can trace its origins back to Newton's systematic way of looking at **gravity**. Although Newton and his predecessors laid a solid foundation for our understanding of the cosmos, scientific understanding of the universe did not stop there.

In the early 1900s, Albert Einstein developed a new theory to describe gravity; he called it the general theory of relativity. In this theory, Einstein hypothesized that gravity was due to the warping of space-time. Very massive objects, such as stars and planets, cause the space-time around them to curve, much like a person on a trampoline causes the surface of the trampoline to curve. This warping will cause other objects to "fall" toward the massive objects.

According to the general theory of relativity, more massive objects will cause space-time to curve much more than less massive objects. In addition to warping space-time, very massive objects that accelerate will also generate ripples in the fabric of space-time. Catastrophic events, such as a collision of two black holes, will produce the strongest ripples. These ripples, or gravitational waves, radiate away from the catastrophic event at the speed of light. The waves carry with them information about the nature of the event themselves. If these waves could be detected, they would give scientists valuable information about the nature of neutron stars and black holes. They may even be able to help scientists understand the earliest stages of the formation of the universe.

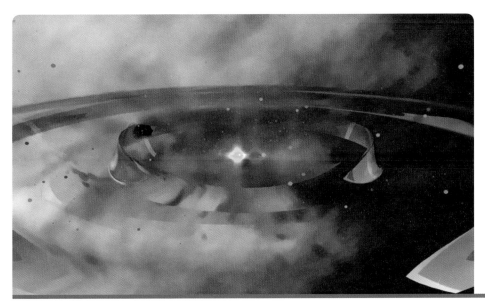

COLLIDING BLACK HOLES

This image depicts a collision between two black holes. What kind of waves would result from such a collision?

STEM and Gravity

Gravitational waves cannot be detected with ordinary tools, such as light or radio telescopes. Instead, scientists and engineers have developed a new technology, called the Laser Interferometer Gravitational-Wave Observatory (LIGO), which is sensitive enough to detect these waves. Currently there are two LIGO facilities, one in Louisiana and one in Washington. Each detector forms the shape of an L with arms that are approximately 4 kilometers long. LIGO detectors have been in operation since 2002. Their goal is to find direct evidence for the existence of gravitational waves.

On February 11, 2016, members of the LIGO team announced that they had detected a gravitational wave emitted from the collision of two distant black holes. This monumental scientific discovery was only possible because of the collaborative efforts of thousands of scientists. This is an exciting time to be an astronomer working with the LIGO scientific community!

Gravitational Fields

Use the gravitational field equations to solve the problems below.

1. A 485 kg sphere sits at 14.0 km due North of a 852 kg sphere. What is the force of gravity on the first sphere due to the second sphere? Compare this to the force of gravity on the second sphere due to the first sphere.

2. Two 2.5 kg bowling balls are 0.50 m apart. What is the force of gravity of the first bowling ball due to the second? Compare this to the force of gravity on the second bowling ball due to the first.

3. A 112 kg man stands 551 m from a building of 25,500 kg. What is the gravitational force of the man due to the building? What is the gravitational force of the building due to the man?

4. A sphere of mass 255 kg is 18.0 meters from a sphere of 895 kg. What is the force of gravity on one sphere due to the other sphere? Compare the force of gravity that one sphere exerts with the force of gravity that the other exerts.

Forces Between Objects

Use the gravitational field equations to solve the problems below.

1. What is the distance between two objects if one (a 185,000 kg object) feels a gravitational force of 0.00200 N due to a 225,000 kg object.

2. Using the universal law of gravitation, solve for r if given two masses (122,000 kg and 225,000 kg) and a gravitational force between the two of 0.00500 N.

3. Using the universal law of gravitation, solve for r between two asteroids with a gravitational force of 0.250 N. Asteroid 1 is 238,000 kg and Asteroid 2 is 489,500 kg.

4. An 800 kg object feels a gravitational force of 0.0001 N due to a 1,200 kg object. What is the distance between the two objects?

Center of Mass and Center of Gravity

Use the center of gravity equations to solve the problems below.

1. A 3.0 kg object sits at 2.0 m west of a 5.0 kg object. A 2.0 kg object sits at 2.5 m east of the 5.0 kg object. Find the center of mass of this system.

2. One 2.0 kg object is 4.5 m north of a second object of 3.0 kg. A third object of mass 17.0 kg is 1.0 m due south of the 3.0 kg object. Find the center of mass of this system.

3. A 1,800 kg car is parked at 40.0 m east of a 8,700 kg bus. A second car of mass 1,700 kg is 3.0 m west of the bus. Find the center of mass of this system.

4. Three asteroids with masses 14,910 kg, 7,250 kg, and 9,510 kg, respectively, are in a row. The first is 512 meters from the middle asteroid, and the third asteroid is 222 meters from the middle asteroid. Find the center of mass of the system.

Force of Gravity

1. What is the force of gravity due to Earth on a 110 kg football player standing on the 50-yard line in his high school stadium? Compare this to the magnitude of the force of gravity on the player due to a 24,000 kg clinic located 92 m away from the football player.

2. A 50 kg boulder stands in a field. What is the force of gravity due to Earth on the boulder? Compare this to the magnitude of the force of gravity on the boulder due to a 6,800 kg backhoe standing 2 m from the boulder.

3. A 760 kg pickup truck is parked 1.5 m away from a school bus of 9,800 kg. Compare the force of gravity of Earth on the truck with the force of gravity of the school bus on the truck.

4. A 25 kg student stands in the playground of her elementary school (38,500 kg), 15 m from the school. Compare the force of gravity of Earth on the student with the force of gravity of the school building on the student.

Using Newton's Law

Use the law of gravitation equations to solve the problems below.

1. A spacecraft orbiting a planet at an altitude of 120 km releases a satellite that falls toward the surface. The planet has a mass of 5.2×10^{23} kg and a radius of 2,800 km. What is the acceleration of the satellite?

2. A satellite orbiting Mars at an altitude of 450 km sends a probe into the atmosphere. Mars has a mass of 6.4×10^{23} kg and a radius of 3,400 km. What is the acceleration felt by the probe due to Mars at the moment it is launched?

3. Calculate the acceleration due to gravity of an object released from a satellite orbiting a planet at 220 km above the surface of the planet. Assume the planet has a mass of 2.3×10^{23} kg and a radius of 1,800 km.

4. Calculate the acceleration due to gravity of an object released from a spacecraft orbiting a planet 250 km above its surface. Assume the planet has a mass of 3.8×10^{20} kg and a radius of 1,250 km.

Acceleration Due to Gravity

1. What is the acceleration due to gravity felt by a spaceship with a mass of 3.2×10^5 kg in an orbit of about 220 km? Earth has a mass of 6.0×10^{24} kg and a radius of 6,400 km.

2. What is the acceleration due to gravity felt by a rocket with a mass of 8.2×10^2 kg and is in an orbit of about 110 km? Earth has a mass of 6.0×10^{24} kg and a radius of 6,400 km.

3. What is the acceleration due to gravity felt by a rocket with a mass of 2.2×10^2 kg and is in an orbit of about 280 km? Earth has a mass of 6.0×10^{24} kg and a radius of 6,400 km.

4. What is the acceleration due to gravity felt by a spacecraft with a mass of 4.2×10^2 kg and is in an orbit of about 95 km? Earth has a mass of 6.0×10^{24} kg and a radius of 6,400 km.

Movements in Space

LESSON OVERVIEW

Lesson Question

■ How are movements of objects in space categorized?

Lesson Objective

By the end of the lesson, you should be able to:

■ Understand the various types of object movements in space.

Key Vocabulary

Which terms do you already know?

- [ ] aphelion
- [ ] asteroid
- [ ] axis
- [ ] celestial sphere
- [ ] equinox
- [ ] gravity
- [ ] meteor
- [ ] meteorite
- [ ] orbit
- [ ] perihelion
- [ ] phase (lunar)
- [ ] revolution
- [ ] revolve
- [ ] rotate
- [ ] rotation
- [ ] satellite
- [ ] solar eclipse
- [ ] solstice
- [ ] tide

dlc.com/ca11044s

Observing Movements in Space

dlc.com/ca11045s

If clocks didn't exist, how would you know what time of day it was? If calendars didn't exist, how would you know what month it was? Ancient Incans did not have clocks or calendars. Instead, they kept their eyes on the sky and watched the movement of the sun, Earth's moon, and stars.

ALTAR ON ISLA DEL SOL
Ancient Incans built altars to their sun god. What are some ways that the sun was important to their civilization?

EXPLAIN QUESTION

How is the way scientists monitor the movements of the sun, moon, and stars today similar to the way ancient cultures monitored them?

How Are Movements of Objects in Space Categorized?

Describing Planetary Motion

An **orbit** describes the movement of a smaller object around a larger object (though objects of similar size can orbit one another). In a solar system, planets orbit one or several stars. In our solar system, Earth and the other planets orbit a star called the sun. A **revolution** marks one complete orbit around the star. Earth takes approximately 365.25 days to complete one revolution around the sun. (This is why every four years is a leap year—we extend the calendar an extra day to account for the additional quarter of a day in Earth's orbit.)

A planet can travel along its orbit in one of two directions. Astronomers describe Earth's orbit around the sun as direct. Orbits in the opposite direction as Earth's are called retrograde. All eight planets in the sun's solar system follow nearly circular orbital paths around the sun. Although the planets do not follow a retrograde revolution, smaller objects such as moons may express this motion.

PLANETARY ORBITS
The planets in Earth's solar system circle the sun in a relatively flat plane. In which direction does Earth orbit around the sun?

The orbits of planets may change due to the gravitational effects from, or collisions with, other objects in the solar system. In our solar system, orbits are determined by the gravitational pull of the sun, which by far has the greatest amount of mass in the solar system. Certainly, the planets have all been impacted by collisions with meteoroids and other bodies, but most of those collisions would not have sufficient force to knock a planet out of its orbit.

If the objects in our solar system are pulling on one another due to the force of **gravity**, one would think that these objects would collide into each another, but another important factor is involved with orbital motion: inertia.

Inertia is the tendency of an object to resist a change in its motion. In other words, an object at rest will not start moving, and an object in motion will not change its direction or speed unless a force acts on it. You have experienced inertia when driving in a car. If the car stops suddenly, you keep moving forward. This is due to inertia. The more mass an object has, the greater its inertia, so you can imagine that the planets have a lot of inertia.

The forces of inertia and gravity must be perfectly balanced for an object to remain in orbit. If the inertia of an object is weaker than the gravitational force between it and another object, the objects will collide. If the inertia of a moving object in space is stronger than the force of gravity with another object, the moving object will continue to move through space rather than enter into an orbit.

When a smaller object collides with a planet in space, the result is generally a large crater on the surface of the planet, rather than a change in the planet's orbit. For instance, 65 million years ago an **asteroid** estimated to be between 170 to 300 kilometers wide struck Earth. It is believed to be one of the biggest objects to strike our planet. It did not change the orbit of Earth; instead, it created the Chicxulub crater and possibly caused the extinction of the dinosaurs.

IMPACT CRATER

When an asteroid or other large space object collides with a planet, it can leave a large crater. What would be felt or seen at the moment of impact?

Collisions in space are not limited simply to objects colliding with planets. Many types of objects in space can experience collisions, and these collisions can impact the motion of the objects due to unbalanced forces causing a change in the direction of motion. For example, an object might spend billions of years in the Kuiper or asteroid belt. Throughout this time, it might come very close to other objects. What happens if two comets or asteroids crash into each other? The collision could cause the objects to break up, forming numerous smaller ones, or the unbalanced forces could cause one or both objects to change directions. A collision between objects in motion could even cause an object to completely change its orbit. For example, astronomers think that collisions between objects in the Kuiper belt can cause objects to move out of the belt and become comets that change their orbit so that they visit the inner solar system. A more potent force for moving one or more planets from their orbits would be the gravitational force of a passing star. The chance of this happening within the next several million years, however, is small.

Gravity affects all matter in the universe. All large astronomical objects are held together by gravity. For example, a galaxy is a huge conglomeration of stars that orbit a massive black hole at their center. Galaxies also attract each other, forming galactic groups. Within galaxies, clusters of stars are held together by the gravitational attraction between the stars that make them up. Two stars can often orbit around a common point in binary star systems. Planets orbit stars and moons orbit planets. All of these objects are held together by gravity. It is gravity that pulls stars and planets into their spherical shapes.

The gravitational pull of an object, such as a moon orbiting a planet, alters the shape of its orbit and the movement of the planet. For example, Earth and the moon are, in effect, a single gravitational system and both orbit around a common center of mass. The moon does not orbit around the center of Earth, but around a point on a line about 4660–4670 km from the very center of Earth. This point is known as the barycenter. This rule also applies to planets orbiting a star, particularly if the planet is big. The barycenter for the Jupiter- sun system is significantly off from the sun's center, just above the sun's surface. Both Jupiter and the sun orbit this point. This tiny orbital path of the sun makes the sun appear to wobble. Astronomers use wobbles of distant stars to detect planets orbiting around them.

Kepler's First Law of Planetary Motion

Johannes Kepler (1571–1630) was a mathematician and an astronomer who changed how scientists looked at Earth's orbit of the sun. In the early 17th century, he published three laws describing planetary motion.

Prior to Kepler, most scientists thought that the orbits of planetary bodies were perfect circles. Kepler used the work of fellow astronomer Tycho Brahe to show that planets' orbits are not circular but elliptical.

An ellipse is an elongated circle. The degree of elongation is called eccentricity. An eccentricity of 0 produces a perfect circle. An eccentricity of 1 produces a line (parabola). An eccentricity between 0 and 1 produces an ellipse. The nearby planets' orbits are closer to 0 than 1, but not zero. Therefore, a planet's orbit forms an ellipse.

Located within every ellipse are two points, called foci. Kepler found that the sun is not located at the center of the ellipse formed by a planet's orbit in our solar system. The sun's center is located at one of the foci.

Thus, according to Kepler's first law of planetary motion, the orbits of the planets are ellipses, and the sun is located at one focus of each of the orbital ellipses.

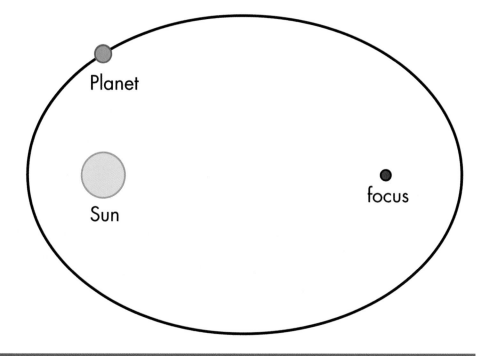

ELLIPSE

Kepler's first law states that planetary orbits are elliptical. What are the defining characteristics of an ellipse?

Kepler's Second Law of Planetary Motion

According to Kepler's second law of planetary motion, the imaginary line joining a planet to the sun sweeps out equal areas of space in equal amounts of time as the planet travels around the ellipse of its orbit.

To understand this law, imagine Earth's elliptical path around the sun. Earth does not travel at a constant speed in its orbit. Instead, the planet accelerates as it nears the point in the ellipse closest to the sun. It slows down as it continues through the part of its orbit farthest from the sun. To visualize this, imagine a line connecting Earth to the sun. As Earth orbits the sun, the line sweeps out equal areas of space within the ellipse in equal amounts of time.

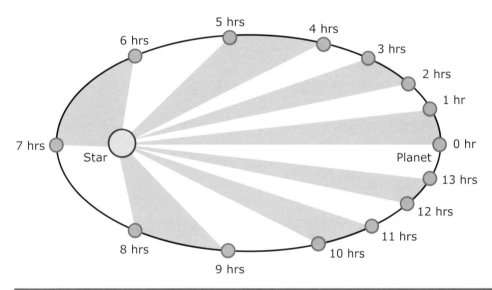

MOVEMENT ALONG THE ELLIPSE

Planets move through an equal area of the ellipse in the same interval of time. How does the speed it takes this theoretical planet to go from point 6 to point 7 compare with the time it takes to go from point 12 to point 13?

Kepler's Third Law of Planetary Motion

According to Kepler's third law of planetary motion, the square of a planet's orbital period (defined as one year for Earth) is directly proportional to the cube of its average distance from the sun.

Kepler's third law examines the relationship between how far a planet is from the sun and the period of its orbit. Consider two planets, Mercury and Mars, orbiting the sun. Mars is almost four times farther from the sun than Mercury is. Thus to complete its orbit, Mars must travel a lot farther than Mercury travels. Mars also takes more time than Mercury to orbit the sun. There is a relationship between distance from the sun and the time it takes to complete a revolution.

This concept can be expressed in mathematical terms as follows:

$$T^2 = \left(\frac{4\pi^2}{GM}\right)a^3$$

The orbital period is represented by T. The distance to the sun can be represented by a. The numbers and variables inside the parentheses represent a constant, so they are sometimes removed from the equation to illustrate more clearly the relationship between orbital period and distance. Kepler's third law can be simplified to the following:

$$T^2 = a^3$$

Returning to the previous example, Mars is about four times as far from the sun as Mercury is. To keep the numbers simple, we'll say that a for Mars is four units and a for Mercury is one unit. Now we can calculate the orbital period for each planet, beginning with Mars:

$$T^2 = 4^3$$
$$T^2 = 64$$
$$T = 8$$

And now let's calculate T for Mercury:

$$T^2 = 1^3$$
$$T^2 = 1$$
$$T = 1$$

Mars's orbital period is eight units, but Mercury's orbital period is one unit. Thus, Mars takes eight times as long to orbit the sun as Mercury takes. In fact, Mercury ($a = 0.4$ AU) has an orbital period of 88 days. Mars ($a = 1.5$ AU) has an orbital period of 687 days, 7.8 times greater than Mercury.

ORBITAL PERIODS

The planets in order from the sun are Mercury, Venus, Earth, Mars, Jupiter, Saturn, Uranus, and Neptune. Which of these planets would have the longest orbital period?

Kepler's third law holds true for both circular and elliptical orbits. Scientists also use this law to estimate the distance between an exoplanet and its central star. (An exoplanet is a planet-like body located outside our solar system.) This law helps scientists to determine if an exoplanet is the right distance from its star to possibly maintain the atmospheric pressure and liquid water temperature range necessary for life as we know it. This range of distance—neither too close nor too far—is called the habitable or "Goldilocks" zone.

Law of Gravitation

Sir Isaac Newton—a mathematician, physicist, and astronomer in the late 17th century—is known for his study of gravity. Gravity is the attractive force between any two objects. Newton discovered that the magnitude of the attractive force depends on the mass of the objects and the distance separating the objects. An object with a larger mass sustains a greater force. At the same time, gravitational attraction is inversely proportional to distance. So as distance increases, gravitational attraction decreases.

Effect of Mass on F	**Effect of Distance on F**
attract with a force of 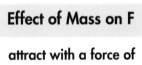	attract with a force of 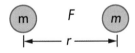
attract with a force of 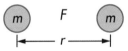	attract with a force of 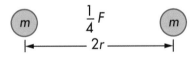
attract with a force of 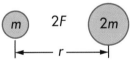	attract with a force of

DISTANCE, MASS, AND GRAVITY

Both distance (*r*) and mass (*m*) affect the force (*F*) of gravity, but in different ways. How would you describe the relationship between mass and gravitational force and the relationship between distance and gravitational force?

Newton's law of universal gravitation thus states that the attractive force of gravity between two objects is directly proportional to the product of their masses. Furthermore, the attractive force of gravity between two objects is inversely proportional to the square of the distance between them. This law can be expressed mathematically by the following equation:

$$F = G\left(\frac{m_1 m_2}{r^2}\right)$$

In this equation, F equals the force of gravity. G equals the gravitational constant (6.67384×10^{-11} N $\times$ m²/kg²). The variables m_1 and m_2 equal the masses of the two objects. The variable r equals the distance between the two objects.

The gravitational force between two objects is directed inward, toward each object's center.

Sample Problem: Law of Gravitation

Earth and the moon are located approximately 3.84×10^8 m apart. Earth's mass is approximately 5.97×10^{24} kg. The moon's mass is approximately 7.35×10^{22} kg. What is the gravitational force between Earth and the moon?

Solution:
To solve this problem, use Newton's law of gravitation. First, identify each variable:

$$G = 6.67 \times 10^{-11} \text{ N} \times \text{m}^2/\text{kg}^2$$
$$m_1 = 5.97 \times 10^{24} \text{ kg}$$
$$m_2 = 7.35 \times 10^{22} \text{ kg}$$
$$r = 3.84 \times 10^8 \text{ m}$$

Now, plug each number into the equation and solve for F:

$$F = \left(6.67 \times 10^{-11} \frac{\text{N} \times \text{m}^2}{\text{kg}^2}\right)\left(\frac{(5.97 \times 10^{24} \text{ kg})(7.35 \times 10^{22} \text{ kg})}{(3.84 \times 10^8 \text{ m})^2}\right)$$

$$F = \left(6.67 \times 10^{-11} \frac{\text{N} \times \cancel{\text{m}^2}}{\cancel{\text{kg}^2}}\right)\left(\frac{4.39 \times 10^{47} \cancel{\text{kg}^2}}{1.47 \times 10^{17} \cancel{\text{m}^2}}\right)$$

$$F = (6.67 \times 10^{-11} \text{ N})(3.00 \times 10^{30})$$

$$F = 20.0 \times 10^{19} \text{ N} = 2.00 \times 10^{20} \text{ N}$$

The gravitational force between Earth and the moon is approximately 2.00×10^{20} N

Rotation

Rotation describes a smooth, circular motion of an object around its center. A planet rotates around an imaginary line through its center called a rotational **axis**. Earth rotates on its axis once a day. Stars and smaller bodies such as moons also **rotate** on their axes. Earth rotates about an axis that tilts at approximately 23.5° from being perpendicular with its orbital plane, though this number varies slightly over time.

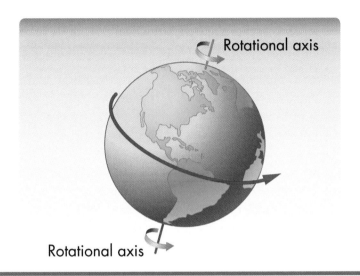

ROTATION

Earth's rotation around its axis is counterclockwise as viewed from above. Is the tilt of Earth's axis constant over time?

A planet's rotation also produces a slight "wobble" in its axis. This wobble, called precession, occurs when the rotational axis changes direction over time. Visualize precession by thinking about a spinning top. When you first spin a top on its axis, it sticks straight up. As it slows down, the axis begins to tip. As the top continues to spin, the axis traces a circle in the air above the top. This is because the top undergoes precession.

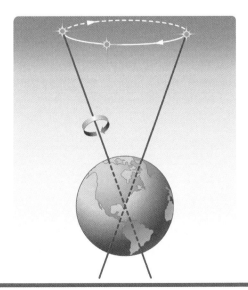

PRECESSION

Precession will change the positions of stars viewed from Earth over time. Which star will precession have the biggest impact on?

Precession of Earth's axis takes about 26,000 years to complete one cycle. This cycle is one of Earth's motions that may have had an effect on past ice ages. However, the speed of precession is not constant, it varies over time. This variation creates another wobble called nutation. Earth's nutation is caused by changes in the gravitational force exerted by the sun and more importantly the moon. This additional wobble has a period of about 18.6 years.

Satellites

A **satellite** describes an object that orbits a larger object, called the primary (non-star). A natural satellite is commonly called a moon. Our solar system contains at least 176 natural satellites. The seven largest satellites include four of Jupiter's moons (Ganymede, Callisto, Io, and Europa); Saturn's largest moon, Titan; Earth's moon; and Neptune's largest moon, Triton.

In our solar system, many natural satellites are tidally locked to their primaries. This means that the same face of the satellite is always turned toward the primary planet. A tidally locked satellite completes one orbit around its primary in the same amount of time as it takes to complete one rotation on its axis. This is why from Earth we always see the same side of the moon.

A TIDALLY LOCKED SYSTEM

The moon is tidally locked to Earth. How does this explain why only one side of the moon is visible from Earth?

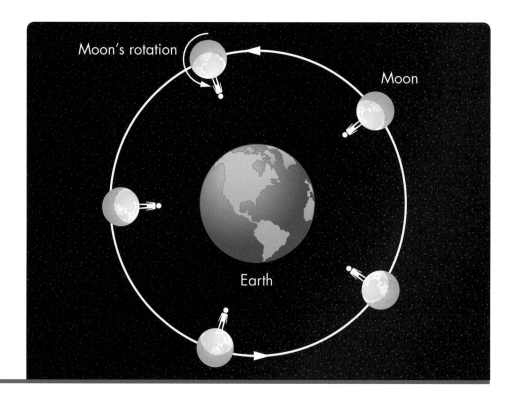

Humans have also made satellites and launched them into space. Sputnik was the first artificial satellite to orbit Earth. It was launched by the Soviet Union in 1957, an event that triggered the space race between the USA and the USSR. During the past half century, humans have launched thousands of pieces of technology into space. The International Space Station is currently the largest operating man-made satellite orbiting Earth.

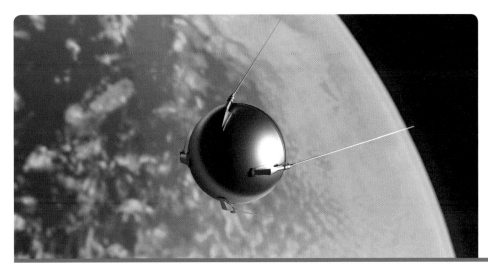

SPUTNIK 1

This was the first artificial Earth satellite launched into orbit in 1957. How can the laws of gravitation be applied to predict the motion of artificial satellites?

Earth's Tides

Water in the oceans rises and falls in a large-scale movement across Earth. Tides represent these slow, gentle changes in sea level with respect to land. In the open ocean, it is very difficult to see the change in water height caused by tides, because sea surface height seldom changes by more than 1 m. The change is more pronounced along the coastline, where water can be seen rising and falling about 3 m every day.

This large-scale, horizontal movement of water across the planet is a result of the forces imposed on Earth by other astronomical bodies in the solar system. Earth is the third of eight planets that **revolve** around the sun. Applying the law of universal gravitation, an object with a greater mass exerts a greater gravitational force than an object with less mass. At the same time, a closer object exerts a stronger gravitational force than an object that is very far away. To visualize this concept, consider the two astronomical bodies that exert a significant gravitational force on Earth—the sun and the moon.

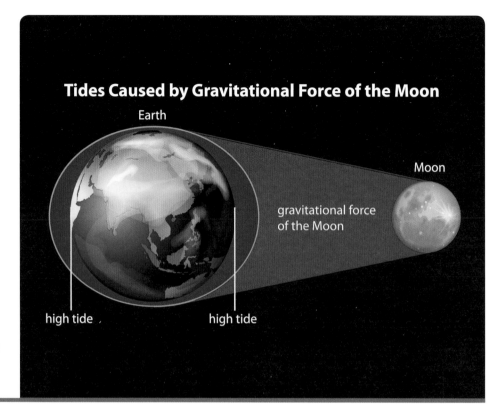

Tides Caused by Gravitational Force of the Moon

Earth

Moon

gravitational force
of the Moon

high tide   high tide

TIDES ON EARTH

The gravitational pull
of the moon and forces
of inertia cause ocean
water to bulge and
form tides. When would
an area experience
high tide?

Earth and the moon do not remain stationary in the solar system. Earth
and the moon revolve around each other around a common center of
mass, called a barycenter. The barycenter is located about 1700 km
below Earth's surface. As the moon and Earth revolve around each
other, the distance between the astronomical bodies varies by as much
as 43,500 km throughout the month. When the moon is closer, it exerts
a stronger gravitational pull on Earth. When the moon is farther from
Earth, its gravitational pull diminishes.

The sun's gravitational pull also influences tides on Earth. The position
of Earth, in its orbit around the sun, varies by as much as 5 million
km. Both the moon and the sun exert powerful gravitational forces on
Earth—the moon because it is so near, and the sun because it is so
massive. However, Earth exerts an even stronger gravitational force
directed inward toward its center. As a result, Earth can hold most
objects with mass close to its surface—including ocean water.

The gravitational tug-of-war between these forces produces the tides along the shore, as well as a global tidal bulge. The tidal bulge is a bulge of water that lifts slightly higher on the planet's surface due to the combined gravitational pull of the moon and the sun. This bulge follows the moon as Earth rotates beneath it every 24 hours and 50 minutes. On the opposite side of Earth, a simultaneous bulge of water forms. The secondary bulge of water is formed by water that is less affected by the moon's gravity pulling on the planet because it is farther away.

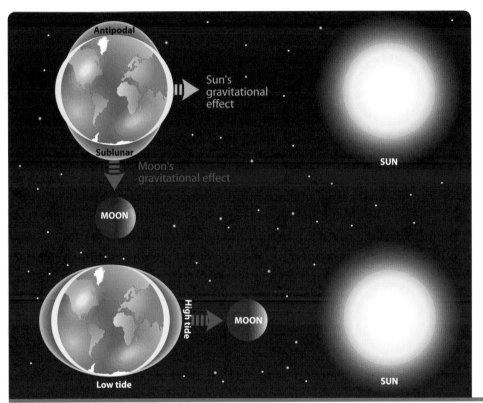

SPRING TIDE

The combination of gravitational pull from the moon and the sun forms an extra-high tide called spring tide. Where is Earth in relation to the sun and moon during a spring tide?

Perihelion and Aphelion

The position of Earth in its orbit around the sun varies by as much as 5 million km. **Perihelion** describes the location in Earth's orbit where Earth is closest to the sun. This point occurs in January. During perihelion, Earth is about 147 million km from the sun. At this time, the sun exerts an enhanced gravitational pull on Earth.

Aphelion describes the position of Earth when it is the farthest from the sun, approximately 152 million km. The planet reaches this point in July. Aphelion is the location in the orbit when gravitational pull from the sun on Earth is least.

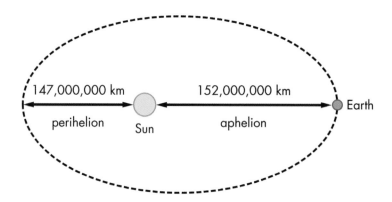

147,000,000 km   152,000,000 km

perihelion   Sun   aphelion   Earth

EARTH'S POSITION

Earth is closest to the sun during perihelion. When is Earth farthest from the sun?

Equinox and Solstice

Recall that Earth tilts at a 23.5° angle, relative to its orbital plane. Therefore, as Earth revolves around the sun, the planet can tilt toward the sun or tilt away from the sun. Twice a year, the planet's tilt is neither toward nor away from the sun. In other words, Earth's axis lines up with the path of its orbit and both poles are equidistance from the sun. This position marks the **equinox**, which happens twice a year. The equinox marks a unique moment when the hours of daylight equal (or nearly equal) the hours of night over a 24-hour day. One equinox occurs on September 22 or 23. This marks the autumnal equinox, or the first day of autumn in the northern hemisphere. The other equinox occurs on March 20 or 21. This marks the vernal equinox, or the first day of spring in the northern hemisphere.

EQUINOX
12 = 12

EQUINOX

An equinox occurs when Earth's axis is not tilted toward or away from the sun. How long would night be at the North Pole during the spring equinox?

Summer Solstice (June 21)

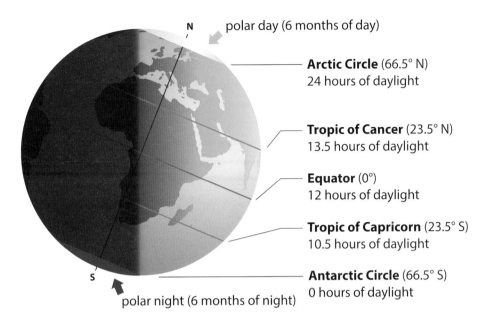

polar day (6 months of day)

Arctic Circle (66.5° N)
24 hours of daylight

Tropic of Cancer (23.5° N)
13.5 hours of daylight

Equator (0°)
12 hours of daylight

Tropic of Capricorn (23.5° S)
10.5 hours of daylight

Antarctic Circle (66.5° S)
0 hours of daylight

polar night (6 months of night)

SUMMER SOLSTICE

During its summer solstice in June, the northern hemisphere experiences the most amount of daylight all year. How much daylight would the southern hemisphere experience on that date?

A **solstice** marks the point when the sun reaches its highest point in the sky when viewed from either the North Pole or South Pole. *Solstice* is derived from the Latin words for "sun" (sol) and "to stand still" (sistere). The solstice marks either the longest day or the shortest day of the year, depending on which hemisphere you are considering.

The northern solstice occurs on June 20 or 21. At this time in its orbit, Earth is close to aphelion, which occurs two weeks later. The northern hemisphere is tilted toward the sun. At this time, the sun is directly over the Tropic of Cancer (23° 26' 16" N latitude) and it is summer in the northern hemisphere. The southern solstice occurs on December 21 or 22. At this time, Earth is close to perihelion, which occurs in early January. The northern hemisphere is tilted away from the sun, which is directly over the Tropic of Capricorn (23° 26' 16" S latitude). At this time it is winter in the northern hemisphere.

In the northern hemisphere, the longest day of the year occurs during the northern solstice. The shortest day of the year occurs during the southern solstice. In the southern hemisphere, the shortest day of the year occurs during the northern solstice. The longest day of the year occurs during the southern solstice.

Earth's tilt, not its distance from the sun, causes the seasons. As Earth revolves in its orbit, the direction in which its axis tilts remains the same. For part of the year, one hemisphere tilts toward the sun while the other tilts away. The hemisphere that tilts toward the sun receives more of the sun's energy because the sun's rays are more direct. This period corresponds to summer for that hemisphere and winter for the hemisphere that is tilted away from the sun. In the northern hemisphere, summer happens around the northern solstice and winter happens around the southern solstice. In the southern hemisphere, summer happens around the southern solstice and winter happens around the northern solstice.

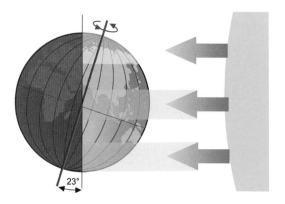 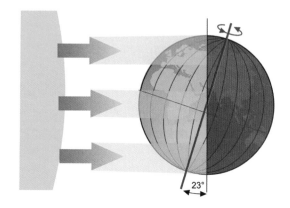

CAUSES OF SEASONS

Earth's axial tilt as it revolves around the sun is responsible for the various seasons of the year. What is the relationship between seasons in the Northern and Southern hemispheres?

Phases of the Moon

The moon does not produce its own light. It acts like a street sign, reflecting light from the sun. The moon revolves around Earth about every 28 days. During this revolution, the portion of the moon illuminated by the sun, when viewed from Earth, changes. The lunar cycle marks these different lunar phases.

The cycle begins with a new moon, a darkened moon without illumination. Four days after a new moon, the illumination increases, producing a waxing crescent. By day 7, the illumination expands to half the moon as viewed from Earth, producing a first-quarter moon. By day 10, the illumination expands to three-fourths of the moon, producing a waxing gibbous. By day 14, the entire moon face as seen from Earth is illuminated, producing a full moon. As the portion of illumination decreases, the lunar phase wanes. By day 18, the illumination decreases to three-fourths of the moon, producing a waning gibbous. By day 22, half the moon is illuminated, producing a third-quarter moon. By day 26, only a sliver of illumination remains, producing a waning crescent. The cycle begins again with a new moon.

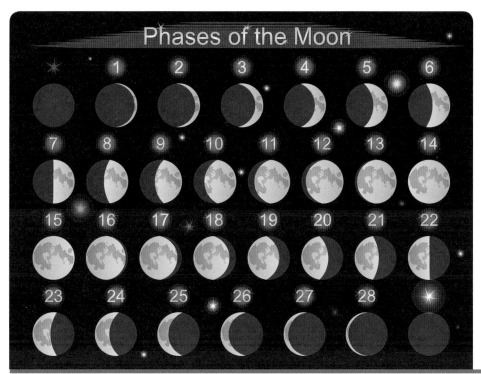

Phases of the Moon

1	2	3	4	5	6
7	8	9	10	11	12	13	14
15	16	17	18	19	20	21	22
23	24	25	26	27	28

MOON PHASES

As the moon orbits Earth, parts of the side of the moon that we can see change. How are these phases related to the moon's orbit around Earth?

Eclipses

Planets and moons revolve in orbits around the sun. Sometimes, these objects align in their orbits, producing an eclipse. An eclipse occurs when one celestial body passes between two others. When this happens, one body's shadow may fall on the other. Earth experiences two main kinds of eclipses—solar and lunar.

A **solar eclipse** is based on the geometry of the sun, moon, and Earth system. When the moon passes between the sun and Earth, it casts a shadow. The shadow directly behind the moon is called the umbra. A wider shadow cast by the moon is called the penumbra. There are three types of solar eclipse. A total solar eclipse occurs when Earth falls within the umbra. A partial solar eclipse occurs when Earth falls within the penumbra. An annular solar eclipse occurs when Earth falls just behind the reach of the umbra.

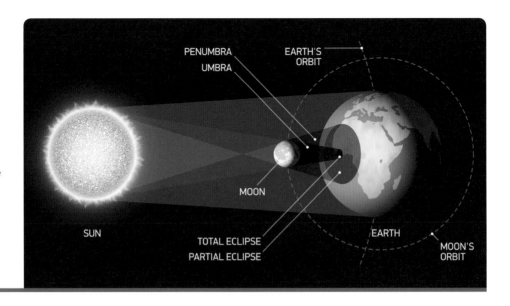

SOLAR ECLIPSE

The moon can appear to entirely block out the sun during a total solar eclipse. Which part of the moon's shadow are you in when you experience a total solar eclipse?

During a lunar eclipse, the moon passes directly behind Earth. As a result, Earth's shadow obscures the moon. A total lunar eclipse occurs when the moon passes through Earth's umbral shadow. Earth prevents sunlight from illuminating the moon. Instead, the moon's outline produces a vibrant red glow. A partial lunar eclipse occurs when a part of the moon passes through Earth's umbral shadow. A penumbral lunar eclipse occurs when the moon passes through Earth's penumbral shadow.

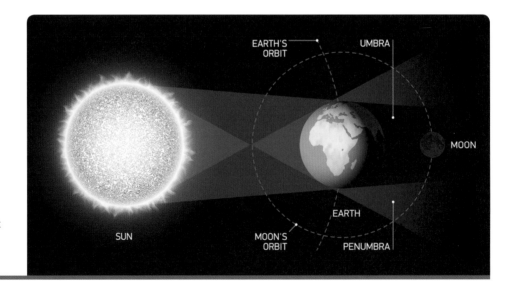

LUNAR ECLIPSE

Earth casts a shadow on the moon during a lunar eclipse. Why isn't there a lunar eclipse every month?

Lunar and solar eclipses do not occur every month because of the moon's orbit around Earth. The moon's orbit is tilted by about 5 degrees, so the only time eclipses occur are when the moon, sun, and Earth are lined up and the moon passes the 0 degree point of tilt in its orbit, called a node. The moon passes a node twice every orbit but the node changes positions relative to Earth and the sun.

Consider the Explain Question

How is the way scientists monitor the movements of the sun, moon, and stars today similar to the way ancient cultures monitored them?

dlc.com/ca11046s

Go online to complete the scientific explanation.

Check for Understanding

A new planet is discovered in the solar system. How could Kepler's laws help describe the planet's orbit around the sun?

dlc.com/ca11047s

STEM in Action

Tracking Movements in Space

Did you know that over 2,000 satellites currently **orbit** Earth? These satellites are used for all sorts of purposes, from transmitting television signals and approving credit card transactions to tracking weather patterns and conducting research in space.

Several kinds of satellites orbit Earth. They are custom-built to complete specific tasks. For example, communication satellites relay telephone messages and radio and television signals. These satellites allow people in the United States to watch live programs from around the world. Weather satellites carry instruments to monitor conditions on Earth. These satellites send information back to scientists who use the information to track conditions on Earth, create weather forecasts, and monitor dangerous storms. Global positioning satellites work in coordination to pinpoint the location on Earth's surface. Members of the military and civilians use these satellites to navigate around the planet.

SATELLITES ORBIT EARTH AT DIFFERENT ALTITUDES

Over 2,000 satellites currently orbit Earth. How do scientists determine the altitude at which a satellite orbits?

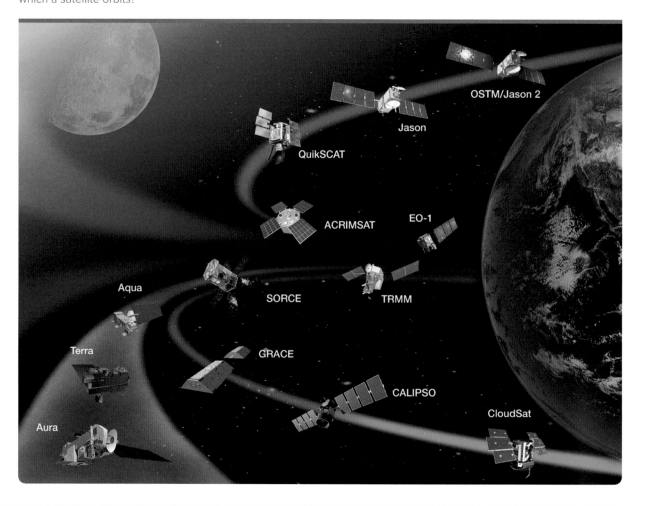

Not all satellites operate at the same height above Earth. Most satellites have a relatively low orbit, 200–1,200 km above Earth. These satellites must travel at approximately 8 km/s to offset the gravitational pull of Earth. Earth imaging and weather satellites often fly at this orbit. The International Space Station also maintains a low Earth orbit of no more than 400 km above Earth's surface.

GOES-13 SATELLITE

Satellite images and data can help prevent loss of life by helping to predict the path and strength of storms. What is the ideal orbit of satellites that are used to track weather events?

The geostationary orbit lies about 36,000 km above Earth. At this distance, satellites orbit Earth once a day. Because the **satellite** orbits at the same rate as Earth rotates, the satellite is always positioned above the same longitude above Earth's surface. Broadcast satellites and relay systems often use geostationary orbits. The benefit of a geostationary orbit is that the satellite remains in the same position throughout the day. To obtain coverage of the polar regions, satellites are placed at low-altitude orbits that move in a near circle, allowing them to gain full coverage of Earth.

Rockets sponsored by governments, and businesses carry satellites into orbit. The rocket must accelerate to more than 40,000 km/h to escape Earth's **gravity**. The rocket is programmed to bring its payload to the proper altitude in space. When in place, the satellite is released. It must maintain an orbital velocity to prevent it from being pulled toward Earth. A typical orbital velocity is 8 km/s at 242 km above Earth. Satellite velocity at a lower orbit must be faster. Once in space, satellites experience no air resistance.

STEM and Movements in Space

Satellites have a variety of uses, including some very important ones, which means they must always be operating effectively. Whose job is it to make sure a satellite works? Aerospace engineers are some of the people responsible for helping to get a satellite into space and making sure it works when it gets there. These individuals are tasked with planning the launch of new satellites into space and monitoring the health and status of satellites already in space. This includes making sure satellites launch properly, are placed in the proper position, and that they follow the correct orbital path. It also involves making sure to time the launch properly, so it does not interfere with the orbits of other satellites and objects in space. Launching a satellite into space is an expensive operation, so it's important for aerospace engineers to get all of the data correct.

TOPEX/POSEIDON SATELLITE

Thousands of satellites orbit Earth, supporting modern technology. What threats face satellites in orbit?

The work of aerospace engineers can start nearly a decade before a new satellite is launched. They must determine what type of signals and data the satellite needs to operate and conduct an orbital analysis to help position the satellite, so it can operate effectively. Once a satellite has been launched and positioned in space, they must send signals to the satellite to confirm it is functioning properly. Through special computer programs, aerospace engineers can program changes into a satellite's software and fix any digital problems that may have occurred. Once a satellite has been positioned and is determined to be working properly, aerospace engineers routinely monitor the health of the satellite by analyzing the data it transmits and sending test signals to make sure it responds properly.

Even if a satellite operations engineer does everything correctly, sometimes a satellite can still malfunction. Aerospace engineers must be on call day and night to help fix a problem, should one arise. For example, if a major network loses its satellite signal or a navigation system receives faulty data, a satellite operations engineer may be called in to see if there's a problem with the satellite.

ASTRONAUT WORKING ON A SATELLITE IN SPACE

Some satellites can be accessed from low Earth orbit for maintenance. Why are geostationary satellites less accessible?

Putting Kepler's Third Law Into Motion

Use the simplified version of Kepler's Third Law ($T^2 = a^3$) to solve the problems below.

1. Suppose an asteroid orbits the sun with a mean radius 11 times that of Earth. What is the period of the asteroid?

2. We know that the orbital period of Haley's Comet is about 75 years. What is its mean radius from the sun as compared to Earth?

3. A student is celebrating her 17th birthday today. Mars is 1.52 times farther from the sun than Earth. How old would she be in "Martian years" if she had lived her entire life in a space colony on Mars?

4. Neptune's orbit period is 164.8 Earth years. What is its orbital radius compared to Earth's?

5. Why is Kepler's Third Law considered a law instead of a theory?

Law of Gravity

Use the equation for Newton's law of gravity to solve the problems below. Use the chart The Planets: Orbits and Physical Characteristics to obtain any information necessary to solve each problem.

1. The planets are held in orbit by the gravitational pull of the sun. What is the gravitational force between Earth and the sun? The sun's mass is approximately 1.9891×10^{30} kilograms.

2. What is the gravitational force between the sun and the planet Jupiter? The sun's mass is approximately 1.9891×10^{30} kilograms.

3. Mass is a measure of the amount of matter that makes up an object. Weight is a function of the gravitational force on an object. You can calculate your weight—i.e., Earth's gravitational force on your body—in units of newtons using the equation for Newton's law of gravity. Your mass (i.e., your weight in kilograms) is m_1, and Earth's mass is m_2. Your weight on the surface of a planet is based on your distance from the planet's center, so r equals Earth's mean equatorial radius (in meters). What is the gravitational force of the planet Earth on your body? In other words, what is your weight in newtons?

4. You would have the same mass no matter where you are in the universe, but if you could travel to other planets, your weight would be different than it is on Earth. You can calculate your weight on other planets using the equation for Newton's law of gravity. The gravitational constant stays the same. Your mass (i.e., your weight in kilograms) is m_1, and the mass of the planet is m_2. Your weight on the surface of a planet is based on your distance from the planet's center, so r equals the mean equatorial radius (in meters) of the planet. What would be the gravitational force of the planet Jupiter on your body? In other words, what would be your weight in newtons on Jupiter?

5. In order to compare your weight on Jupiter to your weight on Earth, you can use dimensional analysis to convert your weight in Newtons on Jupiter to Earth pounds. On Earth, 1 Newton is equivalent to about 0.225 pounds. How many Earth pounds would you weigh on Jupiter?

CONCEPT
3.1

Types of Energy

LESSON OVERVIEW

Lesson Questions

■ What are two main types of energy, and what are some examples of these types of energy?

■ How does the kinetic energy of an object relate to its mass and velocity?

■ What are some examples of conversions between kinetic energy and potential energy in the world around you?

Lesson Objectives

By the end of the lesson, you should be able to:

■ Analyze devices that convert one form of energy into another form of energy, such as conversions between kinetic and potential energy.

■ Solve problems involving the calculation of kinetic energy.

Key Vocabulary

Which terms do you already know?

☐ chemical potential energy
☐ elastic potential energy
☐ elastic rebound
☐ electric potential energy
☐ energy
☐ gravitational potential energy
☐ kinetic energy
☐ mass
☐ potential energy

dlc.com/ca11048s

Lesson Objectives continued

- Compare examples of conversions between kinetic energy and potential energy.
- Construct models of energy depicted as either motions of particles or energy stored in fields.
- Design solutions to real-world problems by using the engineering method.
- Evaluate design solutions according to constraints such as cost, safety, reliability, and aesthetics, and possible social, cultural, and environmental impacts.

Harnessing Wind Energy

Have you ever considered where the energy comes from to charge your everyday technology devices, such as your cell phone? Electrical energy flowing from the outlet in your house is transmitted to your home from a power plant, but what natural resource does the power plant use to generate electrical energy for your home?

dlc.com/ca11049s

EXPLAIN QUESTION

How can you increase the efficiency of a wind turbine when converting wind energy to electrical energy?

WIND FARM

Wind turbines convert the kinetic energy from moving air to mechanical energy. What is the mechanical energy converted to?

What Are Two Main Types of Energy, and What Are Some Examples of These Types of Energy?

Kinetic Energy

Kinetic energy is the **energy** of motion. All moving objects, from tiny molecules to huge bodies in space, have kinetic energy. The kinetic energy of an object is proportional to its **mass** and the square of its velocity. Kinetic energy, denoted as KE, is described by the following equation:

$$KE = \frac{1}{2}mv^2$$

The most obvious examples of kinetic energy are the motions of bodies through water, on land, or through the sky. This includes fish swimming, boats sailing, people running, cars traveling, fan blades rotating, carousels spinning, birds flying, and balls moving in arced paths through the air.

However, there is kinetic energy in many objects that is not as easily noticeable. When a guitar string is plucked, it vibrates very quickly. The guitar string has kinetic energy, and it transfers this energy to the molecules of air around it, causing them to vibrate as well. In fact, all sound is the result of vibrating molecules in the air. This form of kinetic energy is sound energy.

Consider the motion of atoms in a person's hands. When people rub their hands together, their skin feels warm as a result of the increase in kinetic energy. The rubbing motion causes atoms at the surface of the skin to move faster, increasing their kinetic energy. This increase in kinetic energy causes an increase in the temperature of the skin. In fact, temperature is a measure of how quickly atoms in a substance are moving. This form of kinetic energy is called thermal energy.

© Discovery Education | www.discoveryeducation.com ● Image: aijiro / Shutterstock

WARM YOUR HANDS

The kinetic energy from rubbing your hands can make them warm. How does kinetic energy generate warmth?

Elastic Potential Energy

Potential energy is the energy of an object due to its location, shape, or position. There are many forms of potential energy. Perhaps the easiest to understand intuitively is elastic potential energy. When a rubber band is stretched, it has **elastic potential energy**. Think of the rubber band as having the "potential" to snap into motion if it were suddenly released from this position. Furthermore, the degree to which the rubber band is stretched will determine the intensity with which the band will snap when released. The farther the rubber band is stretched, the more potential energy it has. In much the same way, springs store potential energy. When a spring is stretched or compressed, it tries to restore itself to its equilibrium position. The elastic potential energy of a spring is given by the equation:

$$PE_{elastic} = \frac{1}{2}kx^2$$

where k is the spring constant, which depends on the particular properties of the spring. The variable x is the distance the spring is compressed or stretched.

Gravitational Potential Energy

Take a pencil and lift it as high up in the air as possible. When the pencil is released, it will fall toward the ground. Think of lifting the pencil up into the air in the same way as stretching a rubber band. The lifted pencil has the potential to begin moving once released, similar to a rubber band that has been stretched. When an object is lifted, it is moved against the force of gravity, which acts to pull objects downward toward Earth's surface. Similarly, when a rubber band is stretched, it is moved against the elastic force that acts to keep the rubber band at its equilibrium, or rest, position. The more an object is lifted against the force of gravity, the more energy it will have once it is released. **Gravitational potential energy** is said to be "stored" in the object when the object is lifted.

MAXWELL'S WHEEL

Pushing the wheel up to one side of this apparatus increases its gravitational potential energy. The force of gravity then pulls the wheel down, and it moves back and forth. At what point on the apparatus is the gravitational potential energy of the wheel lowest?

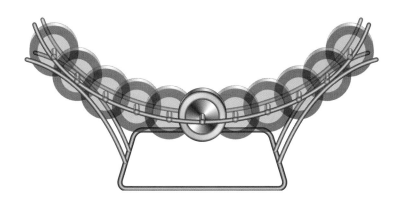

The gravitational potential energy of an object is typically denoted by PE, although to avoid confusion it is sometimes written as PE_{grav}. The gravitational potential energy is proportional to the height h an object is raised above the ground. Suppose the object has a mass m. Then the value of PE is given by the following equation:

$$PE = mgh$$

In this equation, g is the acceleration due to gravity, which is approximately 9.8 m/s² downward.

Chemical and Electric Potential Energy

Two additional forms of potential energy are **chemical potential energy** and **electric potential energy**.

Chemical potential energy is stored in the bonds between atoms and molecules. These bonds can be thought of as attractive forces between different atoms and molecules due to their structural properties. Chemical reactions release the chemical potential energy stored in the bonds. When substances such as coal are burned, they release chemical potential energy in the form of thermal energy and light energy. When our bodies digest food, the chemical potential energy in the food is released to fuel many of our vital biological processes.

Electric potential energy is stored in electric fields between charged particles. We can use the principles of chemical and electric potential energy to discuss the function of a battery. The electrochemical structure inside a battery establishes an electric field between the positive and negative terminals. When negative charges (electrons) move within the battery from the positive terminal to the negative terminal (that is, against the field), their potential energy increases.

TERMINALS ON A BATTERY

A battery stores electrical potential energy. How is that energy released?

When a wire connects the positive and negative terminals, it releases the electric potential energy inside the battery. The electrons move through the wire as electric current from the negative terminal to the positive terminal. The energy of the electric current can be converted into other forms of energy, such as light energy, thermal energy, or mechanical energy. The electric potential energy between two charges, q_1 and q_2, is given by the equation $PE_{elec} = \frac{kq_1q_2}{r}$, where k is Coulomb's constant and r is the distance between the charges.

Energy Stored in Fields

All electromagnetic waves, including visible light waves, are made up of electric and magnetic fields. These fields lie in planes that are perpendicular to one another, and they oscillate in phase with each other. Like mechanical waves, such as sound or water waves, electromagnetic waves carry energy from one location to another. However, unlike mechanical waves, electromagnetic waves do not need a medium in order to travel; they can move through a vacuum. Electromagnetic waves from the sun travel over 90 million miles through empty space in approximately 8 minutes as they transmit solar energy to Earth. This energy provides the heat and light that is necessary to sustain life on the planet.

Electromagnetic Spectrum

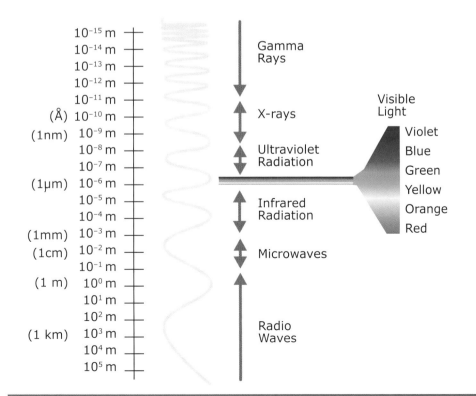

ELECTROMAGNETIC WAVES

Visible light is only part of the electromagnetic spectrum. What are some other forms of electromagnetic waves?

Because electric and magnetic fields both possess energy, the total energy in an electromagnetic wave is the sum of the energy in both of these field components. Both components of the electromagnetic field make an equal contribution to its total energy. The electromagnetic energy density, u, is the amount of total energy per unit volume. In free space, it can be stated in terms of either the amplitude of the electric field, E, or the magnetic field, B:

$$u = \frac{1}{2}\varepsilon_0 E^2 = \frac{1}{2\mu_0}B^2$$

where $\varepsilon_0 = 8.85 \times 10^{-12}$ C^2/N·m^2 is the permittivity of free space, and $\mu_0 = 4\pi \times 10^{-7}$ N·s^2/C^2 is the permeability of free space.

In the particle model of light, electromagnetic radiation is made up of small packets of electromagnetic energy called photons. In free space, these photons travel at the speed of light. The energy and wave frequency of the photons is related through the equation shown below, where f is the wave frequency, and h is a value known as Planck's constant, 6.63×10^{-34} m^2·kg/s:

$$energy_{photon} = hf$$

As the wave frequency of the photon increases, the amount of energy it contains also increases. Photons with high frequencies, such as x-rays or gamma rays, contain more energy than low frequency photons such as radio waves. This is why exposure to gamma rays and x-rays is dangerous to humans while radio waves are harmless. The higher energy forms of radiation contain so much energy, they can knock electrons loose from atoms, causing chemical damage to cells.

An electromagnetic beam consists of photons. Therefore, its total energy density is proportionate to the density of photons per unit area within the beam, n. As the number of photons increases, the beam energy density also increases. However, the energy density is also proportionate to the square of the electric field strength. This means that the photon density must also be proportional to the square of the magnitude of the electric field, $n \propto E^2$.

Energy in Particles

Atoms and molecules have energy because they move and interact with one another. This energy can be transferred between individual particles and, therefore, between larger macroscopic systems. Heat is the energy that is transferred between systems. There are three ways energy can be transferred: conduction, convection, and radiation.

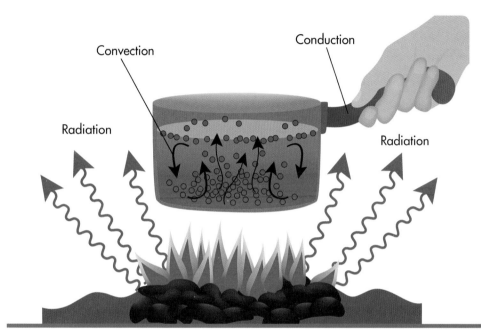

Convection

Conduction

Radiation

Radiation

TYPES OF HEAT

Particles interact in a number of ways. How do particles transfer energy from one to another in each form of heat transfer?

Temperature is a measure of the average kinetic energy of a multitude of particles in a substance. Particles in a higher temperature system move faster than those in a lower temperature system. When the two systems come into contact with one another, the moving particles will collide with each other. When a fast-moving particle collides with a slow-moving particle, some of its kinetic energy is transferred to the less energetic particle. As a result, the slow particle speeds up. In turn, it can collide with its slow-moving neighbors and transfer some energy to them. This process, called conduction, continues until all of the particles have the same average kinetic energy and all parts of the system are in thermal equilibrium. Thermal conduction only occurs if there is a temperature difference between two systems, and the heat is always transferred from hotter regions to colder regions.

Heat transfer can also occur when particles move from one location to another. This heat transfer process is called convection. Forced convection occurs when an outside agent, such as a fan or pump, pushes air or another fluid to another location. Natural convection is the result of differences in density within a fluid. When a substance such as air or water is heated, the particles gain energy and spread apart. Since hotter fluids typically have fewer particles per volume than their cooler counterparts, they have a lower density. Less dense fluids will rise above the more dense fluids. Therefore, hot fluids rise while cooler fluids sink. Convection is the reason why most attics are hotter than basements.

The final method of thermal energy transfer, radiation, occurs because all particles oscillate. As they oscillate, they emit electromagnetic radiation. Energy is radiated, or carried away, from the source by electromagnetic waves. If you place your hands above a fire, your hands will get hot because heat is being transferred upward primarily due to the process of convection. However, if you put your hands next to the fire, they will still feel warm. This heat transfer is due primarily to radiation.

How Does the Kinetic Energy of an Object Relate to Its Mass and Velocity?

Kinetic Energy, Mass, and Velocity

Recall that the **kinetic energy** of a moving **mass** is proportional to its mass and the square of the magnitude of its velocity. Consider a mass m moving at a velocity v. The kinetic **energy** KE of the mass is described by the following equation:

$$KE = \frac{1}{2} mv^2$$

The units of kinetic energy are joules, abbreviated as J.

It is possible to rearrange the equation for kinetic energy to solve for different variables such as velocity. This will be helpful in cases where the total kinetic energy and the mass are known but the velocity is unknown. Solving the above equation for v gives

$$v = \sqrt{\frac{2KE}{m}}$$

VELOCITY OF A BASEBALL

The kinetic energy of a baseball hitting a glove depends on the mass and velocity of the baseball. How would that energy feel if the velocity of the ball increased?

Kinetic Energy, Mass, and Velocity: Sample Problem #1: Calculating the Kinetic Energy of a Soccer Ball

A soccer ball is kicked horizontally across a field with an initial velocity of magnitude 15 m/s. If the soccer ball has a mass of 0.43 kg, what is the kinetic energy of the ball just after it is kicked?

Solution:

We know that the ball is kicked with a velocity of magnitude 15 m/s and that it has a mass of 0.43 kg. Thus,

$$v = 15 \text{ m/s}$$
$$m = 0.43 \text{ kg}$$

We want to solve for kinetic energy KE. We can use the following equation:

$$KE = \frac{1}{2} mv^2$$

Plugging in the known quantities to solve for KE gives:

$$KE = \frac{1}{2} (0.43 \text{ kg})(15 \text{ m/s})^2$$
$$= 48 \text{ J}$$

Thus, the kinetic energy of the soccer ball just after it is kicked is 48 J.

Kinetic Energy, Mass, and Velocity: Sample Problem #2: Calculating the Velocity of a Falling Egg

An egg of mass 0.060 kg is dropped from the top of a building. Just before it reaches the ground, it has a total kinetic energy of 5.9 J. What is the velocity of the egg just before it strikes the ground?

Solution:

We know that the egg has a mass of 0.060 kg and a kinetic energy of 5.9 J before it strikes the ground. Thus,

$$KE = 5.9 \text{ J}$$
$$m = 0.060 \text{ kg}$$

We want to solve for the velocity v. We can write the equation for kinetic energy and rearrange it to solve for v:

$$KE = \frac{1}{2}mv^2$$
$$v = \sqrt{\frac{2KE}{m}}$$

We can plug in the known quantities to calculate v:

$$v = \sqrt{\frac{2KE}{m}}$$
$$= \sqrt{\frac{2(5.9 \text{ J})}{0.060 \text{ kg}}}$$
$$= 14 \text{ m/s}$$

Thus, the egg is traveling at a velocity of 14 m/s downward just before it strikes the ground.

What Are Some Examples of Conversions between Kinetic Energy and Potential Energy in the World Around You?

Conversions between Kinetic and Potential Energy

There are two important facts to remember about **energy**:

1. The total energy in a closed system is always conserved, or constant. We say that a system is closed when only conservative forces, such as gravity, act on it. This is the law of conservation of energy.

2. While the total energy in a closed system is constant, the energy within that system can change from one form to another.

A common example of energy conversion takes place when objects are in free fall. We say that an object is in free fall when the only force acting on the object is the force of gravity pulling the object toward the surface of Earth. In reality, no objects are ever in total free fall because of the force of air resistance. The force of air resistance can be ignored in this lesson.

When objects are lifted up above the ground, they gain **gravitational potential energy**. When they are released, the force of gravity causes them to accelerate toward the ground. As the object falls, it loses gravitational **potential energy** because it decreases in height above the ground, but it gains **kinetic energy** because its speed increases. The amount of gravitational potential energy that an object loses as it falls is exactly equal to the amount of kinetic energy that the object gains. This is a consequence of conservation of energy.

MAN SKIING

This skier needs considerable skill to prevent crashing as he accelerates down the ski slope. How do potential and kinetic energy change as the skier heads down the mountain?

Let us discuss a specific example. Consider an apple of **mass** m at rest on a branch at a height h_1 above the ground. At this time, because the object is at rest, the total energy of the object is in the form of gravitational potential energy, which is given by the following equation:

$$PE_1 = mgh_1$$

Assume that at a later time, a strong gust of wind loosens the apple from its branch, causing it to fall. As the apple falls, it loses gravitational potential energy and gains kinetic energy. For example, when the apple has fallen to a new height, h_2, it has a new potential energy:

$$PE_2 = mgh_2$$

Thus, the loss of gravitational potential energy is given by

$$\Delta PE = PE_1 - PE_2 = mgh_1 - mgh_2$$

The loss in potential energy, ΔPE, is equal to the gain in kinetic energy, ΔKE. Thus, the ΔKE of the apple is given by

$$\Delta KE = \Delta PE$$
$$= mgh_1 - mgh_2$$
$$= mg\,(h_1 - h_2)$$

The apple is initially at rest; so it has no initial kinetic energy. Thus, the change in kinetic energy is given by

$$\Delta KE = \frac{1}{2}mv^2 = mg\,(h_1 - h_2)$$

where v is the magnitude of the apple's velocity at the height h_2.

The last equation is very helpful in solving problems of motion. In fact, it applies not only to objects in free fall but also to objects that are traveling up and down inclines, such as roller coasters or ski trails.

Conversions between Kinetic and Potential Energy: Sample Problem

A roller-coaster car loaded with passengers has a mass of 1,300 kg. The first drop of the roller coaster is 64 m above the ground. The bottom of the first drop is 15 m above the ground. Assuming that the roller coaster comes to rest as it reaches the top of the first drop, determine its speed at the bottom of the first drop.

Solution:

The mass of the car is 1,300 kg. The initial height is 64 m, and the final height is 15 m.

$$m = 1300 \text{ kg}$$
$$h_1 = 64 \text{ m}$$
$$h_2 = 15 \text{ m}$$

The objective is to find the value of v. The roller-coaster car is initially at rest, so the following equation can be used:

$$\frac{1}{2} mv^2 = mg\,(h_1 - h_2)$$

Solving it for v gives

$$v = \sqrt{2g\,(h_1 - h_2)}$$

Note that the mass m cancels out of the equation. We can now plug in the known quantities to solve for v:

$$v = \sqrt{2(9.8 \text{ m/s}^2)(64 \text{ m} - 15 \text{ m})}$$
$$= 31 \text{ m/s}$$

Thus, the speed of the roller-coaster car at the bottom of the first hill is 31 m/s, or approximately 110 km/h. Note that the speed does not depend on the mass of the roller-coaster car.

Other Examples of Energy Conversions

Energy changes form all the time. For example, when people clap their hands, kinetic energy transforms into sound energy and thermal energy. Electrical energy in circuits changes into useful forms of energy such as thermal energy and light energy in light bulbs and mechanical energy in spinning fan blades. Living organisms convert energy from their environment into energy needed for life's functions. For example, plants convert light energy from the sun into **chemical potential energy** during photosynthesis.

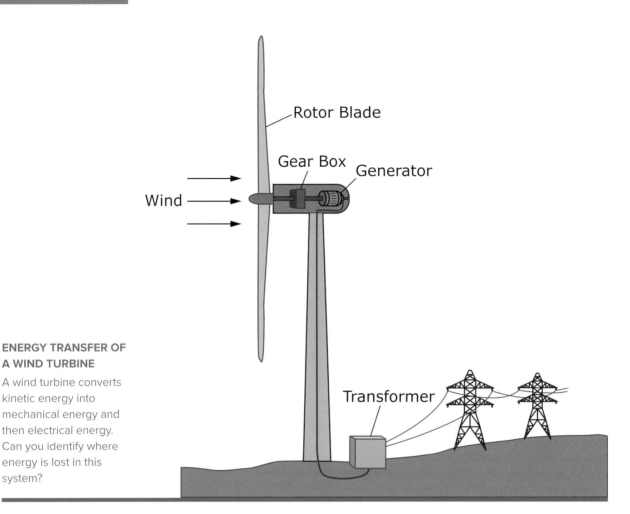

Rotor Blade

Gear Box Generator

Wind

Transformer

ENERGY TRANSFER OF A WIND TURBINE

A wind turbine converts kinetic energy into mechanical energy and then electrical energy. Can you identify where energy is lost in this system?

Sometimes energy changes form many times in a system. For example, when a cannonball is fired, chemical potential energy is released, causing an explosion. This energy is then converted into kinetic energy and gravitational potential energy as the cannonball is launched into the air.

Consider the Explain Question

How can you increase the efficiency of a wind turbine when converting wind energy to electrical energy?

Go online to complete the scientific explanation.

dlc.com/ca11050s

Check Your Understanding

Can you explain two energy transformations that occur when a cannonball is fired upward from a cannon?

dlc.com/ca11051s

S T E M in Action

Applying Types of Energy

The human body needs **energy** in order to perform tasks necessary for survival. We obtain our energy from food. The food that we digest contains **chemical potential energy** that is stored in glucose molecules. Cellular respiration is the process that animal cells use to release chemical **potential energy** from food. The chemical reaction converts glucose molecules into water, carbon dioxide, and ATP molecules. The carbon dioxide is expelled from the body, while the energy obtained is stored in the bonds of ATP molecules.

When our cells need energy, they break down ATP molecules to release chemical potential energy. This chemical energy is then converted into different forms for our bodies to use. We use electrical energy in our brains and **kinetic energy** in our muscles.

Engines in vehicles use chemicals in a different energy conversion. A fuel cell engineer is concerned with these engines and decreasing humanity's dependence on fossil fuels.

HYDROGEN FUEL CELLS

Hydrogen is a highly reactive gas. How can hydrogen be used safely as alternative fuel source?

Steam and gasoline or diesel engines convert kinetic energy from burning a fuel. Steam from water heated by burning fuel turns the central shaft of a steam engine. Controlled explosions of burning fuel inside cylinders of a gasoline or diesel engine also turn a shaft. In all these engines, a transmission turns the shaft's turning into motion of the vehicle.

In contrast, fuel cell engines convert chemical energy into electrical energy. An electrolyte carries charged particles from one electrode to the other in a fuel cell. This generates electricity, which is then used to power the vehicle.

A fuel cell engineer attempts to increase electrical output of a cell or find a fuel that is abundant and cheap. The greatest challenge these engineers face is finding the right electrolyte. Most electrolytes require more energy to make than the fuel cell can output, resulting in a negatively efficient design.

STEM and Types of Energy

Nuclear fusion powers the sun. If it can be controlled in a power plant on Earth, that power plant could possibly produce limitless power, since the fuel, a type of hydrogen, would be cheap.

Fusion scientists use certain magnetic devices to contain hydrogen nuclei in an electrically charged plasma. The most popular of these devices is the tokamak. Heavy magnetic coils surround its donut-shaped inner chamber and produce a magnetic field that holds the plasma and confines it. Fusions within this plasma create particles and radiation, which heat a working fluid outside the tokamak. This heat moves to a secondary fluid to make steam, as in many other power plants.

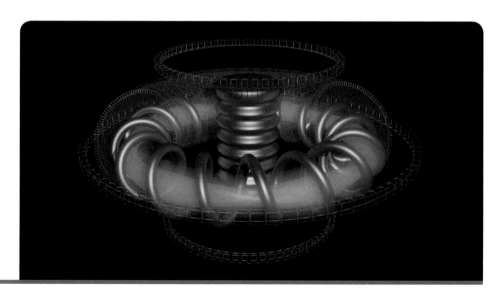

TOKAMAK

A tokamak holds plasma within a magnetic field. How is electrical energy generated from this plasma?

The International Thermonuclear Energy Reactor (ITER) is being built in the south of France. When completed, it will be the largest tokamak on Earth. Scientists will then conduct experiments to produce energy through nuclear fusion and learn how fusion power plants might one day be created.

Kinetic Energy, Mass, and Velocity #1

Use kinematics equations to solve the problems below.

1. A 2300-kg truck is traveling down a highway at 32 m/s. What is the kinetic energy of the truck?

2. A 58-kg boy swings a baseball bat, which causes a 0.140-kg baseball to move towards third base with a velocity of 38.0 m/s. What it the kinetic energy of the baseball?

3. A 35-kg boy is riding an 18-kg bicycle down a path. If the bicycle is moving at 11 m/s, what is the kinetic energy of the boy and the bicycle?

4. Does a 0.14 kg baseball moving at 41 m/s or a 0.058-kg tennis ball moving at 67 m/s have more kinetic energy?

Kinetic Energy, Mass, and Velocity #2

Use kinematics equations to solve the problems below.

1. A 0.450-kg soccer ball has a kinetic energy of 119 J. What is the velocity of the soccer ball?

2. A 0.041-kg bullet has a kinetic energy of 660 J. What is the velocity of the bullet?

3. A paper clip that has a mass of 1.5 grams is thrown into the air and initially has a kinetic energy of 0.013 J. What is the velocity of the paper clip when it is thrown?

Conversions between Kinetic Energy and Potential Energy

Use kinematics equations to solve the problems below.

1. The first hill of a roller coaster is 42.0 meters high. The roller coaster drops to a height of 4.2 meters above the ground at the bottom of this first hill. If the mass of the roller coaster train is 4,500 kg, what is the velocity at the bottom of the first hill? Ignore friction and assume the velocity at the top of the first hill is 0 m/s.

2. The first hill of a roller coaster is 42 meters high. The top of the second hill of the roller coaster is 33 meters high. The mass of the roller coaster train is 4,500 kg.

   a. What is the velocity at the top of the second hill? Ignore friction and assume the velocity at the top of the first hill is 0 m/s.

   b. What type(s) of energy does the roller coaster have at the top of the second hill?

3. A 0.017-kg acorn falls from a position in an oak tree that is 18.5 meters above the ground.

   a. What is velocity of the acorn just before it reaches the ground?

   b. What is the kinetic energy of the acorn when it hits the ground? (Ignore air resistance.)

Conservation of Energy

LESSON OVERVIEW

Lesson Questions

- What is the law of conservation of energy, and what are some examples of it?
- How do we calculate changes in gravitational potential energy of objects near Earth's surface?
- How do we investigate the transformation of potential and kinetic energy?
- How can we demonstrate the law of conservation of energy?

Lesson Objectives

By the end of the lesson, you should be able to:

- Explain the law of conservation of energy using examples.
- Calculate changes in gravitational potential energy of objects near Earth's surface using the equation $\Delta PE = mg\Delta h$.
- Solve problems involving potential and kinetic energy.
- Demonstrate the law of conservation of energy.

Key Vocabulary

Which terms do you already know?

- ☐ chemical potential energy
- ☐ conservation of energy
- ☐ distance
- ☐ elastic collision
- ☐ energy
- ☐ gravitational potential energy
- ☐ inelastic collision
- ☐ joule
- ☐ kinetic energy
- ☐ potential energy
- ☐ thermal energy

dlc.com/ca11052s

Using Energy

When you are tired or hungry, you might say that you don't have a lot of energy or that you need to drink a cup of coffee to increase your energy supply. But what is energy? Energy is what allows you to walk across a floor, throw a ball, or pick up a bag of groceries. Energy is also what powers the electrical devices in our homes and runs the cars that we drive. Without it, we wouldn't be able to grow food, move around our neighborhoods, or communicate with each other. Where does energy come from? How can we get more energy?

dlc.com/ca11053s

EXPLAIN QUESTION

▌ **How do we harness the energy found in hydrogen to power fuel cells?**

BOWLING

When a bowling ball collides with a set of pins, the ball slows down and the pins fall over. Which objects are gaining energy? Which objects are losing energy?

What Is the Law of Conservation of Energy, and What Are Some Examples of It?

Conservation of Energy

The law of **conservation of energy** says that the total amount of **energy** in the universe is constant and does not change over time. In the example of the bouncing ball, the energy stored in the ball changes from potential, or stored, energy to **kinetic energy** (the energy of motion) as the ball falls and bounces; the kinetic energy then changes back to **potential energy** as the ball returns to the top of its bounce. However, as the ball continues to bounce, some of its kinetic energy transforms into **thermal energy** and sound. In other words, the ball's energy changes form. Energy cannot be destroyed; it cannot be created; it just exists.

BOUNCING BALL

The bouncing basketball shows potential and kinetic energy in action. What would the figure look like if all of the kinetic energy were transformed back into potential energy?

Consider a system where no energy is transformed into thermal energy or sound. The following equation shows that potential and kinetic energy (that is, total mechanical energy) are conserved:

initial mechanical energy = final mechanical energy

$$KE_i + PE_i = KE_f + PE_f$$

(where *i* and *f* are initial and final values)

In other words, the initial sum of kinetic and **potential energy** is equal to the final sum. This equation can be rewritten to relate the change in kinetic and potential energies:

$$KE_f - KE_i = PE_i - PE_f$$
$$\Delta KE = -\Delta PE$$

The change in kinetic energy is equal to minus the change in potential energy.

Measuring Energy

We measure energy in units called joules (J). One **joule** is equal to one newton-meter.

One thousand joules is about equal to one British thermal unit (Btu). Your kitchen stove's output may be measured in Btu's. One Btu is the amount of thermal energy necessary to raise the temperature of one pound of water by one degree Fahrenheit. Thus, about 2,000 Btu's—or about 2,100,000 joules—are necessary to make a pot of coffee.

Why use joules rather than Btu's? The reason is simple: The joule is a metric unit, and scientists use metric units rather than British (or English standard) units. Metric units are related by factors of 10, making conversions easier. For this same reason, scientists measure length in meters rather than feet and measure mass in kilograms rather than pounds. The joule is the international (SI) unit used for energy.

Measuring Energy: Sample Problem

A student climbs a ladder to free a 0.62 kg basketball stuck on a garage roof. The student drops the ball from a height of 4.4 m. The ball falls to the ground. This is Stage 1. The ball bounces back to a height of 4.4 m. This is Stage 2. What is the change in kinetic and **gravitational potential energy** during each stage of the ball's journey?

Solution:

During Stage 1, the ball starts from rest at a height of 4.4 m. Newton's laws for one-dimensional projectile motion will determine the speed of the ball when it hits the ground. If the ball falls from height h, the speed v is

$$v = \sqrt{2hg}$$
$$= 2\sqrt{(4.4 \text{ m})(9.8 \text{ m/s}^2)}$$
$$= \sqrt{86.2 \text{ (m/s)}^2}$$
$$v = 9.3 \text{ m/s}$$

The initial speed is 0.0 m/s and the final speed is 9.3 m/s. The ball's mass is 0.62 kg. The initial kinetic energy is

$$KE_i = \frac{1}{2}mv_i^2$$
$$KE_i = 0.0 \text{ J}$$

The final kinetic energy is

$$KE_f = \frac{1}{2} mv_f^2$$
$$= \frac{1}{2} (0.62 \text{ kg}) (9.3 \text{ m/s})^2$$
$$= 27 \text{ J}$$

The change in kinetic energy is

$$\Delta KE = KE_f - KE_i$$
$$= 27 \text{ J} - 0 \text{ J}$$
$$\Delta KE = 27 \text{ J}$$

Mechanical energy is conserved, so the change in potential energy plus the change in kinetic energy is a constant:

Initial mechanical energy = final mechanical energy
$$\Delta PE = -\Delta KE$$
$$\Delta PE = -27 \text{ J}$$

The ball gains 27 J of kinetic energy and loses 27 J of potential energy.

During Stage 2, the ball reverses its motion. It moves upward with an initial speed of 9.3 m/s. Its initial kinetic energy is now:

$$KE_i = \frac{1}{2} mv_i^2$$
$$= \frac{1}{2} (0.62 \text{ kg}) (9.3 \text{ m/s})^2$$
$$= 27 \text{ J}$$

The ball comes to rest for an instant at its original height, so the final kinetic energy is 0 J. The change in kinetic energy is:

$$\Delta KE = KE_f - KE_i$$
$$= 0 \text{ J} - 27 \text{ J}$$
$$\Delta KE = -27 \text{ J}$$

Energy is conserved, so the change in potential energy is minus the change in kinetic energy:

$$\Delta PE = \Delta KE$$
$$\Delta PE = 27 \text{ J}$$

The ball loses 27 J of kinetic energy and gains 27 J of potential energy. Mechanical energy, which equals 27 J, is conserved during both stages.

Gravitational Potential Energy

Picture the bouncing basketball again, only this time, toss it into the air. When the ball is thrown upward, its initial kinetic energy is converted into gravitational potential energy. Although the magnitudes of the ball's kinetic and potential energies change along the way, their sum remains constant. In other words, the law of conservation of energy still applies—energy exists and does not disappear.

As you might guess, sometimes other forces, such as friction, do work on objects in motion. Consider a group of skiers skiing down a mountain. Does friction affect their speed down the mountain? Of course it does. As the skiers move down the mountain, they encounter more friction, which keeps them from gaining more speed during the run and slows them down near the end of the run by converting kinetic energy into thermal energy. When an object sliding across a surface slows down because of friction, some of its kinetic energy is converted into thermal energy.

Chemical Potential Energy

Thermal energy is a form of energy that many of us use every day to cook our food and heat our homes. Fossil fuels such as coal and oil are used to convert **chemical potential energy** into thermal energy. As human population and energy demands increase, additional quantities of fuel are needed to meet the energy needs. Chemical potential energy found in fossil fuels is not infinite. Unlimited supplies of coal and other fossil fuels do not exist—once fossil fuels are converted to other forms of energy, they are gone. They are not a renewable form of energy.

FOREST FIRE

As wood burns, chemical potential energy within the wood is transformed into heat energy. The chemical potential energy converted into what other forms of energy?

The extraction of fossil fuels has a variety of impacts on the environment. One process, commonly known as fracking, involves water being injected into oil- or gas-bearing rocks. The injected water contains chemicals that may alter the biogeochemistry of the geosphere. Many of the elements extracted during mining and drilling are not commonly found in large quantities near the surface. They may cause problems when they enter the biosphere. Heavy metals, released from mining activities and the use of its products, are particularly hazardous to living things.

According to the U.S. Energy Information Administration, in 2017, fossil fuel power plants made up approximately 62% of the total power generation across the United States. Fossil fuel power plants convert the chemical potential energy into thermal energy and then into electrical energy to distribute to homes.

Fossil Fuel Powered Steam Turbine Electricity Generation

FOSSIL FUEL ENERGY CONVERSION

Why do you think fossil fuel power plants are more efficient in converting energy than alternative energy power plants?

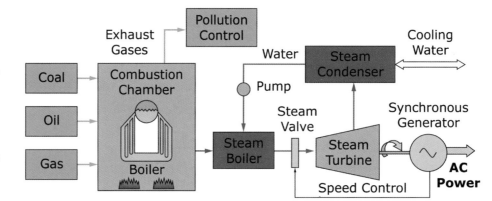

How Do We Calculate Changes in Gravitational Potential Energy of Objects Near Earth's Surface?

Solving Problems Involving Gravitational Potential Energy

Potential energy is the stored **energy** all objects possess. **Potential energy** can be **gravitational potential energy**, which is the stored energy of an object based on its vertical position in a gravitational field; elastic potential energy, which is the stored energy of a stressed or compressed object; **chemical potential energy**; electromagnetic potential energy; or nuclear potential energy.

Gravitational potential energy is the result of gravitational attraction on an object. Near the surface of Earth, the gravitational potential energy depends on the height and mass of an object. As an object's height increases, so does its gravitational potential energy. Thus, the gravitational potential energy is directly related to the height of the object above the ground. On the ground, the height is $h = 0$.

TROPICAL RAIN FOREST

The water has gravitational potential energy at the top of the waterfall, which transforms into kinetic energy as it flows over the edge of the falls. Into what other forms of energy does the gravitational potential energy of the falling water transform?

The gravitational potential energy of an object also depends directly on its mass (m) and acceleration due to gravity (g).

These relationships can be summarized in the equation:

$$PE_{grav} = mgh$$

Sometimes we are interested in the change in gravitational potential energy as an object moves from one height to another, expressed as Δh. In this case, we can modify the formula:

$$\Delta PE_{grav} = mg\Delta h$$

This equation states that change in gravitational potential energy (ΔPE_{grav}) is equal to the mass (m) of the object times the acceleration of gravity on Earth (g) times the change in height (Δh) of the object.

Gravitational Potential Energy: Sample Problem

At a fall festival, a crane raises a giant pumpkin 20.0 meters into the air before dropping it on a wrecked car. The pumpkin weighs 450 kg, and the acceleration of gravity due to Earth is 9.8 m/s². What is the gravitational potential energy of the pumpkin relative to the ground when the crane has raised it?

Solution:

The change in the gravitational potential energy of the pumpkin is the product of the mass of the pumpkin, the height that the crane raises the pumpkin above the ground, and the gravitational acceleration:

$$\Delta PE_{grav} = mg\Delta h$$
$$= (450 \text{ kg})(9.8 \text{ m/s}^2)(20.0 \text{ m})$$
$$\Delta PE_{grav} = 8.8 \times 10^4 \text{ J}$$

The gravitational potential energy relative to the ground of the pumpkin when it is raised is 8.8×10^4 joules.

How Do We Investigate the Transformation of Potential and Kinetic Energy?

Elastic Potential Energy

Elastic **potential energy** is **energy** stored in an object due to stress or compression. For example, a drawn bow has elastic **potential energy**. The amount of energy stored is related to the amount of stretch of the device. The farther back the bowstring is pulled, the more energy is stored.

Springs are special instances of elastic potential energy because they can be compressed or stretched. If a spring is neither stretched nor compressed, it is at a zero potential energy position. However, once force is applied to the spring, the potential energy changes.

SPRING

Elastic potential energy, which is the energy stored in elastic materials like springs, is due to stretching or compressing. What kind of energy becomes evident when the spring is stretched or compressed many times in a short time interval?

The potential energy of the spring is directly related to the square of the **distance** it is stretched, x, and to the elastic property of the spring, called the spring constant, k.

This relationship can be expressed in the equation:

$$PE_{spring} = \frac{1}{2} kx^2$$

This equation shows that you can find a spring's potential energy by multiplying the spring constant (k) by the amount of compression or stretch squared (x) and dividing by two. Once the spring is released, the potential energy transforms into **kinetic energy**.

Elastic Potential Energy: Sample Problem: Jack-in-the-Box

Suppose a jack-in-the-box has a spring constant of 80 N/m. How much elastic potential energy is stored in the jack-in-the-box if its spring is compressed 10 cm?

Solution:

The elastic potential energy of the jack-in-the-box is found by multiplying the spring constant (80 N/m) by the amount of compression squared (10 cm = 0.1 m).

$$PE_{spring} = \frac{1}{2} kx^2$$

$$= \frac{1}{2}(80 \text{ N/m})(0.1 \text{ m})^2$$

$$PE_{spring} = 0.4 \text{ j}$$

The elastic potential energy of the jack-in-the-box is 0.4 J.

Electric Potential Energy

Have you experienced the build-up of static electricity in your body? Imagine that you are walking across a carpet in the wintertime, when the humidity is very low. If you touch certain objects, you will notice that a spark jumps between you and the object. You also may have observed the same type of electricity when combing or brushing your hair in a dry atmosphere, This electricity is due to the separation of charged particles by friction.

Such charged particles that experience an electric force have electric potential energy. When a charged particle is subjected to an electric force, the particle moves in a way that lowers its electric potential energy and raises its kinetic energy.

LIGHTNING

Lightning is the release of enormous electric potential energy. What accounts for the initial high levels of potential energy that seeks release?

A particle with charge q_1, measured in coulombs (the SI unit of charge, expressed as C), will experience a force due to a second particle with charge q_2, also measured in coulombs. If the particles are separated by distance r, measured in meters, they will have electric potential energy related to the product of their charges and indirectly to the distance between them. This relationship can be expressed in the equation

$$PE_{elec} = k\frac{q_1 q_2}{r}$$

where PE_{elec} is the electric potential energy, q_1 and q_2 are the charges, r is the distance between the charges, and k is the coulomb constant associated with the medium in which the charges exist. The value for k in a vacuum is 8.99×10^9 N·m²/C². Like any form of energy, electric potential energy is measured in joules.

Electric Potential Energy: Sample Problem: Charged Particles

A particle with a charge of -1.2 nC (nano-coulomb, or 10^{-9}C) is located at a distance of 2.3 cm from a particle with charge of 2.8 nC (2.8×10^{-9} C). The first particle is released from rest. The second particle is fixed at its location. What is the change in electric potential energy when the first particle has moved 1.0 cm?

Solution:

The charge of the first particle is -1.2 nC $= -1.2 \times 10^{-9}$ C. The charge of the second particle is 2.8 nC $= 2.8 \times 10^{-9}$ C. The particles are separated initially by 2.3 cm $= 0.023$ m. The initial electric potential energy of the charges is

$$PE_{elec\ (i)} = k\frac{q_1 q_2}{r_f}$$

$$= \left(8.99 \times 10^9\ \frac{N \cdot m^2}{C^2}\right) \frac{(-1.2 \times 10^{-9}\ C)(2.8 \times 10^{-9}\ C)}{0.023\ m}$$

$$= -1.3 \times 10^{-6}\ J$$

The particles have opposite charges, so they will be attracted. The first particle moves toward the second particle. When the first particle has moved 1.0 cm, the particles are separated by 2.3 cm $-$ 1.0 cm $= 1.3$ cm $= 0.013$ m. The electric potential energy is then

$$PE_{elec\ (i)} = k\frac{q_1 q_2}{r_f}$$

$$= \left(8.99 \times 10^9\ \frac{N \cdot m^2}{C^2}\right) \frac{(-1.2 \times 10^{-9}\ C)(2.8 \times 10^{-9}\ C)}{0.013\ m}$$

$$= -2.3 \times 10^{-6}\ J$$

The change in electric potential energy is therefore

$$\Delta PE_{elec} = PE_{elec,f} - PE_{elec,I} = -2.3 \times 10^{-6} \text{ J} - (-1.3 \times 10^{-6} \text{ J}) = -1.0 \times 10^{-6} \text{ J}$$

The electric potential energy has decreased by 1.0×10^{-6} J. Energy is conserved, so the particle's kinetic energy must increase by the same amount. Thus, the particle's speed increases as it moves toward the second particle.

Kinetic Energy

Kinetic energy, the energy of motion, depends on the mass of an object as well as its speed. Remember the bowling ball spinning down the lane to hit the pins as its potential energy transformed into various kinds of kinetic energy, including sound and **thermal energy**? The mass of the bowling ball and the speed with which it is thrown determine the amount of kinetic energy it possesses, and thus releases. For example, a heavier ball will release more energy than a lighter ball if both are thrown at the same speed.

The kinetic energy (*KE*) of an object in motion is equal to one-half the mass (*m*) of the object times the square of its velocity:

$$KE = \frac{1}{2} mv^2$$

This equation shows you that kinetic energy is directly proportional to the square of its velocity. In other words, if an object's velocity doubles, its kinetic energy increases by a factor of four.

ROLLER COASTER AND KINETIC ENERGY

Roller coasters are designed to convert potential to kinetic energy—for a thrill! How does the kinetic energy change if more people fill the car, or if the initial velocity is 1 m/s higher?

Kinetic Energy: Sample Problem: Roller Coaster

Suppose you are exploring an amusement park that has just opened a new roller coaster. What is the kinetic energy of a 630 kg roller coaster car that is moving with a speed of 20.5 m/s?

Solution:

Multiply the mass of the car by the square of its speed and divide by two.

$$KE = \frac{1}{2}\, mv^2$$

$$= \frac{1}{2}\, (630 \text{ kg}) \,(20.5 \text{ m/s})^2$$

$$KE = 1.3 \times 10^5 \text{ J}$$

To two significant figures, the kinetic energy of the car is 1.3×10^5 joules. If you double the speed, the kinetic energy is quadrupled.

How Can We Demonstrate the Law of Conservation of Energy?

Demonstrating with a Falling Object

According to the law of **conservation of energy**, no matter which form of **energy** we study, the energy will remain constant in an isolated system. **Potential energy** transforms into **kinetic energy**, or **thermal energy**, or sound, but the total amount always remains the same.

PENDULUM CLOCK

The simple harmonic motion of a pendulum demonstrates the law of conservation of energy. What kind of energy keeps the pendulum in motion? What provides this energy?

The law of conservation of energy can be demonstrated by measuring the speed of an object after it falls from a certain height. Imagine a 21 kg piece of space junk dropped at rest from a rocket 440 km above Earth's surface. What is the change in **gravitational potential energy** relative to the ground of the space junk at this height?

$$\Delta PE_{grav} = mg\Delta h$$
$$= (21 \text{ kg}) (9.8 \text{ m/s}^2) (4.4 \times 10^5 \text{ m})$$
$$\Delta PE_{grav} = 9.1 \times 10^7 \text{ J}$$

The gravitational **potential energy** of the space junk relative to the ground is 9.1×10^7 J. If the space junk falls 220 km, its potential energy with respect to its initial position changes by the following:

$$\Delta PE_{grav} = mg\Delta h$$
$$= (21 \text{ kg}) (9.8 \text{ m/s}^2) (-2.2 \times 10^5 \text{ m})$$
$$\Delta PE_{grav} = -4.5 \times 10^7 \text{ J}$$

In the real world, the space junk will lose energy to friction because of the air rushing past as it falls. If we ignore this friction for this example, then the decrease in gravitational potential energy should equal the increase in kinetic energy:

$$\Delta KE = -\Delta PE$$
$$\Delta KE = 4.5 \times 10^7 \text{ J}$$

The junk fell from rest, so the initial kinetic energy was 0 J. The final kinetic energy is then 4.5×10^7 J.

We can check conservation of energy by measuring the speed of the junk. If energy is conserved, the junk's speed will be

$$v = \sqrt{\frac{2KE}{m}}$$

$$= \sqrt{\frac{2(4.5 \times 10^7 \text{J})}{21 \text{ kg}}}$$

$$v = 2.1 \text{ km/s}$$

In the real world, the speed will be less than 2,100 m/s due to energy lost to friction.

Demonstrating with a Spring

To find the elastic potential energy of a spring, measure how much the spring is compressed. Compress the spring with a mass. Then, release the mass upward. The initial stored elastic potential energy equals the change in gravitational potential energy of the mass when it reaches its highest point.

The speed of the mass as it leaves the spring gives another way to check conservation of energy. A motion detector measures the speed of the mass. Using the speed, we can determine the kinetic energy.

COMPRESSED SPRING
The potential energy of compressed springs is used in mattresses, pogo sticks, and car shock absorbers. Can you find other daily and industrial uses?

Imagine a spring with a spring constant of 2,500 N/m. A 15-kg block is placed on the spring. A student compresses the spring by 12 cm below the spring's natural rest point. At this point, the elastic potential energy of the system is as follows:

$$PE_{spring} = \frac{1}{2} kx^2$$

$$= \frac{1}{2} (2500 \text{ N/m}) (0.12 \text{ m})^2$$

$$PE_{spring} = 18 \text{ J}$$

The student then releases the spring. A motion detector measures the speed of the mass as it leaves the spring. The elastic potential energy of the spring is transformed to kinetic energy of the mass. The speed of the mass as it leaves the spring will be

$$v = \sqrt{\frac{2KE}{m}}$$

$$= \sqrt{\frac{2PE_{spring}}{m}}$$

$$= \sqrt{\frac{2(18\text{J})}{15 \text{ kg}}}$$

$$= \sqrt{2.4(\text{m/s})^2}$$

$$v = 1.5 \text{ m/s}$$

In the real world, the speed of the mass will be less than this amount. A real spring will continue to vibrate after it is released. This fact means that some of the initial elastic potential energy will convert to kinetic energy of the spring.

Demonstrating with a Paddle Wheel

Nineteenth-century British physicist James **Joule** devised another way to test conservation of energy. (James Joule is the scientist for whom the unit of energy is named.) Joule used a paddle wheel in a tank of water. He connected the wheel to a set of masses. Joule let the masses fall a certain height. As the masses fell, they caused the wheel to turn. Friction between the paddle wheel and the water caused the water's temperature to rise.

Joule's experiment showed that the initial gravitational potential energy of the masses changed to the kinetic energy of the paddle wheel, and then to the thermal energy of the water.

Consider the Explain Question

| **How do we harness the energy found in hydrogen to power fuel cells?**

Go online to complete the scientific explanation.

dlc.com/ca11054s

Check Your Understanding

| **Using a bouncing ball as an example, can you describe the conservation of energy?**

dlc.com/ca11055s

in Action

Applying Conservation of Energy

Devices such as your cell phone and laptop need **energy** to operate. Therefore, almost all of these electronic devices have a battery that stores the energy needed to operate the device. Look at a cellphone or another similar electronic device. Can you locate the battery? Many batteries are small and portable. Other batteries, such as those used in cars, are much larger and heavier.

In an effort to make renewable forms of energy more efficient and cost-effective, there must be a way to store the energy once it is collected. For instance, solar energy is only generated in significant quantities on sunny days. Most people still want to use electricity and heat their homes on cloudy days. Therefore, there must be a way to save the solar energy and use it at a later time. Batteries solve this storage problem. However, batteries can only store a finite amount of energy and they take time to recharge. Scientists and engineers are currently designing new types of batteries that store more energy and that take less time to charge.

Do you know how batteries store energy? Batteries consist of two electrodes, called the cathode and the anode, and a chemical fluid, called an electrolyte. Chemical reactions within the battery release stored **chemical potential energy** and cause a current to flow through the battery. The battery will continue to supply energy until all of the chemical reactants have been used up. Some batteries, such as lithium-ion batteries, are rechargeable. When they are connected to an external power source, the chemical processes are reversed and the battery can be reused. Other batteries, including the commonly used alkaline batteries, are not rechargeable. When all of the chemical energy stored in the battery has been released, the battery must be disposed of.

STEM and Conservation of Energy

One of the oldest and most commonly used forms of renewable energy in the United States is called hydroelectric energy. It is generated at hydroelectric power plants such as Niagara Falls. In order to create a hydroelectric power plant, a river is dammed to create a reservoir of water that can be released when needed. Although water is a renewable resource, the damming of a river can negatively impact the surrounding environment and can damage the delicate ecosystems that depend on the river.

When the water in a dam is allowed to drop from a high elevation to a lower elevation, its stored **gravitational potential energy** is converted into **kinetic energy**. At the bottom, the water flows very quickly because it has a lot of kinetic energy. This energy is used to turn the blades of a turbine. The turbine is connected to an electrical generator that converts the kinetic energy into electrical energy. Do you live near a hydroelectric power plant? If you do, it is likely that some of the electricity that comes into your home was generated from the **potential energy** stored in water.

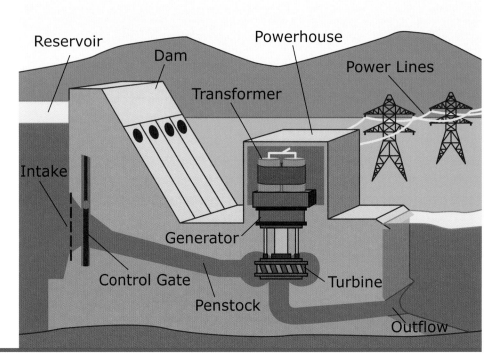

PARTS OF A HYDROELECTRIC POWER STATION

Energy is generated by hydroelectric power plants when water flows through a dam. What are the advantages of hydroelectric power?

The people who design and maintain hydroelectric power plants are called mechanical engineers. In order to build a new power station, an engineer must first assess the terrain and then develop a design that meets the energy needs and that maintains the integrity of the surrounding environment and ecosystem. Engineers frequently used computer-aided design tools to develop prototypes, run simulations, and analyze potential designs. Once a design has been selected, mechanical engineers also oversee the construction of the power plant. Since mechanical engineers are responsible for such a wide variety of tasks, they must have good problem-solving skills, have a solid knowledge of mathematics, and be able to think creatively.

HYDROELECTRIC POWER PLANTS

A hydroelectric dam converts the energy of falling water to electrical energy. Why is hydroelectric power considered a renewable energy?

Measuring Energy

Use the law of the conservation of energy and the formulas for one-dimensional projectile motion, gravitational potential energy, and kinetic energy to solve the problems below. Neglect friction, air resistance, and other dissipative forces in all problems. Use $g = 9.8$ m/s².

1. A metal ball bearing with mass 5.0 g falls out of a factory machine and drops to the concrete floor 3.0 m below. It bounces back up to its starting point. Find the changes in the bearing's potential and kinetic energies as it a) travels from the machine down to the floor, and b) travels up from the floor back to its starting point.

2. A tennis player strikes a tennis ball from underneath with her racket. The ball is sent straight up with an initial velocity of 19 m/s. How high above the striking point will the ball travel?

3. A cameraman sitting near the open door of a news helicopter accidentally drops his 140-g mobile phone out the door at an altitude of 990 m. How fast will the phone be falling when it strikes the ground?

4. A 500.0-kg roller coaster car travels with some initial velocity along a track that is 5.0 m above the ground. The car goes down a small hill and then coasts back up a higher hill. The second hill is 12.0 m above the ground. What must the initial velocity of the car be in order for the car to be going 3.0 m/s at the top of the second hill?

5. A student designs an experiment to demonstrate the conservation of gravitational potential and kinetic energy. She drops a wooden block from rest through a photogate 2.0 m below. If energy is conserved, how fast should the block be travelling when it passes through the photogate?

6. A pinball machine's plunger has a spring constant of 22 N/m, and is compressed by 0.040 m to start a 0.0060 kg pinball.

   • What is the elastic potential energy before the ball is released?

   • What is the kinetic energy of the pinball the instant it leaves the spring?

   • What is the speed of the pinball the instant it leaves the spring?

   • If the pinball is moving at 1.3 m/s as it is deflected horizontally across the top of the pinball machine, how much higher above the ground is this part of its path when compared to its starting position?

Solving Problems Involving Gravitational Potential Energy

Use the formula for gravitational potential energy to solve the problems below. Neglect friction and other dissipative forces in all problems. Use $g = 9.8$ m/s².

1. A boy with mass 25 kg climbs into a small tree. He sits on a branch that is 2.0 m above the ground. What is his gravitational potential energy with respect to the ground?

2. A work crew is using a pulley to lift a small piano up the outside of a building to a second-floor balcony. The piano has mass 180 kg. At a height of 3.0 m, what is the piano's gravitational potential energy with respect to the ground?

3. A cat with mass 4.0 kg jumps down to the floor from a bookcase 2.0 m high. What is the cat's change in gravitational potential energy?

4. A student lifts a 1.5 kg book from a chair seat 41 cm off the ground to a table that is 71 cm off the ground. What is the book's change in gravitational potential energy?

Elastic Potential Energy

Use the formula for elastic potential energy to solve the problems below. Neglect friction and other dissipative forces in all problems. Use $g = 9.8$ m/s^2.

1. To store stacks of clean plates, a cafeteria uses a closed cart with a spring-loaded shelf inside. Customers can take plates off the stack one at a time through a hole in the top. A stack of plates compresses the spring 0.40 m. The spring constant is 240 N/m. What is the elastic potential energy of the spring?

2. Customers take plates from the cart described above. As a result, the spring moves up to be compressed by only 0.30 m. What is the change in elastic potential energy?

3. In her garage, a bicyclist hangs a box of bike parts from a long spring attached to the ceiling. The spring stretches 0.80 m with the box attached and has a spring constant of 150 N/m. What is the elastic potential energy stored in the spring?

4. The bicyclist from Problem 3 returns from the bike shop with more parts, which she puts in the box. Now the spring stretches down 1.0 m. What is the change in the elastic potential energy stored in the spring?

Electric Potential Energy

Use the formula for electric potential energy to solve the problems below. Neglect friction and other dissipative forces in all problems. Use $k = 9.0 \times 10^9$ N m²/C².

1. A fixed source charge particle of 4.1 nC and a second particle with charge 2.4 nC are separated by a distance of 3.5 cm.
   a) What is the electric potential energy between the particles?
   b) If the second particle is released, will it move toward or away from the source charge?

2. Two small spheres carry charges of 1.9 nC and −2.8 nC, respectively. They are initially separated by a distance of 2.5 cm.
   a) What is the electric potential energy between the spheres?
   b) If the spheres are free to move, will they move toward or away from each other?

3. A fixed particle with charge −8.8 nC and a second particle with charge −4.3 nC, respectively, are initially separated by a distance of 0.11 m. They are released and the second particle moves 0.030 m.
   a) What is the change in electric potential energy?
   b) Did the second particle move toward or away from the source charge?
   c) How was the electric potential energy used?

Kinetic Energy

**Use the formula for kinetic energy to solve the problems below.
Neglect friction and other dissipative forces in all problems.
Use $g = 9.8$ m/s².**

1. An egg with mass 50.0 g falls out of a nest. A short time later, the egg is falling at 12 m/s. What is its kinetic energy?

2. A toy cannon launches a 46-g golf ball straight up into the air with a kinetic energy of 6.8 J. What must the ball's velocity be as it leaves the cannon?

3. A hockey player shoots a puck across the ice with kinetic energy 63 J and velocity 28 m/s. What is the mass of the puck in grams?

4. A child is riding downhill in a wagon with a combined mass of 28 kg. Suppose the wagon's speed increases from 2.4 m/s to 3.7 m/s.
   a) What is the change in the kinetic energy of the wagon and child?
   b) What is a likely source of this change in kinetic energy?

Laws of Thermodynamics

dlc.com/ca11056s

LESSON OVERVIEW

Lesson Questions

- What is thermodynamics, and how does it explain the transfer of energy by work or heat?
- What is the difference between an open, a closed, and an isolated system?
- What determines an object's internal energy? What are the laws of thermodynamics?
- How can we distinguish reversible from irreversible processes?

Lesson Objectives

By the end of the lesson, you should be able to:

- Cite evidence that internal energy is the total energy within an object or a system, and includes the kinetic (rotation, vibration, and translation) and potential energy of the particles that make up the object or system.

Key Vocabulary

Which terms do you already know?

- ☐ closed system
- ☐ entropy
- ☐ gas
- ☐ heat energy
- ☐ heat
- ☐ internal energy
- ☐ irreversible process
- ☐ isolated system
- ☐ laws of thermodynamics
- ☐ open system
- ☐ reversible process
- ☐ thermal energy
- ☐ work

Lesson Objectives continued

- Apply the laws of thermodynamics to describe systems.
- Explain the difference between open, closed, and isolated systems, and provide examples.
- Understand how the laws of thermodynamics govern the behavior of matter and energy.
- Distinguish between reversible and irreversible processes.

How Vehicle Engines Function

dlc.com/ca11057s

When was the last time you took a trip in a car, bus, train or plane? Or maybe you mostly walk from place to place—even so, the goods you use probably arrive at the store by some kind of delivery vehicle. If the goods traveled a long distance to reach the store, then many different vehicles may have been involved in transporting them. What sorts of engines power these vehicles? How do they work? What is the history and technology behind them?

TRUCK ENGINE

A process occurs in which energy is transferred from the fuel of a motor vehicle to the rotational motion of the vehicle's wheel and axle. How does the engine of a vehicle such as a truck or a car function when such a scenario takes place?

EXPLAIN QUESTION

How do the laws of thermodynamics determine the function and efficiency of various technology systems?

What Is Thermodynamics, and How Does It Explain the Transfer of Energy by Work or Heat?

What Is Thermodynamics?

Many artificial and most natural systems involve the transfer of energy as **heat**. Thermodynamics is the area of physics that looks at processes in which energy is transferred by heat and **work**. For instance, an internal combustion engine converts the chemical energy in gasoline into **thermal energy** and eventually into work to turn the car's axle. **The laws of thermodynamics** govern the processes that take place inside an internal combustion engine. Examples of thermodynamics are everywhere. When a pot of water is heated on a stove, thermodynamics predicts how the thermal energy from the stove will affect the temperature of the water over time.

CAR ENGINE

The processes inside an internal combustion engine are one example of the laws of thermodynamics in action. How does energy change forms in an internal combustion engine?

What Is Thermal Energy and How Is It Transferred?

Thermal energy is a form of energy. Heat is the transfer of thermal energy from one object to another. Thermal energy is transferred any time a lower-temperature object is brought into contact with a higher-temperature object. Thermal energy flows from higher-temperature objects to lower-temperature objects. For example, if a teacup at room temperature is filled with tea, heat transfers thermal energy from the hot tea to the room-temperature cup. This transfer of thermal energy will increase the temperature of the cup. That is why people generally think twice before touching a hot cup of tea.

Eventually, heat will transfer enough energy that the two objects (the tea and the cup) will reach a state of thermal equilibrium. Thermal equilibrium occurs when two objects (or systems) are in thermal contact, but there is no longer any exchange of thermal energy between them. At thermal equilibrium, both the tea and the cup have the same temperature. Eventually, the tea and the cup will also reach thermal equilibrium with the air. The cup and the tea will give up thermal energy to the air until all three have the same temperature.

What Is the Difference between an Open, a Closed, and an Isolated System?

What Is a System?

A system is simply a collection of one or more distinct objects. In thermodynamics, it is often useful to define a system to help analyze a situation. It is also useful to define an environment that surrounds the system. Once the system is defined, the environment is anything external to the system that can influence it.

A system and its environment can be defined in any way that is convenient for analysis. For instance, in the case of a pot of boiling water, it may be convenient to define the system as the metal pot and the water inside it. Everything else is the environment. Therefore, **thermal energy** transferred from the stove to the pot of water would be an input of energy from the environment to the system.

Types of Systems

To study thermodynamics, it is useful to define different types of systems.

In a **closed system**, mass cannot enter or leave the system, but energy is free to enter or leave the system. A greenhouse is an example of a closed system (assuming it is sealed to the outside environment). Mass cannot enter or leave the greenhouse. However, energy can enter or leave, because both light and **heat** can pass through the windows of the greenhouse. Different types of closed systems can be built. These are systems that can exchange both heat and **work**, or just one of the two, with the environment.

A CLOSED SYSTEM

A greenhouse is an example of a closed system, because mass cannot enter or leave the system (assuming the structure remains closed). What forms of energy can be exchanged in a greenhouse system?

In an **open system**, both mass and energy can enter or leave the system. The Atlantic Ocean is an example of an open system, because mass can enter the system via currents from other bodies of water. Energy can also enter the system from a variety of sources, such as light from the sun or geothermal energy from Earth's crust.

AN OPEN SYSTEM

This image shows heat signatures of the Atlantic Ocean. The Atlantic Ocean is an example of an open system, because mass in the form of ocean currents, as well as energy, can enter the system. What are the sources of energy in an ocean system?

In an **isolated system**, neither energy nor mass can enter or leave the system. The only truly **isolated system** is the universe itself. However, in practice, some systems can closely approximate an isolated system, because they allow very little energy or mass to enter or leave.

What Determines an Object's Internal Energy?

What Is Internal Energy?

The **internal energy** of an object is the sum of all the kinetic and potential energies of each molecule in the object. It is a useful concept for understanding **the laws of thermodynamics**.

Determining the internal energy of an ideal monatomic **gas** is simplest. Monatomic means that there is just one atom per molecule rather than two or more atoms bonded together. Molecules of a **gas** are in constant motion, constantly bouncing off the other molecules of the gas. The motion of these molecules accounts for the kinetic energy of the gas. The faster the molecules move, the greater the kinetic energy, since kinetic energy is directly proportional to the square of the magnitude of the object's velocity. In a gas, the velocity of the molecules increases as the temperature increases.

Therefore, the kinetic energy increases as the temperature increases. The internal energy also depends on the gravitational potential energy of these molecules due to their position.

The internal energy of a liquid or solid can be determined as well. However, it is more complicated, since the internal energy depends more heavily on the energy stored in the chemical bonds between atoms and molecules. The internal energy of a solid or liquid has more potential energy from these interactions than does the internal energy of a gas system.

What Are the Laws of Thermodynamics?

The Zeroth Law of Thermodynamics

The most basic law of thermodynamics has a rather unusual name. Scientists realized after discovering the first and second laws of thermodynamics that this law needed to be stated first. So, it was named the zeroth law to make sure it was placed before the first and second laws.

When two objects are at different temperatures and left in contact with one another, it makes sense that they will eventually reach the same temperature. When this happens, the two objects are in thermal equilibrium. The zeroth law of thermodynamics states that if two objects, A and B, are in thermal equilibrium, and A is also in thermal equilibrium with a third object, C, then B and C must also be in thermal equilibrium. This statement is the thermodynamic equivalent of a similar mathematical principle known as transitivity: If x is equal to y, and x is equal to z, then y is equal to z.

The First Law of Thermodynamics

As noted earlier, the **internal energy** of a system is the sum of all the energies of the molecules in the system. This includes all the kinetic energy and potential energy of the molecules. The internal energy of a system can increase in one of two ways: (1) if **thermal energy** is added to the system, or (2) if **work** is done on the system. Using this idea, an important relationship can be stated. The change in internal energy of a system (ΔU) is equal to the thermal energy added by **heat** to the system (Q) plus the work done on the system (W). In equation form, this is written

$$\Delta U = Q + W$$

This relationship, called the first law of thermodynamics, is one of the great laws of physics. It is another way of stating the principle of conservation of energy.

BOILING WATER

Heating the pot of water raises the internal energy of the system as predicted by the first law of thermodynamics. What is the evidence that work is being done on the water?

Thermal energy added to the system is considered positive and, therefore, increases the internal energy of the system. If thermal energy leaves the system, then Q will be negative and the internal energy will decrease. Work in the first law of thermodynamics is defined as work done on the system. If work is done on the system, it will increase the internal energy of the system (since energy is entering the system). If work is done on the system, then W will be positive, and the internal energy of the system will increase. If work is done by the system, then W will be negative, and the internal energy of the system will decrease.

One good example of the first law in action is a cooling system in an air conditioner. Several devices operate on a refrigerant, a substance that boils at less than room temperature, and take it through a thermodynamic cycle.

- A compressor compresses low pressure vapor to high pressure vapor ($W > 0$).
- A condenser cools high pressure vapor to high pressure liquid ($Q < 0$).
- An expansion (or throttle) valve expands high pressure liquid to low pressure liquid and vapor ($W < 0$).
- An evaporator boils low pressure liquid and vapor to low pressure vapor again by absorbing thermal energy from a room ($Q > 0$).

This cycle cools a room and exhausts hot air to the environment outside the room. The internal energy of the refrigerant changes in every step of this process but returns to the same value every time it passes through the same point in the cycle.

The Second Law of Thermodynamics

The first law of thermodynamics is a restatement of conservation of energy. All processes in nature conserve energy. However, examples of processes that conserve energy and yet never actually happen can also be described. For instance, if you drop a rock from a cliff, the gravitational potential energy is converted to kinetic energy as it falls. The energy is conserved. Now imagine the reverse process. If the same rock suddenly rose from the ground and returned to its initial height, energy would also be conserved. Obviously, that doesn't happen naturally. There are other examples of this kind. When a plate shatters on the floor, energy is conserved. Energy would also be conserved if the plate were to suddenly reassemble itself and restore the chemical bonds that were broken. Yet that never happens either. Why?

The second law of thermodynamics helps to answer this question by explaining which processes occur in nature and which do not. It can be stated in a variety of ways, but the most general form of the second law of thermodynamics involves the concept of entropy. Entropy can be thought of as a measure of the order or disorder of a system. More disordered systems have higher **entropy**. In terms of entropy, the second law of thermodynamics states that:

In any natural process, the total entropy of a system and its surrounding environment must increase.

This makes sense when applied to the example of a plate shattering on the floor. When the plate shatters, the disorder of the system increases and therefore is allowed by the second law. A plate that naturally puts itself back together would decrease the disorder (that is, increase the order) of the system. This would violate the second law of thermodynamics and, therefore, could never naturally occur.

IRREVERSIBLE PROCESSES

The second law of thermodynamics predicts that plates can shatter because entropy increases in this process. How much work would have to be done to the plate to get it back to its original state?

An equivalent form of the second law of thermodynamics relates to thermal energy directly and states as follows:

Thermal energy can flow spontaneously from a higher-temperature object to a lower-temperature object, but thermal energy will never flow spontaneously from a lower-temperature object to a higher-temperature object.

The Third Law of Thermodynamics

The third law of thermodynamics sets a limit on the temperatures that objects can reach. The third law states as follows:

At absolute zero all processes stop and entropy reaches a minimum value.

In practice, it is not possible for all processes to stop entirely. Hence, absolute zero is an unattainable limit.

How Can We Distinguish Reversible from Irreversible Processes?

Engines

A **reversible process** is one that can be done in reverse without changing the total energy of the system. Are there reversible processes? Are, for example, the processes of engines reversible? In reality, no fully reversible processes exist, due to factors such as friction and turbulence. No matter how efficient engines are, some amount of energy is lost to the surroundings. This means that they can never convert 100% of the energy that is put into them into useful **work**. An idealized engine, called a Carnot engine, is defined in theoretical terms. Such an engine requires that its processes are entirely reversible.

Instead, only irreversible processes exist. These processes cannot be reversed without changing the energy of the system. While the Carnot engine cannot exist in the real world, it is possible to define systems that change states so gradually that the processes causing the changes can be considered "nearly reversible." This is because there is only a small change in the energy of the system.

Consider the Explain Question

| How do the laws of thermodynamics determine the function and efficiency of various technology systems?

Go online to complete the scientific explanation.

dlc.com/ca11058s

Check Your Understanding

| Go online to check your understanding of this concept's key ideas.

dlc.com/ca11059s

STEM in Action

Applying the Laws of Thermodynamics

People have always tried to control the temperature of their environment by burning wood or other fuels as a source of warmth. The options for cooling a space were much more limited, however. Before the turn of the 20th century, indoor cooling was limited to trapping the cooler nighttime air in a room for as long as possible, or having thick stone walls that took a lot of energy to **heat** up. The first practical air conditioner was invented in the early 1900s. Air conditioners essentially **work** like heat engines, but in reverse. They make use of the fact that phase changes can both absorb and release **thermal energy**, depending on the direction of the change. When a **gas** condenses and becomes a liquid, it releases thermal energy into its environment. However, when a liquid evaporates and becomes a **gas**, it absorbs thermal energy from its surroundings, thus cooling them.

WIND TOWER

This wind tower was the first form of air conditioning. How do the laws of thermodynamics explain how it could be used used to make ice?

Air conditioners use the principles of thermodynamics to cool the air inside a room. Warm air from indoors flows over cold, low-pressure evaporator coils filled with a fluid known as a refrigerant. Within the coils, the refrigerant absorbs some of the thermal energy from the indoor air. In the process, the refrigerant evaporates from a liquid to a gas. This lowers the temperature of the air, which may then be circulated throughout the building using a fan. The evaporator coils are usually inside the building, built into the furnace unit.

Next, the refrigerant is pumped outside the building where the compressor puts the refrigerant under high pressure. This compression causes more unwanted thermal energy to build up in the refrigerant, so a second fan is used to blow ambient outdoor air over the hot condenser coils and out into the atmosphere. This is why you often feel a gust of hot air when walking by the part of an air conditioner that is outside a building. The outdoor air absorbs the thermal energy from the condenser coils and cools the pressurized refrigerant. The liquid refrigerant is then pumped through an expansion valve, where it cools—without gaining or losing heat—before going back inside the building as liquid refrigerant. Just like a heat engine, an air conditioner runs in a repeating thermodynamic cycle. The refrigerant is constantly being converted from a liquid to a gas and back to a liquid again.

HOW AN AIR CONDITIONER WORKS

This diagram explains how an air conditioner functions. What role do the laws of thermodynamics and changes in volume, pressure, and temperature of air play in an air conditioning system?

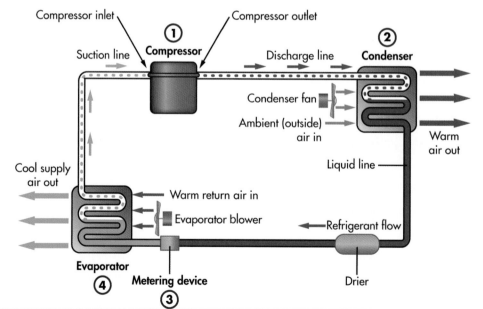

Another kind of cooling device is the evaporative cooler, sometimes called a swamp cooler, which uses the heat of evaporation of water to cool a space. An evaporative cooler works well in hot, dry climates such as deserts. Instead of passing over cooling coils, in an evaporative cooler the outdoor air is used to evaporate water from a pad; the evaporating water both cools and humidifies the air as it enters the building. Evaporative coolers cost less, and use less energy, than compressor-based air conditioners, but their reliance on evaporation limits their use to arid climates.

STEM and the Laws of Thermodynamics

The invention of air conditioning had an impact on architecture and on urban development. Architects could use materials and design features that were less hindered by the need to insulate against the heat. For instance, glass skyscrapers became much more widespread because architects did not need to worry as much about radiant heat from the sun coming through the windows. The availability of air conditioning also meant that many more people were willing to live in climates with long, hot summers. Cities like Los Angeles, Phoenix, and Las Vegas have grown as large as they have in part because of the availability of air conditioning. The city of Dubai in the United Arab Emirates also would not exist without the availability of air conditioning.

FLOATING PAVILION

Energy efficient structures such as the Floating Pavilion in the Netherlands are designed to reduce the negative impact that a structure can have on the environment. What thermodynamic principles do you think are used in its design?

But running air conditioners is expensive and uses a great deal of energy, and although they cool the air inside a building, the heat they dump outdoors raises the temperature of the city itself. Today, concern for the environment along with dwindling natural resources have led many architects to reconsider their building designs and return to the design principles used before the advent of modern heating and cooling technologies. **The laws of thermodynamics** can be used to heat and cool a structure without relying on external energy sources. Insulating materials can be used to trap the heat inside a building and prevent the indoor temperature from dropping. Passive solar designs utilize a building's exposure to the sun to retain solar energy during cold seasons and eliminate it during warmer seasons. Even the material used to line the roof of a structure can be used to regulate the amount of heat circulating within a building. In order to create energy-efficient homes and buildings, an architect must have a thorough understanding of the laws of thermodynamics.

First Law of Thermodynamics

Use the first law of thermodynamics to solve the problems below.

1. This question has two parts.

   A. A small, closed chamber of gas is heated. When the gas in the chamber expands, it does 5 J of work on a piston. The gas has an initial energy of 8 J and a final energy of 30 J. Considering the equation for the first law of thermodynamics ($\Delta U = Q + W$), does the work done in this scenario have a positive or negative value? Explain.

   B. How much heat is added to the gas in the chamber?

2. 150 J of work is done on a closed system, and 270 J of heat is added to the system. Does the internal energy of the system increase, decrease, or stay the same? If the internal energy changes, state the change in energy.

3. In an isothermal system, a chamber is filled with gas and a piston rests atop the chamber. The initial internal energy of the system is 3,500 J. When heat is added to the gas, the piston rises. If 2,000 J of heat is added to the system, how much work will the gas do on the piston? (Assume this is an ideal system in which energy transfer is 100% efficient.)

Electricity and Magnetism

Image: Bosca78 / E+ / Getty Images

© Discovery Education | www.discoveryeducation.com

LESSON OVERVIEW

Lesson Questions

■ How did the study of the photoelectric effect lead to a better understanding of the dual nature of light?

■ What are some common examples of electric and magnetic forces at work?

■ What is Coulomb's law, and how can it be used to describe the relationship between attractive and repulsive forces?

■ How are electromagnetic waves generated?

■ How do electricity and magnetism relate to the more general phenomenon of electromagnetism?

Key Vocabulary

Which terms do you already know?

- [ ] Coulomb's law
- [ ] distance
- [ ] electric field
- [ ] electromagnetic wave
- [ ] electromagnetism
- [ ] electron
- [ ] energy
- [ ] frequency
- [ ] induction
- [ ] magnetic field
- [ ] photoelectric effect
- [ ] photon
- [ ] plasma
- [ ] transverse waves
- [ ] vector
- [ ] voltage

dlc.com/ca11060s

Lesson Objectives

By the end of the lesson, you should be able to:

- Relate the study of the photoelectric effect to advances in understanding the dual nature of light.

- Cite evidence that demonstrates common examples of electric and magnetic forces.

- Relate the acceleration of a charged particle to the generation of electromagnetic waves.

- Distinguish the behavior and interactions of electricity and magnetism as related forces of electromagnetism that can be used in technological devices to transmit and capture information and energy.

- Analyze electrostatic forces between objects using mathematical representations of Coulomb's law to describe and predict the effects of electrostatic forces between objects.

Interactions of Electricity and Magnetism

Have you ever seen the aurora borealis or perhaps the aurora australis? These awe-inspiring phenomena are direct results of electric and magnetic forces. Solar winds emit energy from the sun, and this energy interacts with Earth's magnetic field. This interaction sets off a series of events that can result in vivid light displays. Why don't we see the light displays in all locations on Earth and throughout the day?

dlc.com/ca11061s

EXPLAIN QUESTION

How does the interaction between electric and magnetic energy produce phenomena such as the aurora borealis?

THE NORTHERN LIGHTS

Electric and magnetic forces are everywhere. How do they create the spectacular light shows known as the northern lights?

How Did the Study of the Photoelectric Effect Lead to a Better Understanding of the Dual Nature of Light?

The Photoelectric Effect

In the **photoelectric effect**, a metal emits electrons when light shines on it. The incident light transfers **energy** to the electrons of the atoms that make up the metal. The energy causes the electrons to overcome their attraction to atomic nuclei, making them "free" electrons. These free electrons can produce a current in a circuit connected to the metal.

This phenomenon, called the photoelectric effect, may sound simple. But the explanation provided by Einstein revolutionized physics in the early 1900s. Named because of the connection between light and electricity, the photoelectric effect could be explained only by thinking about light as distinct energy packets, called photons, not as waves. Why?

Researchers observed that a curious aspect of the photoelectric effect is that only certain frequencies of light cause electrons to be emitted. For example, red light, no matter how intense, does not produce free electrons in a metal. On the other extreme, even the dimmest of blue lights cause **electron** emission. If light is purely a wave, then increasing the intensity of red light should eventually provide enough energy to free electrons. However, scientists found that even very intense red light did not cause the metal to release electrons. This fact reveals the particle nature of light.

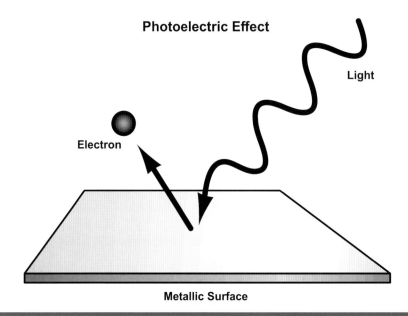

Photoelectric Effect

Light

Electron

Metallic Surface

PHOTOELECTRIC EFFECT

The photoelectric effect describes how electrons can be ejected from an atom when light is absorbed. What requirement must be met for light to result in the ejection of an electron?

As well as being a wave, light should be thought of as photons, or packets of energy. That would explain why the different frequencies of light affected metal in the experiment differently. This shift in thinking opened the door for quantum theory and launched one of the most persistent scientific conundrums in history: the wave-particle duality of light.

The Compton effect provides more evidence of the particle nature of light. In 1922, the physicist Arthur Compton did experiments in which he crashed gamma-ray and X-ray photons into electrons. After the collisions, the photons had lower energy and the electrons had higher energy, just as you would expect from a collision between two particles.

Dual Nature of Light

Einstein's explanation of the photoelectric effect (that light is made of particles called photons) consistently explains experimental data. On the other hand, a long history of experiments prove that light is a wave. Light can interfere and diffract. These are wavelike behaviors. Yet, the photoelectric effect and other experiments seem to confirm that light is composed of discrete packets with energy determined by the light's **frequency**. Both interpretations seem accurate. Light behaves like both waves and particles. Scientists have found that the conditions of an experiment determine which characteristic of light will be revealed.

It is not just light that can be a particle or a wave. With the right experimental setup, matter itself can be coaxed into acting like a wave. Electrons and other small-scale particles can act like waves by interfering and diffracting and by showing other wavelike properties. Larger scale objects, such as a bowling ball, would have such small wavelengths that only their particle nature can be observed. In theory, all matter and all light acts like waves and particles.

What Are Some Common Examples of Electric and Magnetic Forces at Work?

Electrical Forces

An electrical force is an attraction or repulsion between two charged objects. Every charged particle is surrounded by an **electric field**. Any other charged particle in that field will experience an electrical force due to the original charged particle. The intensity of the electric field at a point is defined to be the force a positive test charge would experience at the position.

THE TRUMP GLOBE

Any metal object, including the Trump Globe displayed at Columbus Circle in New York City, can hold electrical charge. What would happen to this sculpture if it were not grounded to Earth by a metal pole?

The magnitude of the electrical force that a particle exerts on another particle is directly proportional to the product of their charges and inversely proportional to the square of the **distance** between them. The direction of the force is along the line joining the particles. As with other forces, the motion and acceleration caused by electrical forces can be described by Newton's laws of motion.

One big difference between electrical forces and gravitational forces is that gravitational forces act only to attract two bodies to one another, whereas electrical force can be attractive or repulsive. Gravity, like electricity, is a force that acts on two bodies.

An example of electrical force in everyday life is when someone's feet rub on the floor before touching a metal doorknob. A spark will jump. The spark can cross through air due to **energy** from the electrical force.

Electrical forces all trace back to the fundamental electrical force between electrons and protons. In an atom, the electrical force is many orders of magnitude stronger than the gravitational force, and many of the fundamental characteristics of atoms and molecules are determined by electrical forces.

What Is Coulomb's Law, and How Can It Be Used to Describe the Relationship between Attractive and Repulsive Forces?

Coulomb's Law

Charges in electric fields are subject to forces. Coulomb's law describes the electrostatic force between two charged particles.

When charged particles are in motion, the forces become complex. For charges at rest, the formulation of Coulomb's law states: The magnitude of the force of interaction between two point charges is directly proportional to the product of the magnitudes of charges and inversely proportional to the square of the **distance** between them. In the equation form, Coulomb's law is written as follows:

$$F = \frac{kq_1q_2}{d^2}$$

where F is the electrical force, q_1 and q_2 are the charges, d is the distance between the charges, and k is a constant (approximately 8.99×10^9 N·m^2/C^2) called Coulomb's constant.

The sign of the calculated value of the force can be used to determine whether the force is attractive or repulsive. If the two charges have the same sign, the calculated force will be positive. This means that a positive electrical force is repulsive. If the two charges have opposite signs, the calculated force will be negative. This means that a negative electrical force is attractive.

ELECTROSTATIC FORCES

In this experiment, repulsive forces between each pair of charged objects push them away from each other. Is the electrical force between each pair positive or negative?

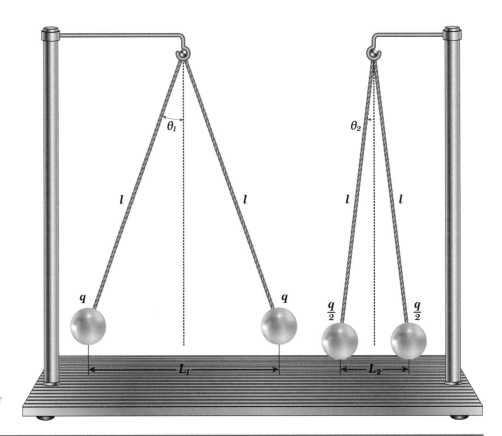

Electrostatic force, like gravitational force, is inversely proportional to the square of the distance between the two charges. This inverse square "law" is shared with other physics phenomena that include gravitation, electrostatics, electromagnetic radiation, acoustics, and other domains. One reason for the similarity is that because point sources of **energy** or fields spread out in all directions, the total area covered represents an increasingly larger sphere. Because the surface area of a sphere increases with the square of its radius, the intensity of the source would decrease with the square of the distance.

This means that the electrostatic force between any two charged objects quickly becomes smaller as the distance increases. Suppose the distance between two charges is twice as big. Then the electrostatic force becomes $1/(2)^2$, or one-fourth, as strong as it was before. Making the distance three times as large makes the force one-ninth as large. The force on charges that are four times as far away as two similar charges is only one-sixteenth as big. On the other hand, if the distance is one-half as large, the force is four times larger. Two charges that are a tenth as far apart as two similar charges will experience a force 100 times as big.

Coulomb's Law: Sample Problem

Two charges experience a repulsive force of 64 N. What will the force be if the distance between the two charges is quadrupled?

Solution:

The magnitude of force that a particle exerts on another particle is directly proportional to the product of their charges and inversely proportional to the square of the distance between them: $F = \dfrac{kq_1q_2}{d^2}$.

If q_1 and q_2 are the charges and d is the original distance between them, then

$$F = \frac{kq_1q_2}{d^2} = 64 \text{ N}$$

If the distance is quadrupled, the new force F_2 can be calculated as follows:

$$F_2 = \frac{kq_1q_2}{(4d)^2}$$
$$= \frac{kq_1q_2}{16d^2}$$
$$= \left(\frac{1}{16}\right)\frac{kq_1q_2}{d^2}$$
$$= \left(\frac{1}{16}\right)F$$
$$= \left(\frac{1}{16}\right)(64 \text{ N})$$
$$= 4.0 \text{ N}$$

This can also be verified by thinking about the fact that the force is inversely proportional to the square of the distance. If r is replaced by $4r$, the new force will be 1/16 of the old force. Thus, the new force will be 4.0 N.

Magnetic Forces

Magnetic forces affect magnetic objects. Magnetic fields arise either from permanent magnets or from the flow of electrons in a current. The motion of electrical charge and, therefore, the motion of an **electric field** give rise to a **magnetic field**. Any moving charge creates a magnetic field.

Single electrical charges can exist, but no one has ever found an isolated magnetic pole. In a permanent magnet, the motion of electrons that resembles "spin" gives each atom a magnetic field, and the alignment of many of these atoms forms a permanent magnet. There are always two poles to a magnet: a north pole and a south pole. Magnetic field lines always loop around and close in on themselves. Like poles of different magnets repel, while opposite poles attract.

An everyday example of magnetic force is the force that holds a magnet to a refrigerator. During manufacturing, a refrigerator magnet has a strong magnet applied that shapes its magnetic orientation and strength. A compass, which works based on Earth's magnetic field lines, is another example of a common use of magnetic forces.

COMPASS

The magnetic dial in a compass indicates Earth's magnetic north. How could the compass be used to show the direction of Earth's magnetic field?

Just as the moving electric field around a moving charge produces a magnetic field, the movement of electrical charge in a conductor produces a magnetic field. An electromagnet is an example of this kind of magnetic field. Current passes through continuous loops of wire in a coil, each loop contributing its magnetic field. Just as a permanent magnet is made stronger by the alignment of many small atomic magnetic fields, so an electromagnet is made stronger by more wire loops that carry the electric current.

PERMANENT MAGNET

Magnetic fields form around permanent magnets. What is the relationship between the north and south poles of a magnet?

This is not the only connection between electric and magnetic fields. An electric field is present with one or more electrical charges, but an electric field can be produced by a magnetic field that is in motion. This can be observed if a coil of wire is in a circuit that has no source of electric current. If a constant magnetic field is present in the coil, nothing will happen. But if the magnetic field changes its strength or moves with respect to the coil, an electric current will appear in the coil.

How Are Electromagnetic Waves Generated?

Acceleration of Charged Particles

Charged particles create electric fields. When a charged particle moves, that **electric field** changes. A changing electric field induces a **magnetic field**. If a charged particle accelerates, then the induced magnetic field also changes and a changing magnetic field induces an electric field. The acceleration does not have to be an increase in the magnitude of the velocity. It could also mean a change in direction, as would be the case if a charge moves in a circle.

While electric and magnetic fields have different characteristics, they are coupled together. The mutual interaction between electric and magnetic fields is known as **electromagnetism**.

Particle accelerators take advantage of the relationship between charged particles and electromagnetic fields. They tune electromagnetic fields to create tight beams of charged particles that are accelerated to speeds close to the speed of light. These charged particles collide with a target or other particles. The resultant collisions can be studied to reveal the structure and makeup of subatomic particles.

How Electromagnetic Waves Propagate

Electricity and magnetism are related through electromagnetism. Electromagnetic waves are generated when electric and magnetic fields fluctuate simultaneously.

Several principles combine to help explain electromagnetic propagation. Faraday's law of **induction** explains how a changing magnetic field induces an electric field. This law of induction explains how electric generators work. These devices use moving magnets to induce electrical current.

This law of induction is not enough to explain how electromagnetic waves propagate. Maxwell's equations, a set of four mathematical relationships, describe the underpinnings of electric and magnetic fields. A summary of these four points is as follows:

■ Electrical charges give rise to electric fields.
■ Magnets always come in pairs with opposite poles.
■ Electric current induces a magnetic field.
■ A changing magnetic field can induce a current in a wire.

These concepts explain how electric and magnetic fields interact to create electromagnetic waves that propagate as light.

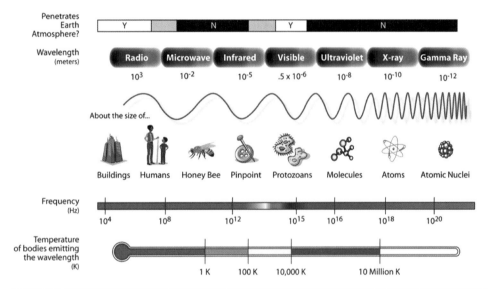

ELECTROMAGNETIC SPECTRUM

Electromagnetic waves are detectable by various devices, and some by the human eye. How do scientists use the electromagnetic spectrum for research?

How Do Electricity and Magnetism Relate to the More General Phenomenon of Electromagnetism?

Electricity

Electrical charge is a fundamental property of particles. Examples of charged particles include electrons, which have a negative charge, and protons, which have a positive charge. Charged particles give rise to an **electric field** whether they are in motion or not.

The strength of an electric field at any point depends on the magnitude of the charge as well as the distance from the charge. Any charge in an electric field will experience a force. Another way to think about this is that any two charged particles experience an electrical force. In this way, gravitational forces, in which two masses experience a resultant gravitational force, can be a helpful analogy.

When charged particles move, a current is created. Electrical current is precisely the flow of charged particles, so electricity is related to moving charges.

A changing **magnetic field** can make charged particles move. This means that shifting magnets around near a metal wire can induce an electric current in the wire. The reason the wire needs to be a metal is that metals have a molecular structure that freely releases electrons and allows them to flow. Materials that do not release electrons will not sustain a current.

Magnetism

Some materials are naturally magnetic, such as lodestone. Other materials can become magnetic if placed in an external magnetic field. Still other materials, such as wires, can have a magnetic field induced around them. Electromagnets, which work as an electric current passes through coils of wire, use this principle.

When charged particles move, their moving electric fields create magnetic fields. That is why a current in a wire is surrounded by a magnetic field. The strength and structure of the magnetic field depend on the strength and direction of the current. Like electric fields, magnetic fields can exert forces on charged particles.

One important difference between electricity and magnetism is that a single charged particle can create an electric field. The charge can be positive or negative. Magnetic poles always come in pairs: a north pole and a south pole.

Earth is a giant magnet, having north and south magnetic poles. These are near, but not actually at the geographic north pole and south pole. Research has shown that the planet's magnetic field has flipped several times in its history.

Electromagnetism

Concepts of **electromagnetism** describe the combined effect of electric and magnetic fields as they induce and respond to forces. Electromagnetic waves are transverse **energy** waves that propagate in a direction perpendicular to both the magnetic and electric fields.

An electromagnet is a coil of wire wrapped around a metal (usually iron) core. When current flows through the wire, the core becomes a magnet. More turns of the wire create a stronger magnet. Generators, transformers, and many other modern devices depend on electromagnets.

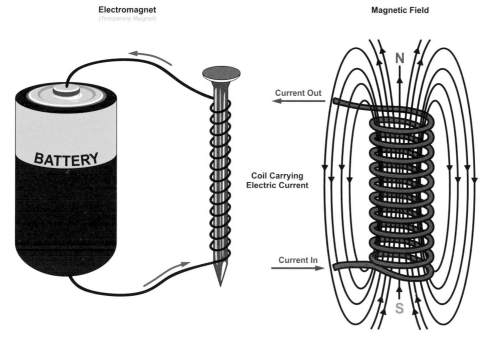

Electromagnet
(Temporary Magnet)

BATTERY

Magnetic Field

N

Current Out

Coil Carrying
Electric Current

Current In

S

ELECTROMAGNETISM

A nail surrounded by coil and connected to a battery cell produces an electromagnetic field. What rules govern the properties of the field?

Consider the Explain Question

| How does the interaction between electric and magnetic energy produce phenomena such as the aurora borealis?

dlc.com/ca11062s

Check Your Understanding

| Can you provide evidence that electricity and magnetism are really only one force: electromagnetism?

dlc.com/ca11063s

 **in Action**

Applying Electricity and Magnetism

You use electricity every day; without it, your life would be very different from what it is now. You would not be able to talk on a cellphone, watch television, search the Internet on a computer, or use a toaster to make toast. But do you know where electricity comes from and how it can be generated?

An electric current is a group of the same type of charges moving in the same direction. Generators produce an electric current by moving a wire through a **magnetic field** or, equivalently, by changing the magnetic field near a stationary wire. In one commonly used design, a coil of wire is wrapped around a magnet, and the magnet is spun about a fixed axis. The moving magnetic field causes a current to flow through the wire. This design allows the mechanical **energy** of the spinning magnet to be converted to electrical energy.

Generators convert mechanical motion into an electric current. Motors do just the opposite; they convert the energy of moving charges into mechanical energy.

In a motor, a coil of wire is wrapped around a piece of metal that is attached to a shaft. The coil is surrounded by fixed permanent magnets. When a current flows through the coil, the resulting magnetic field of the current interacts with the magnetic field of the permanent magnets, which makes the coil spin. What devices do you use that contain motors? Locate the motor in one of your devices and examine it to see if you can locate the coil of wire and the permanent magnets.

HOW A MOTOR WORKS

Current flowing through a coil induces a magnetic field. What will cause the coil to spin?

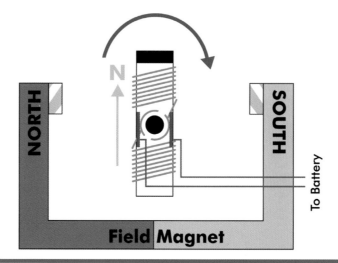

STEM and Electricity and Magnetism

Without an understanding of **electromagnetism**, scientists would not be able to study a critical piece of the puzzle of nature, and we would not know nearly as much about our solar system, galaxy, and beyond.

Light is an **electromagnetic wave**. Visible light makes up only a small part of the much larger electromagnetic spectrum that ranges from radio waves to gamma rays. Every part of the electromagnetic spectrum plays a role in our understanding of the origin and structure of the universe. Think about the awe-inspiring pictures that you have seen of outer space. These pictures are possible because scientists know how to interpret and manipulate data hidden inside electromagnetic waves.

People who study the universe outside of Earth are called astronomers. Since astronomers study distant stars, planets, and galaxies, they are unable to collect data and specimens directly. Instead, they must rely on information contained in the electromagnetic radiation that comes to Earth from far reaches of outer space. Astronomers use telescopes to collect their data. These telescopes are much more sophisticated than the telescope that you might use to look at the moon from your backyard. Professional telescopes are equipped with digital cameras and computers that allow astronomers to analyze the electromagnetic radiation and use the results to map unknown regions of outer space.

SEEING THE UNIVERSE IN A WHOLE NEW LIGHT

ALMA is a special telescope that will allow astronomers to view hidden gases in the universe. What new information about the universe will astronomers learn using this telescope?

Coulomb's Law

Use electricity and magnetism equations to solve the problems below.

1. Two copper spheres are currently 1.2 meters apart. One sphere has a charge of $+2.2 \times 10^{-4}$ C and the other has a charge of -8.9×10^{-4} C. What is the force between the charged spheres? Is the force attractive or repulsive?

2. Two metal rods in a factory are oppositely charged and placed 8.9 cm apart. One rod has a charge of $+7.5 \times 10^{-7}$ C and the other has a charge of -5.1×10^{-5} C. What is the force between the rods? Is it an attractive or repulsive force?

3. Two charged objects in a laboratory are brought to a distance of 0.22 meters away from each other. If the force between the spheres is 4,550 N and the charge on one object is 9.9×10^{-5} C, what is the charge on the other object?

4. What is the force between two protons that are separated by 1.0 mm? The charge of a proton is 1.6×10^{-19} C.

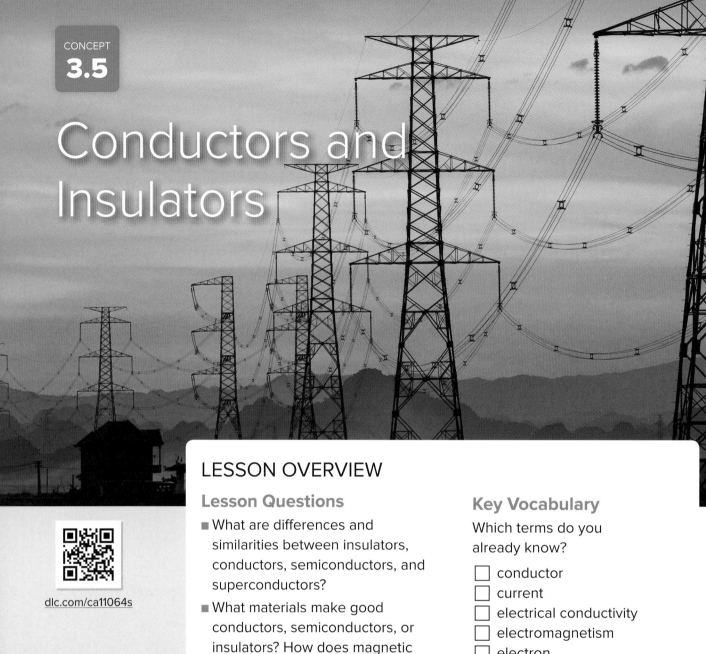

CONCEPT
3.5

Conductors and Insulators

dlc.com/ca11064s

LESSON OVERVIEW

Lesson Questions

- What are differences and similarities between insulators, conductors, semiconductors, and superconductors?
- What materials make good conductors, semiconductors, or insulators? How does magnetic induction create an electric current in a conductor? What are the features of the electric charge on an insulator?

Lesson Objectives

By the end of the lesson, you should be able to:

- Compare insulators, conductors, semiconductors, and superconductors. Classify materials as conductors, semiconductors, or insulators.
- Explain how magnetic induction creates electric current in conductors.
- Provide evidence that electric charge is generally static on insulators.

Key Vocabulary

Which terms do you already know?

- ☐ conductor
- ☐ current
- ☐ electrical conductivity
- ☐ electromagnetism
- ☐ electron
- ☐ induction
- ☐ insulator
- ☐ magnetic field
- ☐ metallic
- ☐ metals
- ☐ resistance
- ☐ semiconductor
- ☐ static electricity
- ☐ superconductor
- ☐ transistor

Birds on a Wire

Have you ever wondered why birds on a telephone wire do not get electrocuted? After all, if you come anywhere near a power line, you will find many "High Voltage" warnings instructing you to not touch any wires or even to go near them. The secret of the birds lies in how electricity moves.

dlc.com/ca11065s

EXPLAIN QUESTION

How does the structure of a material explain its behavior as a conductor or an insulator?

BIRD ON A WIRE

Occasionally, a bird will get electrocuted while on an electrical wire. Why do you think this might happen?

What Are Differences and Similarities between Insulators, Conductors, Semiconductors, and Superconductors?

Conductors and Insulators

Different materials can be classified according to how easily an electric **current** can pass through them. An electric current is a flow of electrons through a material. Different materials have different forces between the particles inside that affect how easily electrons can move about inside the material. In some materials, such as **metals**, negatively charged electrons can move about easily. In others, such as most plastics, electrons cannot move easily through the material.

The **electrical conductivity** of a substance expresses how well the material conducts current. The higher the electrical conductivity, the more easily a current can flow through the substance. Copper has a very high electrical conductivity, while diamond has a very low electrical conductivity.

Conductors are materials that conduct electricity well. Metals are good conductors. For this reason, the electric current in circuits usually runs along a **metal** wire. Electrons can move easily through a conducting material.

Insulators are materials that do not conduct electricity or that conduct electricity very poorly. They are the opposite of conductors. Insulators can be used for safety reasons to prevent the flow of a current. Usually **metal** wires in circuits are coated with a plastic insulating jacket. Electrons cannot move easily through an **insulator**.

THE FIRST TELEGRAPH CABLE, 1837

This piece of telegraph cable, used in the first experimental telegraph, is made up of five copper wires embedded in a wood and resin base. What is the function of the copper wires? What is the function of the wood base?

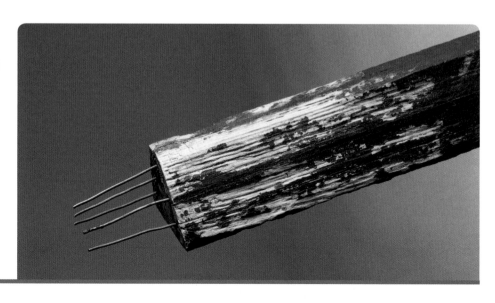

Semiconductors

Semiconductors are materials with an electrical conductivity in between conductors and insulators. Computers, televisions, cell phones—in fact, nearly all modern electrical devices—use semiconductors. Semiconductors are used in the chips that a computer uses to operate. They are used in circuit components called diodes and transistors. These devices are used as tiny switches in circuits that control the flow of current. The microprocessor chips used in computers hold thousands of these tiny diodes and transistors.

USE OF SEMICONDUCTORS

A transistor is made by joining two types of semiconductors. Why are transistors such useful devices in electronic circuits?

Superconductors

Some materials have a very high level of conductivity. In theory, if their temperature is low enough, they have an infinite conductivity because they have no **resistance** to the flow of electrons. These materials are called superconductors, and they are materials that conduct electricity with no resistance.

Superconductors are therefore very efficient for transmitting electric current. One difficulty with superconductors is that all currently known superconducting materials work only at very low temperatures. In fact, the temperature at which most materials can act as a **superconductor** is only −138°C, or equivalently 135 K. However, recently, there have been advances in room temperature superconductors. This class of **superconductor** operates at temperatures of 35°C or 308.15 K.

Mercury is an example of a superconductor, which becomes a superconductor at the extremely low temperature of −269°C, or equivalently 4.2 K.

What Materials Make Good Conductors, Semiconductors, or Insulators?

Materials and Conductivity

Materials that conduct electricity effectively are conductors. Examples of conductors include **metals**. Electrical devices use conductors to transmit **current** through the device. Common electric wires usually are made from copper or aluminum, both of which are metals. Copper and aluminum have particularly high electrical conductivities.

Materials that do not conduct electricity are insulators. Examples of insulators include glass, paper, and plastic. Power cords for electric devices such as computers or cell phone chargers are made from a rubber or plastic insulating coating around a **metal** conducting wire. Rubber and plastic have particularly low electrical conductivities.

Semiconductors are materials with a moderate level of **electrical conductivity**. Examples of semiconductors include silicon and germanium. In fact, pure silicon and pure germanium are better insulators than conductors. Semiconductors are made by combining the pure silicon or germanium with small amounts of certain other materials, including arsenic or boron. The additional material allows electrons to move slightly more freely through the silicon or germanium. Silicon chips used in computers are made from this sort of impure silicon.

CONDUCTIVITY TABLE

This table summarizes the properties of insulators, conductors, and semiconductors. What feature of a material determines whether it is a good, intermediate, or poor conductor of electricity?

Material	Conductivity	Examples
Insulator	Low or none at all	Glass, paper, plastic
Conductor	High	Metals
Semiconductor	Intermediate	Impure silicon, germanium

Extraction of Metals

Metals such as silver and gold are excellent conductors; however, the cost of the metal inhibits the use of the material in industries with high production needs, such as the manufacturing of the wiring found in your home. Copper, however, is a lower cost option with similar conductive performance and is one of the most widely used metals in industry. Copper is used for electrical wiring, heating coils, appliances, and plumbing. Aluminum is another low-cost conductive metal that is used in many industrial applications. Between 1965 and 1974, home builders attempted to use aluminum wiring in homes due to the lightweight nature of the metal and conductive properties. Unfortunately, many house fires were reported, as the aluminum wiring would form an electrically resistant oxide surface when attached to the outlet connection and become a fire hazard.

People obtain minerals and valuable rocks, such as coal, by mining. This generally involves digging into the ground to expose and remove the valuable deposits. Subsurface mines are created by digging tunnels deep beneath the ground. This technique is typically used when concentrated deposits are located at significant depth beneath Earth's surface.

When large or dispersed deposits are located at relatively shallow depths, surface mining techniques may be used. This usually involves removing large amounts of soil and rock covering wide areas. Strip mining exposes a near-surface rock layer. Open-pit mining and quarrying carve away at surface or shallow deposits. Copper extraction is often done in open pit mines. Mountaintop removal is an extreme form of surface mining in which entire mountain peaks are exploded and removed to gather the resources within.

A major concern of any mining project is the waste formed by the process. The waste materials can cause problems with the local water supply. In the case of copper mining, gases are also a byproduct. When the copper is extracted from its ore through a smelting process, the acidic gas sulfur dioxide is produced. This forms acid rain when it meets water vapor in the air.

How Does Magnetic Induction Create an Electric Current in a Conductor?

Magnetic Induction

Motors and electric generators are devices that power many things, including cars, electric fans, and automatic doors. Nearly all the electrical power generated by commercial energy companies used in homes is thanks to electric generators. Electric generators use magnetic **induction** and properties of conductors.

ELECTRIC MOTOR

Electric motors rely on magnetic induction to operate. What are the two main separate parts of an electric motor?

Magnetic induction occurs when a changing **magnetic field** produces a **current** in a **conductor**. The laws of **electromagnetism** state that a changing magnetic field causes charged particles to feel a force. Placing a **conductor** in a changing magnetic field causes the electrons in the conductor to feel a force. Electrons that feel a force from a magnetic field will flow through a conductor. The flow of electrons creates an electric current. Thus, a changing magnetic field induces a current.

Faraday's Law

Faraday's law is the physical law that describes how current is induced by a changing magnetic field. Faraday's law states that the electromotive force, or EMF, induced by a changing magnetic field is related to how fast the magnetic flux changes with time, or, more specifically:

$$\varepsilon = \frac{-N(\varphi_2 - \varphi_1)}{t_2 - t_1}$$

In this equation, ε is the EMF, N is the number of turns of the wire, and t_1 and t_2 are the initial and final times, respectively. The phi symbols, φ_1 and φ_2, are the initial and final values, respectively, for the magnetic flux.

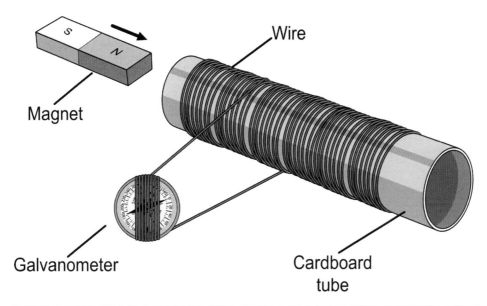

Magnet

Wire

Galvanometer

Cardboard tube

MAGNETIC INDUCTION
Faraday's model is easy to recreate. If you do not have a galvanometer, how else might you determine that an electrical current was being produced?

Magnetic flux is defined as the strength of the magnetic field multiplied by the surface area of the wire loop. It is important to remember that this definition applies only for uniform magnetic fields that are perpendicular to the area of the wire loop. The direction of the induced current is dictated by the "right-hand rule." This means if you point the thumb of your right hand in the direction of the current, the direction in which your fingers curl is the direction of the magnetic field. If the EMF from the above equation is negative, the current flows in the opposite direction.

Faraday's Law: Sample Problem

The following diagram shows a wire, looped three times into a circle with a radius of 10 cm, and placed in a magnetic field (B) of 0.1 T. The tesla (symbol T) is a unit of measure of the strength of a magnetic field.

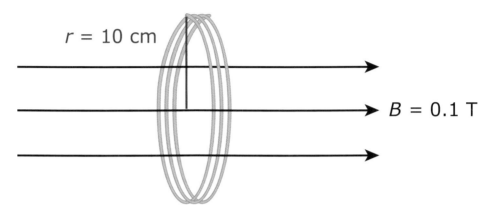

$r = 10$ cm

$B = 0.1$ T

FARADAY'S LAW

A 0.1 Tesla magnetic field passes through a three-turn wire loop with a radius of 10 centimeters. How does the number of turns of this type of wire loop affect the EMF generated in the loop?

What would be the EMF induced in this wire if the magnetic field were increased from 0.1 T to 1 T over a period of 30 seconds?

Solution:

To solve this problem, use the equation for Faraday's law. In this setup, N is 3 and the initial flux is 0.1 T times the surface area of the circle:

$$\phi_1 = (0.1 \text{ T}) [\pi(0.1 \text{ m})^2] = 3.14 = 10^{-3} \text{ T} \times \text{m}^2$$

The surface area of the wire is not changing, but the strength of the magnetic field is. The final magnetic field is 10 times that of the initial magnetic field, meaning the final flux will be 0.031 T $\times$ m². The initial time can be set to zero, meaning the final time is 30 seconds. Putting all of this into the equation for EMF results in the following calculation:

$$\varepsilon = -3 \left(\frac{0.031 \text{ T} \times \text{m}^2 - 3.14 \times 10^{-3} \text{ T} \times \text{m}^2}{30 \text{ s}} \right) = -\left(\frac{0.028 \text{ T} \times \text{m}^2}{10 \text{ s}} \right) = -0.003 \text{ V}$$

The units for EMF are volts (V), so the induced EMF in this wire is -0.003 volts.

What Are the Features of the Electric Charge on an Insulator?

Insulators and Static Charge

Static electricity is the accumulation of electric charge in a substance or object.

Electric charges can move freely in a **conductor**, so conductors are good carriers of electric **current**. Electric charges in insulators cannot move freely, which is why insulators are very poor conductors of electricity.

INSULATORS

This insulated electric cable is stored on wooden spools. Why are some electrical cables much thicker than others?

Insulators can store an electric charge even though the charge cannot move freely. Electric charge can be built up on insulators in the form of static electricity, since a charge on an **insulator** does not move, or does not move very much. It often is easier to store a charge on an insulator than on a **conductor** because the charge cannot easily transfer from the insulator onto another object. The charge remains static on the insulator.

Consider the Explain Question

How does the structure of a material explain its behavior as a conductor or an insulator?

Go online to complete the scientific explanation.

dlc.com/ca11066s

Check for Understanding

A 12-V battery is connected in parallel with resistor R1 = 12 Ω and resistor R2 = 4.0 Ω. Can you calculate the power rating of each resistor in the circuit?

dlc.com/ca11067s

STEM in Action

Applying Conductors and Insulators

Why do conductors and insulators behave the way they do? Research into this question connects physics with chemistry and engineering. Engineers use the answer to this question to look for new materials and ways to combine and re-purpose old materials. Part of this quest is the discovery and application of new semiconductors and superconductors.

Semiconductors are materials that offer more **resistance** to conducting a **current** than a **conductor**; however, they offer much less resistance than an **insulator**. Semiconductors are often created by adding impurities to materials that are normally insulators. Common semiconductors are made by combining the elements silicon, gallium, or germanium with atoms of other elements. Engineers take what they know about these materials and apply them to new and different technologies. Many superconductors are newly discovered materials that have been combined with known materials. Semiconductors are essential parts of computer chips and many other electronic devices, offering the advantage of controlled conductivity when the impurities used and the temperature of the material are managed.

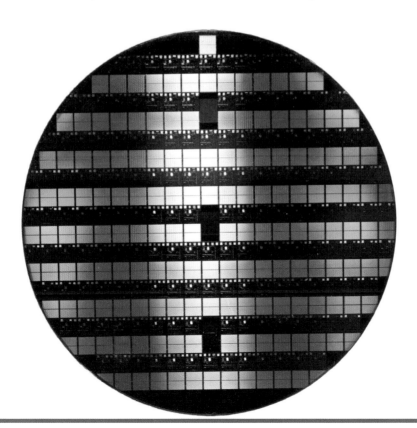

MICROCHIP

This microchip is composed of electronic circuits on a thin wafer of silicon, which is a commonly used semiconductor. How does a semiconductor control the flow of current in the chip?

Superconductors, like semiconductors, are made from materials that do not necessarily conduct well under normal circumstances, but offer virtually no resistance to the flow of electricity when supercoiled. Some superconductors are made from familiar material, such as helium, that is put under extremely high pressure or brought to extremely low temperatures. Research into finding superconductors combines many areas of science. Much research on superconductors focuses on development and use of superconducting magnets and superconducting wire in power plants.

STEM and Conductors and Insulators

Have you ever had a job to do but did not have the correct tool to complete it? A tool—or any product—should be constructed of the right material to do its job well, and these materials must be able to perform as needed. Materials engineers require a firm understanding of physics to develop, produce, and test materials that are used in many products, including superconducting magnets. Research into superconductivity continues to turn up surprising features and new technological applications.

GOOD INSULATOR

These insulators are preventing the power line from touching the tower. Why is glass used as the insulator?

The work of a materials engineer involves both fundamental science and applied science, and focuses on superconducting materials and their formation, structure, and magnetic and electrical properties. Materials engineers develop devices that use superconducting magnets because these magnets can create an extremely strong **magnetic field**. The medical technology called magnetic resonance imaging (MRI) uses superconducting magnets that have been designed by materials engineers. The strong magnetic field helps create images of organs and other soft tissues inside the body. Medical doctors can then interpret these images to help diagnose and manage health issues.

Superconducting magnets can also be used in maglev technology to levitate heavy objects such as passenger trains. Maglev is named for and is based on magnetic levitation. Objects such as the JR-Maglev in Yamanashi, Japan, are suspended and accelerated using magnets rather than traditional methods. The magnets are used to keep the trains levitated above and to move the trains along and above the tracks. Because there is no physical contact between the trains and the tracks, there is no friction between them, so the amount of wear and tear on the trains and tracks is greatly reduced. Theoretically, the contactless trains are able to travel much faster than traditional trains.

MAGLEV TECHNOLOGY
How can maglev trains move without wheels?

The speed record for maglev trains is 603 km/h, attained by the CJR's MLX01 superconducting maglev in 2015 in Japan. This speed is 28 km/h beyond the speed record of conventional trains set by the French TGV (*Train a Grande Vitesse*, or high-speed train) in 2007.

Conductors and Insulators: Faraday's Law

Use Faraday's law to solve the problems below.

1. A single-turn square loop of wire measuring 2 meters on all sides sits in a magnetic field of 5 T. The magnetic field is decreased to 1 T over a period of 15 seconds. What is the e.m.f. induced in the wire?

2. A circular wire turned 5 times sits in a 2 T magnetic field. The magnetic field is increased to 10 T over a period of 25 seconds, which induces a −5.03 V e.m.f. What is the radius of the wire loop?

3. Imagine a circular loop with a 2-meter radius in a 5 T magnetic field that decreases to 1 T over 2 minutes. How would the current induced in this situation differ from the current induced in the same loop sitting in a 1 T magnetic field that increases to 5 T over 2 minutes?

4. A 10-turn circular loop with a radius of 50 cm sits in a magnetic field that increases from 0.5 T to 2.5 T. If −0.157 V are induced in the wire, how quickly does the magnetic field change?

Nuclear Physics

LESSON OVERVIEW

Lesson Questions

- How are two isotopes of the same element different?
- How do unstable isotopes decay radioactively?
- How do scientists use the properties of radioactive decay to determine the age of objects?
- What is the difference between nuclear fission and nuclear fusion?

Lesson Objectives

By the end of the lesson, you should be able to:

- Identify distinguishing features of isotopes.
- Summarize the processes of how radioactive isotopes decay.
- Demonstrate how radioactive decay can be used to calculate the age of objects that contain radioactive isotopes.
- Compare the processes of fission and fusion.

Key Vocabulary

Which terms do you already know?

- ☐ alpha particle
- ☐ beta particle
- ☐ chain reaction
- ☐ daughter isotope
- ☐ electron
- ☐ element
- ☐ energy
- ☐ half-life
- ☐ isotope
- ☐ neutron
- ☐ nuclear fission
- ☐ nuclear fusion
- ☐ nuclear reaction
- ☐ nuclear reactor
- ☐ nucleus (atom)
- ☐ parent isotope
- ☐ plasma
- ☐ proton
- ☐ radioactive decay
- ☐ radioactivity
- ☐ strong nuclear force
- ☐ transmutation

dlc.com/ca11068s

Thinking About Solar Energy

What is your favorite time of year? For many, their favorite season is summer with its warm, bright, sunny days. Both the bright light and warm air temperature are products of solar energy reaching Earth.

dlc.com/ca11069s

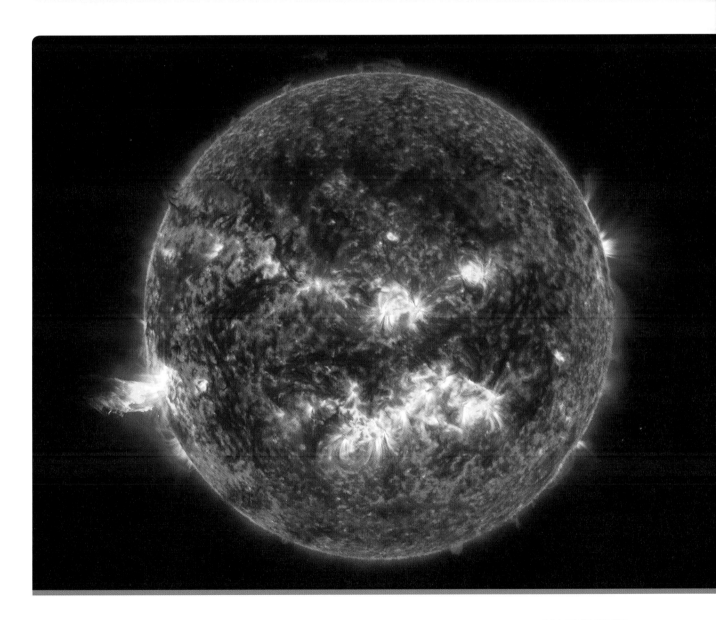

EXPLAIN QUESTION

| How do the nuclei of radioactive elements break down, and how can we make use of the process?

SOLAR ENERGY

This image of the sun shows how energy moves on its surface. What do you see that represents energy?

How Are Two Isotopes of the Same Element Different?

What Is an Isotope?

Electrons, neutrons, and protons are the building blocks of atoms. The neutrons and protons are found in the nucleus of atoms. A nucleon is any particle in the nucleus, so it refers to protons and neutrons collectively. The number of nucleons is called the atomic mass number.

The number of protons in the nucleus of an atom determines the type of **element**. For instance, if an atom has two protons, it is a helium atom. The number of protons also matches the atomic number of the element. For example, helium is said to have atomic number 2.

Not all atoms of the same element have to have the same number of nucleons. Different atoms of the same element can have a different number of neutrons. For instance, helium comes in two stable forms. Helium-3 has one **neutron** and helium-4 has two neutrons. Each of these different versions of helium is called an **isotope**. Note that the number after the hyphen is the atomic mass number. Helium-3, for example, has three nucleons.

Elements can be written using the following general notation:

$$^A_Z X$$

Here, A is the atomic mass number. Z is the number of protons in the nucleus, which is also the atomic number.

HYDROGEN ISOTOPES

Hydrogen can have different numbers of nucleons. How would these differences be shown using the general notation?

The Nuclei of the Three Isotopes of Hydrogen

Protium	Deuterium	Tritium
1 proton	1 proton 1 neutron	1 proton 2 neutrons

Carbon is another element that occurs in different isotopes. Carbon atoms always have six protons, but can have anywhere from 5 to 10 neutrons. The isotopes of carbon can be written as

$$\begin{array}{|c|c|c|c|c|c|} \hline {}^{11}_{6}C & {}^{12}_{6}C & {}^{13}_{6}C & {}^{14}_{6}C & {}^{15}_{6}C & {}^{16}_{6}C \\ \hline \end{array}$$

Certain isotopes of an element occur in nature much more frequently than others. For instance, carbon-12 ($^{12}_{6}C$) accounts for about 98.9 percent of all carbon atoms in nature. The main factor that affects the frequency of a particular isotope is its stability. Certain isotopes of carbon, such as carbon-12 and carbon-13, are stable.

Other isotopes are unstable. The unstable isotopes will decay radioactively at a continuous, predictable rate. When unstable isotopes decay, they emit radioactive particles. Eventually they also transform into different elements.

How Do Unstable Isotopes Decay Radioactively?

The Forces inside the Nuclei of Atoms

Except for hydrogen, all elements contain multiple protons. Since every **proton** has a positive charge, there is a repulsive electric force between each pair of protons in an atom's nucleus. It would be sensible to expect the electric force between the protons to be quite large given how close together the protons are in the nucleus and the fact that electric force is proportional to the inverse square of the distance, as given by Coulomb's law. Therefore, the following question arises: How does the nucleus of an atom stay intact and not rip itself apart?

Atoms remain stable in most cases because there is another force present—the **strong nuclear force**. It is an attractive force that acts on all nucleons in a nucleus. Protons and neutrons attract other protons and neutrons through this force. The strong nuclear force is powerful enough to overcome the electric force, but it acts only at very small distances. The strong nuclear force is effective only if nucleons are closer together than about 10–15 m. When nucleons are further apart, the electric force overpowers the strong nuclear force and can separate the nucleus of an atom. As long as the nucleons stay close together, the strong nuclear force prevails and the nucleus of the atom remains stable.

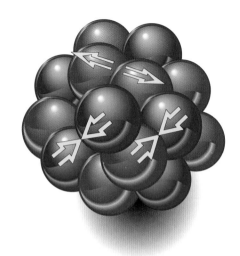

STRONG NUCLEAR FORCE

Protons and neutrons attract other protons and neutrons. How is the strong nuclear force distinguished from other forces in the nucleus?

One interesting property of the strong nuclear force is that it requires that the number of protons and neutrons in a nucleus be similar. If too many or too few neutrons are present, the atom may be unstable.

Types of Radioactive Decay

Many isotopes of elements that are found in nature are unstable. In unstable elements the protons and neutrons will not naturally stay together indefinitely. Instead, their nuclei eventually decay. The nuclei will eventually emit particles and transform themselves into something different. This process is called **radioactive decay**. It can happen very quickly or very slowly depending on the **isotope** involved. For instance, a sample of radon-218 atoms decay and become polonium-214 atoms in a fraction of a second. On the other extreme, a sample of uranium-238 atoms will over the course of billions of years decay into thallium-234.

So far, scientists have found three types of naturally occurring radioactive decay: alpha decay, beta decay, and gamma decay.

In alpha decay, an atom emits a helium-4 nucleus (^4_2He) . This particle is known as an **alpha particle**. After the decay, the original atom has lost two protons and two neutrons. One example of an alpha decay process is

$$^{230}_{90}Th \rightarrow {}^{226}_{88}Ra + {}^4_2He$$

In this **nuclear reaction**, the original thallium atom is known as the **parent isotope**. The radium atom is known as the **daughter isotope**. Note that the total number of nucleons in the decay products remains the same, $226 + 4 = 230$. Likewise, the total number of protons also remains the same $88 + 2 = 90$.

The daughter nucleus in alpha decay contains two less protons than does the parent nucleus. It has become an entirely different **element**. The process of changing from one element to another is known as **transmutation**.

Another form of radioactive decay is called beta decay. Beta decay involves the emission of beta particles when a neutron decays into a proton, electron, and a subatomic particle called an antineutrino. An example of beta decay is

$$^{3}_{1}H \rightarrow {}^{3}_{2}He + e^- + \overline{v}$$

In this case, the e⁻ represents the electron and the Greek letter nu (v) with a bar over it, $\overline{v}$, represents the antineutrino.

A final form of radioactive decay is known as gamma decay. In gamma decay, a gamma ray (γ) is emitted, which is a high-**energy** photon.

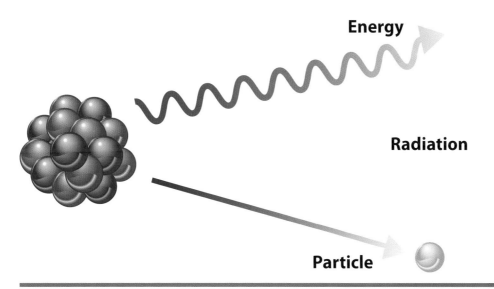

Energy

Radiation

Particle

RADIOACTIVE DECAY OF AN ATOM

The process of radioactive decay in an atom results in loss of a particle. What kinds of particles can be lost during radioactive decay?

The Rate of Decay of Radioactive Isotopes

A sample of radioactive material is made up of a large number of individual atoms. The radioactive decay of these atoms does not happen all at once. It happens gradually over time. It is impossible to predict when any individual atom will decay because radioactive decay is a random process. The only thing that can be determined is the average rate at which a large sample will decay over time. This rate varies by isotope. The number of decays is proportional to the number of particles in the sample.

Decay is a one-way process. Once an atom decays, the process cannot be reversed. The amount of time for half of a sample of a particular isotope to decay is constant. This amount of time is known as the **half-life** of the isotope.

Suppose a particular radioactive isotope has a half-life of one minute and that there is a sample of 120 g of the isotope. After one minute, there will be 60 g of the isotope in the sample. After two minutes, there will be 30 g of the isotope in the sample. After three minutes, there will be 15 g of the isotope in the sample.

The percentage of a remaining atom can be calculated using the equation:

$$N_{(t)} = N_0 e^{-\lambda t}$$

- N_t is the remaining amount of the substance after a given time (t).
- N_0 is the initial amount of the substance.
- λ is the decay constant. The decay constant is a measure of how likely a give atom is to decay in one second. This can be calculated using the equation:

$$\lambda = \frac{0.693}{t_{1/2}}$$

- $t_{1/2}$ is the half-life of the isotope.

Rate of Decay of Radioactive Isotopes: Sample Problem

Sodium-24 has a half-life of approximately 15 hours. What percentage of the original sample is left after one day?

Solution:

- $t_{1/2}$ is 15 hr
- The decay constant $= \dfrac{0.693}{15\ \text{hr}} = \dfrac{0.046}{\text{hr}}$
- $t = 24$ hours
- $N_{(t)} = 1e^{-(0.046)(24)}$
- $N_{(t)} = 0.33$ or 33%

The decay of a sample of radioactive isotopes leads to an exponential decline in the number of nuclei present in the original isotope of the sample. The decay rate can be plotted on a time graph. The number of atoms of the original isotope is plotted on the y-axis and time is plotted on the x-axis.

Decay Series

Often, unstable isotopes decay in a chain. They gradually transform from one element to another in a long process of transmutations. For instance, uranium-238 usually decays in a preferred pattern that is specific to that isotope of uranium. First, it becomes thorium-234 in an alpha decay process that has a half-life of 4.5 billion years.

This thorium isotope then decays to become protactinium-234 in a beta decay process that has a half-life of 24 days. Next, protactinium decays with a half-life of 6.7 hours to turn back into uranium. This time, however, it is uranium-234. This process of decay continues, yielding numerous other elements along the way. Eventually, this decay series ends as a stable isotope of lead—lead-206.

How Do Scientists Use the Properties of Radioactive Decay to Determine the Age of Objects?

Radiometric Dating

One of the most useful applications of **radioactive decay** is the ability to determine the age of objects formed thousands or even billions of years ago. The process mkes use of the decay rate of particular isotopes. It is known as radiometric dating.

Carbon-14 dating is one type of radiometric dating. It is a common technology in use today for determining the age of organic substances that are less than about 50,000 years old. All plant life on Earth uses carbon dioxide (CO_2) from the atmosphere. CO_2 contains atoms of carbon, which are mostly carbon-12 atoms. However, a small proportion of the carbon is the radioactive **isotope** carbon-14. Furthermore, this proportion has remained relatively constant for tens of thousands of years. This is due to the effects of cosmic rays that bombard Earth's upper atmosphere. They are constantly producing more radioactive carbon-14 even though existing carbon-14 is gradually decaying.

Since animals eat plants, all living organisms on Earth absorb material with a steady proportion of carbon-14. Once a plant or animal dies, it stops absorbing this source of carbon. The existing carbon-14 in the organism then decays at a steady rate. Carbon-14 has a **half-life** of 5,730 years. This means that after 5,730 years, half of the carbon-14 atoms in the sample have decayed and no longer exist. After 11,460 years, another half of the remaining carbon-14 atoms have decayed, leaving only one quarter of the original carbon-14 atoms, and so on. Therefore, if scientists can determine the proportion of carbon-14 left in a sample, they can use this information to reconstruct the age of the sample.

Archaeologists frequently use carbon-14 dating because the useful range of this method works for dating many human and animal ancestors. However, if a sample is much older than 50,000 years, the carbon-14 in the sample has decayed to such a low proportion that it is very difficult to get an accurate estimate of the age. Therefore, scientists use isotopes of other elements with longer half-lives to date older samples. For instance, geologists use uranium-238 to date the age of rocks. Uranium-238 has a half-life of 4.5 billion years, making it useful for dating material over geologic timescales.

CARBON DATING

The proportion of carbon-14 in a sample allows scientists to determine its age. What limits this method to dating samples older than a certain age?

What Is the Difference between Nuclear Fission and Nuclear Fusion?

Nuclear Fission

In 1938, German scientists—Otto Hahn, Lise Meitner, Otto Frisch, and Fritz Strassmann—made an interesting discovery. They found that by firing neutrons at uranium atoms, the atoms could be split into much smaller elements such as radium and beryllium. This was surprising. Previously, nuclear decay had produced only very small particles, such as the **alpha particle** and a slightly reduced version of uranium itself. This new process was named **nuclear fission**. It led to the first **nuclear reactor** in 1942 and the first nuclear bomb in 1945.

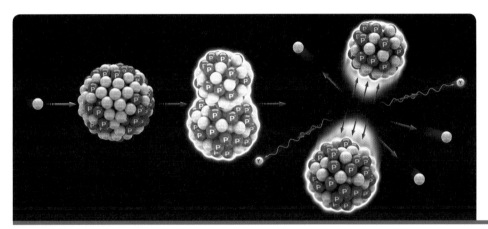

NUCLEAR FISSION
Nuclear fission is the process by which some atomic nuclei split apart into different nuclei. Why does nuclear fission result in the release of energy?

Nuclear fission occurs only in large atoms, such as uranium or plutonium. It occurs much more readily in certain isotopes of these elements than others. For instance, fission occurs more readily in the uranium-235 **isotope** than it does in the much more common uranium-238 isotope. Nuclear fission, in uranium-235, begins when a **neutron** is absorbed into the uranium-235 nucleus. The absorption causes the nucleus of the uranium atom to increase in internal **energy**. The extra internal energy then causes the atom to elongate. Once elongated, the strength of the **strong nuclear force**, which holds atoms together, weakens. The strength of the electric force begins to dominate. Since the electric force is repulsive between protons in the nucleus, it causes the uranium nucleus to split into two similarly sized pieces, known as fission fragments. These two pieces are different elements whose identity depends on the number of protons in each piece. Usually the two pieces do not have the same proportion of protons. Often one piece has roughly 60 percent while the other has roughly 40 percent of the protons. One example of a nuclear fission reaction is:

$$n + {}^{235}_{92}U \rightarrow {}^{134}_{54}Xe + {}^{100}_{38}Sr + 2e$$

Since a fission reaction like this releases additional neutrons, scientists realized that a **chain reaction** could be produced. The neutrons released by the original uranium atom can go on to split additional uranium atoms. Those atoms in turn emit yet more neutrons. The reaction can spread quickly.

Nuclear Fusion

Nuclear fission involves breaking up a single large atom into smaller parts—the fission fragments. In contrast, **nuclear fusion** involves combining two smaller nuclei (or other subatomic particles) to form larger elements. Fusion is theoretically possible for any elements with a smaller number of nucleons than iron (Fe). However, for practical purposes, it is feasible in the laboratory with only very small elements of hydrogen and helium.

The energy in the sun is mostly due to nuclear fusion reactions between hydrogen atoms, producing helium atoms and gamma rays. One example is:

$$^1_1H \rightarrow\ ^2_1H + ^3_2He + \gamma$$

Scientists are currently trying to develop commercial nuclear fusion reactors on Earth. Fusion reactors would produce energy more cleanly and safely than nuclear fission reactors.

Consider the Explain Question

How do the nuclei of radioactive elements break down, and how can we make use of the process?

Go online to complete the scientific explanation.

dlc.com/ca11070s

Check Your Understanding

Go online to check your understanding of this concept's key ideas.

dlc.com/ca11071s

STEM in Action

Applying Nuclear Physics

Radioisotopes have numerous applications in areas such as medicine, industry, and agriculture. Radiation from cobalt-60 is extensively used in cancer treatment. The radiation is targeted to the tumor location where it will damage the DNA of actively dividing cancer cells, resulting in the death of these cells. Medical devices and equipment are sometimes sterilized by the same method. Other radioactive isotopes are used as tracers for diagnosis and to conduct research on metabolic processes. In this case, weak radioisotopes are linked to a medication that is targeted to a specific organ or tissue. The radioisotope-tagged medication is injected into the patient and its localization patterns determined by detectors scanning the body.

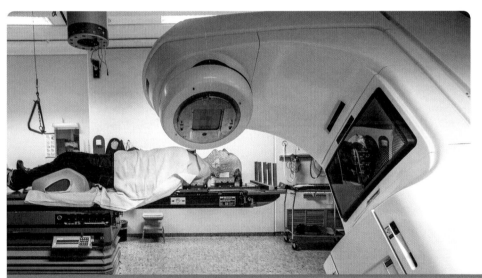

RADIATION THERAPY
Radiation from cobalt-60 is being used in cancer treatment. How are cells affected by this treatment?

In industry, radioactive isotopes are commonly used to measure thicknesses of materials and to analyze for defects. In a technique called industrial radiography, a machine containing a radioisotope is aimed at an object to be tested, and a film placed behind the object. Any radiation that can pass through defects in the object will be detected on the film. The examination of pipelines for leaks cannot be accomplished by any other method. A similar method is used to test other objects for structural defects in welds and materials such as aircraft engines, automobiles, bridges, and even roadways. Specialized radiation detectors can be used to assess the thickness of material by assessing the amount of energy lost by particles as they pass through.

In some cases, the industrial use of radioisotopes is in the product. Does your home have a smoke detector? Most smoke detectors used in homes are ionization-type smoke detectors. Did you know that these detectors use the radioactive element americium-241 to create a signal when smoke is present? Where does this radioactive element come from and how does this work? Within the smoke detector, the decaying americium releases α particles, which enables a current to flow between two oppositely charged metal plates. Smoke from a fire absorbs the α particles, the current stops flowing, and the alarm is triggered.

SMOKE DETECTOR

This home smoke detector contains a radioactive isotope. How do ionizing smoke detectors work?

STEM and Nuclear Physics

As the human population grows, so does its energy demands and much of the energy used today relies on the use of fossil fuels. Fossil fuels have several drawbacks, including their non-renewability and the negative environmental impacts associated with their use. Nuclear energy, which is more efficient and less polluting than fossil fuels, is used in many parts of the world to supply energy. Today's nuclear reactors utilize **nuclear fission** to produce the energy used to generate electricity. The main drawbacks to this process are the safe storage of radioactive waste and the risk of meltdown.

Nuclear engineers and scientists are attempting to replicate the sun's mechanism for producing energy by designing **nuclear fusion** reactors. Fusion reactors would not have many of the safety concerns that fission reactors do. A fusion reaction that is uncontrolled will just stop, rather than having to be cooled or risk disaster like a fission reaction. The waste from a fission reaction is sometimes considerable and might be a hazard for billions of years, whereas the waste from a fusion reaction is minimal and would be completely gone in as little as 50 years. Fusion reactors would produce 3–4 times more energy than fission reactors.

So far, the only practical use for manmade nuclear fusion has been a destructive one, the hydrogen bomb. Also called the thermonuclear bomb, the hydrogen bomb uses an initial nuclear fission reaction to produce the high temperatures and pressures needed for the fusion reaction. In a nuclear fusion reactor, two forms of hydrogen, deuterium and tritium, are heated to a temperature of over a million degrees Celsius until they form **plasma**. The **plasma** is extremely fragile on Earth since the density and pressure found in stars cannot be replicated, so it is contained within a magnetic field. This type of reaction takes massive amounts of energy and has not been contained within the confines of a power plant for more than a second or two. Plasma physicists and engineers are working hard to try to overcome the hurdles of the extreme temperatures and pressures required to initiate a fusion reaction. They expect fusion reactors to be a principal energy source of the future.

INSIDE A FUSION REACTOR

The ideal configuration of a fusion reactor is based on a torus-shaped magnetic containment field, called a tokamak reactor. Why is magnetic containment needed?

Determining the Products of Nuclear Decay

For the problems below, determine whether the reaction is alpha or beta decay and identify the missing parent or daughter isotope.

1. $^{242}_{96}\text{Cm} \rightarrow {}^{A}_{Z}X + {}^{4}_{2}\text{He}$

Type of reaction: _____

Daughter isotope: _____

2. ${}^{A}_{Z}X \rightarrow {}^{224}_{91}\text{Pa} + {}^{4}_{2}\text{He}$

Type of reaction: _____

Parent isotope: _____

3. ${}^{A}_{Z}X \rightarrow {}^{29}_{13}\text{Al} + \bar{e} + \bar{\nu}$

Type of reaction: _____

Parent isotope: _____

4. $^{172}_{79}\text{Au} \rightarrow \,^{A}_{Z}X + \,^{4}_{2}\text{He}$

Type of reaction: _____

Daughter isotope: _____

5. $^{45}_{19}\text{K} \rightarrow \,^{A}_{Z}X + e^{-} + \bar{\nu}$

Type of reaction: _____

Daughter isotope: _____

6. $^{A}_{Z}X \rightarrow \,^{175}_{78}\text{Pt} + \,^{4}_{2}\text{He}$

Type of reaction: _____

Parent isotope: _____

7. $^{204}_{81}\text{Tl} \rightarrow ^{A}_{Z}X + e^{-} + \bar{\nu}$

Type of reaction: _____

Daughter isotope: _____

8. $^{A}_{Z}X \rightarrow ^{19}_{9}\text{F} + e^{-} + \bar{\nu}$

Type of reaction: _____

Parent isotope: _____

Discovery EDUCATION

Radiometric Dating

Use what you know about radiometric dating to solve the problems below.

1. A rock shelf is composed of potassium-40, which has a half-life of approximately 1.3 billion years. The newest layer of rock is pure potassium-40. The oldest layer contains 25% potassium-40. Approximately how old is this oldest layer of rock?

2. Element X has a half-life of 12,000 years. If a fossil sample containing element X is 36,000 years old, what percentage of the original amount of element X would you expect to find in the sample?

3. A species of rodent went extinct 66,000 years ago. A team of archaeologists finds a skeleton of a rodent of this species. A sample of the skeleton contains 2.72×10^{16} atoms of carbon-14. If this particular rodent was among of the last of its species to die, how many atoms of carbon-14 did its skeleton have originally?

4. Archaeologists are using carbon-14 found in organic samples to find the age of a recently uncovered tomb. Presently, the samples in the tomb contain 3.0×10^{18} atoms of carbon-14. If the samples originally contained 9.2×10^{19} atoms of carbon-14, approximately how old is the tomb?

5. A geologist is analyzing a rock sample that she knows is 1,400 years old. If two half-lives have passed during this time, what is the half-life of element X?

Radiometric Dating

LESSON OVERVIEW

Lesson Questions

- How do scientists use radiometric dating techniques?
- What assumptions do scientists use to explain Earth's geologic history?
- What relative dating techniques so scientists use?
- How do scientists describe gaps in the rock record?

Lesson Objectives

By the end of the lesson, you should be able to:

- State the underlying assumptions that scientists use to explain Earth's geologic history.
- Identify relative dating techniques and explain how scientists use them.
- Explain how scientists describe gaps in the rock record.

Key Vocabulary

Which terms do you already know?

- ☐ decay rate
- ☐ deuterium
- ☐ half-life
- ☐ isotope
- ☐ protium
- ☐ radioactive decay
- ☐ radiometric dating
- ☐ tritium

dlc.com/ca11072s

Investigating Earth's Past

dlc.com/ca11073s

Have you ever picked up a rock and been curious about its age or how it was first formed, or seen a highway cut into a hillside and wondered about the age of each of the unique layers of rock revealed beneath the surface of Earth?

REVEALING EARTH'S HISTORY LAYER BY LAYER

The layering of rocks helps scientists to describe and explain the relative time during which events occurred. What techniques are available to insert specific dates into that timeline?

EXPLAIN QUESTION

How are radiometric dating techniques used to understand and learn about Earth's history?

How Do Scientists Use Radiometric Dating Techniques?

Radiometric Dating Techniques

Using relative dating principles, such as the principles of original horizontality, superposition, and **fossil** succession, scientists are able to determine the chronological order in which events occurred. These methods, however, are not capable of determining the actual number of years that have elapsed since an event occurred or a rock formed. Determining such a specific age is referred to as absolute dating and the resulting age is called the **absolute age**.

The most common method of absolute dating is the use of radiometric methods. Radiometric dating refers to the dating of material based on the decay of radioactive atoms that were present when the material formed. **Radioactivity** is a property of certain elements, such as uranium, and radioactive elements spontaneously emit **radiation**.

Radiometric dating techniques are used to date rocks and organic material that has not yet fossilized, such as bone or charcoal. Radiometric methods can be directly applied only to **igneous** rocks and certain metamorphic rocks, so accurate dates cannot be determined for all rocks. When dating igneous rocks, scientists assume that the amount of a radioactive element present in a rock added to the amount of the decayed elements is equal to the original amount of the radioactive element. When dating metamorphic rocks, radiometric methods can sometimes assign ages to only the most recent metamorphic event the rock endured. Radiometric dating is not always reliable in metamorphic rocks, especially if a metamorphic event took place over a long period of time. Radiometric dating methods cannot be applied to **sedimentary** rocks. There are two reasons for this:

- Radiometric clocks must be set in a molten state. That's why igneous rocks, and in some very special cases metamorphic rocks, are candidates. Sedimentary rocks never experience a molten state.
- Sedimentary rocks are formed out of the detrital matter of source rocks. As such, they are a conglomeration of many other rocks of differing ages whose histories don't preserve a single radiometric age.

To understand radiometric dating, you need to know about the structure of atoms.

Atoms

All of the materials that are around you—the solids, liquids, and gases—are made of several tiny particles called atoms. Each atom is made of smaller particles called protons, neutrons, and electrons. Protons and neutrons are located in an atom's center, called the nucleus (or **atomic nucleus**). Each **proton** and **neutron** within an atom's nucleus has about the same mass. Electrons **orbit** the nucleus, and for most purposes, an **electron**'s mass is so small that it is not considered to be significant when determining the total mass of an element.

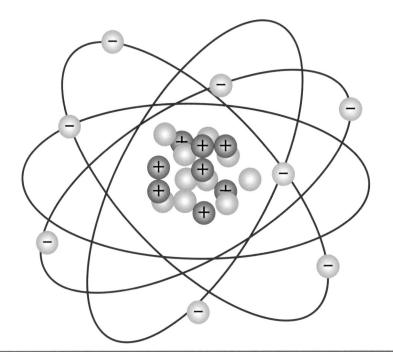

ATOMIC MODEL

An atomic model shows protons and neutrons in a nucleus, surrounded by orbiting electrons. Which particles are charged in an atom?

There are many different types of atoms, but an element is a substance that is made up of only one type of atom. Hydrogen, oxygen, carbon, iron, and gold are just a few examples of elements, and each of these elements is made of only one type of atom.

The characteristic that defines each element is the number of protons in its atomic nucleus, which is called the **atomic number**. For example, every hydrogen atom has only one proton in its nucleus. In contrast, every carbon atom has six protons in its nucleus, and every gold atom has 79. On a **periodic table** of elements, elements are organized from those with the lowest to those with the highest atomic number.

Isotopes

Recall that every atom of a given element has the same number of protons, but atoms of a single element can have different numbers of neutrons. Isotopes are atoms of the same element that have different numbers of neutrons, and most elements have several isotopes.

The name of an **isotope** is commonly written as the name of the element, followed by a hyphen, followed by the isotope's **mass number** (the sum of the isotope's protons and neutrons). For example, the most common isotope of carbon is called carbon twelve and is written as carbon-12, or C-12. It has 12 particles in its nucleus—6 protons plus 6 neutrons. However, another isotope of carbon, called carbon-13 (or C-13), has 13 particles in its nucleus—6 protons plus 7 neutrons, and carbon-14, or C-14, has 14 particles in its nucleus—6 protons plus 8 neutrons.

Approximately 99 percent of the carbon in nature exists as C-12, and approximately 1 percent exists as C-13. C-14 only exists in nature in trace amounts—it is unstable and over thousands of years decays to form an isotope of nitrogen. (This property of C-14 plays an important role in absolute dating, as shall be discussed.)

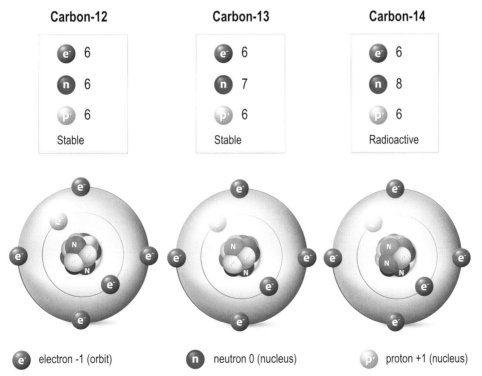

Carbon-12	Carbon-13	Carbon-14
e⁻ 6	e⁻ 6	e⁻ 6
n 6	n 7	n 8
p⁺ 6	p⁺ 6	p⁺ 6
Stable	Stable	Radioactive

e⁻ electron -1 (orbit)   n neutron 0 (nucleus)   p⁺ proton +1 (nucleus)

CARBON ISOTOPES

The most common form of carbon is C-12, but there are other isotopes. How do scientists use carbon to date ancient objects?

Some isotopes have special names, such as hydrogen-1 (H-1), which is usually called hydrogen but is also called protium, which is an isotope that accounts for more than 99 percent of all hydrogen in nature. Another hydrogen isotope, hydrogen-2 (H-2), is called deuterium, and a third hydrogen isotope, hydrogen-3 (H-3), is called tritium, which is extremely rare on Earth—it forms in trace amounts in the atmosphere. Like C-14, it is unstable, and it decays over time to form an isotope of helium.

Since most of the mass in an atom is contained in its protons and neutrons, isotopes with higher mass numbers have greater mass. For example, most of the hydrogen in ordinary water (also called dihydrogen oxide) is H-1. However, another form of water, called heavy water, contains a massive amount of the H-2 isotope. Both types of molecule are still water and have the same chemical formula, H_2O. Heavy water is chemically similar to normal water, but it is not quite identical because the nucleus in H-2 has twice the mass of the nucleus in H-1.

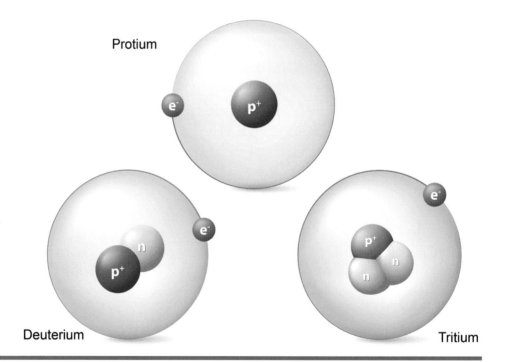

HYDROGEN ISOTOPES

Deuterium (H-2) has twice the mass of the ordinary isotope of hydrogen (H-1). How does the mass of H-3 compare to the mass of H-1?

Radioactive Decay

Most isotopes in nature are stable, which means they do not change under normal conditions. But some isotopes are considered to be unstable and will spontaneously decay, or break down, over time. Unstable isotopes are described as being radioactive. Radioactivity is the spontaneous breakdown, or decay, of an unstable atomic nucleus, which is also accompanied by the **emission** of radiation. Radioactive isotopes are atoms with unstable nuclei that also emit particles and energy.

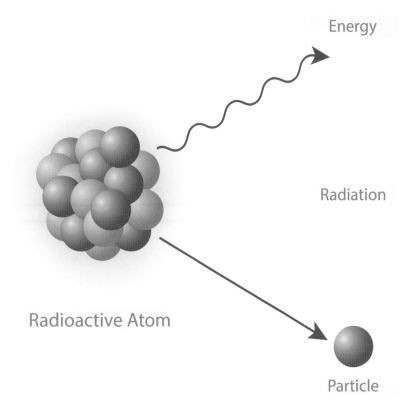

Energy

Radiation

Radioactive Atom

Particle

RADIOACTIVITY
The nuclei of unstable isotopes can decay, releasing radiation. How does an isotope change when it decays?

Radioactive decay is the process by which one element naturally changes into another element by the emission of charged particles from the nucleus of its atom. An unstable isotope that decays is called a **parent isotope**. The new element that forms from a parent isotope is called a **daughter isotope**. For example, hydrogen-3 (H-3), also called tritium, is a parent isotope that decays and changes to the daughter isotope helium-3 (He-3). Carbon-14 (C-14), also called radiocarbon, is a parent isotope that decays to the daughter isotope nitrogen-14 (N-14).

Half-Life

The rate of decay of radioactive isotopes is measured in units called half-lives (abbreviated $t_{1/2}$), which is the amount of time it takes for half a sample of a parent isotope to decay and form a daughter isotope. Half-lives of different types of radioactive isotopes can range from a few microseconds to millions of years. However, the **half-life** for any specific type of **radioactive isotope** is constant.

It is important to understand that radioactive isotopes undergo exponential decay, a term used to describe a quantity that decays by a fixed percent at regular intervals. The result of this process is that by the end of each half-life, one half of the remaining parent isotope will have decayed into a daughter isotope.

To explain how half-life works, we will use an imaginary parent isotope (X) and an imaginary daughter isotope (Y). In this example, X has a half-life of five years ($t_{1/2}$ = 5 yr). We begin with a pure sample of X—one hundred percent X and zero percent Y. At the end of five years, one-half (50%) of the sample will still be parent isotope, but the other half (50%) of the sample will be daughter isotope—different elements.

However, this does not mean that all of X will decay into Y in two half-lives (2 $t_{1/2}$ = 10 yr). Instead, one-half of the remaining parent isotope will decay into Y by the end of the second half-life. In other words, half again—or one-fourth (25%) of the original sample—will be X, and three-fourths (75%) will be Y at the end of two half-lives. At the end of three half-lives, one-eighth (12.5%) of the original sample will be X and seven-eighths (87.5%) will be Y.

Half-life remains constant over the entire life of the decay, and as time passes, more and more parent isotope decays into daughter isotope, which means that the ratio between parent isotope and daughter isotope is changing. To continue with the preceding example, one-sixteenth (6.25%) of the original sample will be X and fifteen-sixteenths (93.75%) will be Y at the end of four half-lives.

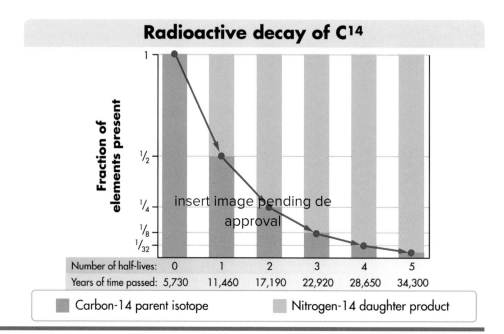

CARBON-14

Radioactive decay is exponential. What happens to the amount of the parent isotope after each half-life?

Half-Life: Sample Problem and Data

Uranium-235 (U-235) has a half-life of 700 million years and decays into lead-207 (Pb-207). The following data table shows how the amount of U-235 in a rock changes over time:

	After 1 half-life	After 2 half-lives	After 3 half-lives	After 4 half-lives
% of original U-235 remaining	50	25	12.5	6.25

How old will the rock be when 93.75% of its U-235 has become Pb-207?

Solution:

After one half-life, 50% of the rock's U-235 will have become Pb-207.
After two half-lives, 75% of the rock's U-235 will have become Pb-207.
After three half-lives, 87.5% of the rock's U-235 will have become Pb-207.
After four half-lives, 93.75% of the rock's U-235 will have become Pb-207.

The data also shows that the half-life of U-235 is 700 million years:

$$700 \text{ million years} \times 4(\text{half-lives}) = 2{,}800 \text{ million years}$$

So, when 93.75% of the rock's uranium-235 has become lead-207, the rock will be 2,800 million, or 2.8 billion, years old.

Different Isotopes – Different Time Scales

Different radioactive isotopes decay at different rates. For example, the half-life of lead-203 is twelve days, the half-life of carbon-14 is 5,730 years, and the half-life of uranium-238 is 4.5 billion years. These different radioactive isotopes provide measurements for different time scales.

Some radioactive isotopes are useful for determining ages on relatively recent timescales. For example, carbon-14 can be used for measuring the age of the remains of organisms that died up to 50,000 years ago. After that, too much of the parent isotope has decayed to be measured accurately.

Other radioactive isotopes have half-lives that range from 700 million years to more than 100 billion years and are useful for determining ages on relatively long timescales. The ages of Earth rocks, moon rocks, and meteorites are measured by the decay of isotopes with long half-lives.

The table that follows shows the decay rates of isotopes commonly used for radiometric dating.

Decay Rates			
Parent Isotope	Daughter Isotope	Half-Life (years)	Used to Date...
Uranium-235 (U-235)	Lead-207 (Pb-207)	7.04×10^8	various rocks and minerals
Potassium-40 (K-40)	Argon-40 (Ar-40)	1.25×10^9	mica, hornblende; glass from meteorite impacts
Uranium-238 (U-238)	Lead-206 (Pb-206)	4.47×10^{10}	various rocks and minerals
Thorium-232 (Th-232)	Lead-208 (Pb-208)	1.40×10^{10}	various rocks and minerals
Samarium-147 (Sm-147)	Neodymium-143 (Nd-143)	1.06×10^{10}	meteorites; mafic igneous rocks
Rubidium-87 (Rb-87)	Strontium-87 (Sr-87)	4.88×10^{10}	potassium-bearing minerals; felsic whole rocks

DECAY RATES

The half-lives of radioactive isotopes vary. How does the length of a radioactive isotope's half-life determine the types of substances it can be used to date?

The Age of Earth

A major challenge in determining Earth's age is that much of the evidence from Earth's past has been destroyed because Earth's oldest rocks have been recycled and destroyed by the processes of **plate tectonics** and the **rock cycle**. Rock material from Earth's early crust is extremely rare, because most of it has been recycled into Earth's interior several times. Even so, ancient rocks more than 3.5 billion years old are found on all of Earth's continents.

In 2014, scientists found rocks in the Jack Hills of Australia that they described to be the oldest known rocks on Earth ... and they were. They estimated the rocks to be 4.375 billion years old.

Silicate minerals are the largest and most important class of rock-forming minerals, making up about 90 percent of Earth's crust, and this age estimate was made by examining crystals of a silicate mineral called zircon, which is very hard and durable and is highly resistant to weathering and geologic processes. Grains of zircon are commonly found in sand, and ratios between uranium and lead isotopes in these zircons provided the estimate of their absolute age.

Lunar rocks have not been disturbed by plate tectonics because the moon does not have a hot enough core to drive a tectonic system. This has enabled scientists to find rocks on the Moon that are more ancient than rocks found on Earth, the oldest having been dated between the ages of 4.4 and 4.5 billion years. However, the giant impact hypothesis suggests that Earth is at least as old as the Moon. In this hypothesis, a space object the size of Mars, such as an asteroid, impacted early Earth while it was still molten, and fragments of Earth and other debris from this impact formed the moon.

MAGNIFICENT DESOLATION

Astronauts collected rocks on moon's surface more ancient that any found on Earth. Why are some moon rocks older than the oldest on Earth?

Many scientists suggest that the best age for Earth is determined by viewing Earth, the moon, and meteorites as part of the same evolving system. A meteorite is a stony or metallic body that has fallen to Earth from space. It is believed that all of these objects evolved at about the same time, because many radiometric dating tests have been done on meteorites, and the results show that they formed between 4.53 and 4.58 billion years ago. Currently, the approximate age of Earth has been estimated as 4.6 billion years by radiometric dating of Earth rocks, lunar rocks, and meteorites.

Consider the Explain Question

| **How are radiometric dating techniques used to understand and learn about Earth's history?**

Go online to complete the scientific explanation.

dlc.com/ca11074s

Check Your Understanding

| **Go online to check your understanding of this concept's key ideas.**

dlc.com/ca11075s

STEM in Action

Applying Radiometric Dating

Most of what we know about the history of the many varieties of species that have evolved to live on Earth comes from studying their fossils left behind in **sedimentary** rocks. However, radiometric dating techniques are most useful in analyzing igneous rocks and metamorphic rocks. There are many kinds of **igneous** rock; some of the most common are granite, pumice, and obsidian.

When magma cools, it forms a type of rock called igneous rock. If the magma is formed below Earth's surface, it tends to cool very slowly, and the resulting igneous rock is called intrusive. If the magma cools at or near Earth's surface, it tends to cool more quickly and is called extrusive igneous rock. Layers of igneous rock that are associated with layers of sedimentary rock can be useful for establishing the age of the sedimentary rocks—or at least narrowing the age. That's because radiometric dating can be used on some kinds of igneous rocks but not on sedimentary rocks or fossils.

JOHN DAY FOSSIL BEDS

The John Day Fossil Beds in Oregon yield fossils that span a time period across 40 million years. How do scientists use radiometric dating to estimate the absolute ages of the fossils?

Why are radiometric dating techniques less useful for dating sedimentary rocks or fossils? Sedimentary rocks are made of sediments of other types of rock that formed long before the sedimentary rock initially formed. For example, a grain of quartz in sandstone likely eroded from granite. Dating the quartz grain would show the age of the granite, not the sandstone.

So how is radiometric dating used to date sedimentary rocks and fossils? One of the most common methods is bracketing. Brackets are punctuation marks, such as [ ] or { }; they enclose information between the marks. Bracketing contains the date of sedimentary rock between the known dates of other rocks. Scientists date layers of igneous rock above and below sedimentary rocks and fossils in an effort to closely estimate the fossils' age.

FOSSILS LOCATED BETWEEN LAYERS OF ASH

In this diagram, geologists have used radiometric dating to date the layers of volcanic ash. The fossils in the top layer of sedimentary rock are between 495 and 510 million years old, and the fossils in the bottom layer of sedimentary rock are between 520 and 545 million years old. How many years of Earth's history are between the two fossil layers?

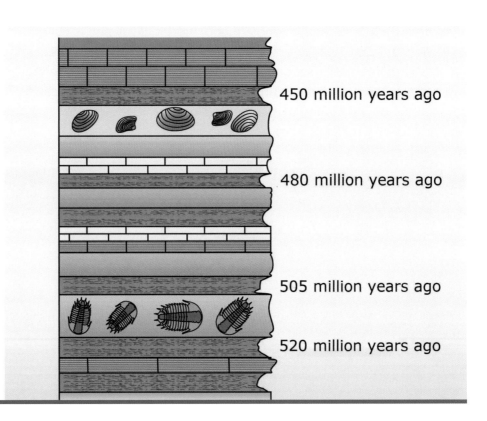

450 million years ago

480 million years ago

505 million years ago

520 million years ago

STEM and Radiometric Dating

Geophysicists generally consider radiometric dating to be the most reliable absolute dating method. But there are several other methods of absolute dating. One of these is called **fission** track dating.

Fission track dating is based on the constant decay rate of uranium-238 isotopes. When U-238 atoms emit charged particles from a **mineral** or glass, they leave a trail of damage behind called fission tracks. These tracks are similar to the tire marks left behind on a racetrack when dragsters "peel out" from the starting line. Just like a racetrack, when scientists observe a lot of tracks, they know that there has been a lot of fission activity. In fission track dating, the number of tracks can be used to determine the time and the uranium concentration. Scientists count the number of tracks per unit area and use this number to calculate the time that has passed since the original material first formed.

Fission track dating is just one of the radiometric dating techniques used by the scientists and technicians affiliated with the United States Geological Survey (USGS). The USGS is a federal agency that studies Earth and the causes of natural disasters. The people employed by the USGS come from a wide variety of scientific backgrounds. They share their unique knowledge and abilities in an effort to understand previous geological events that have taken place in Earth's history so that they can protect and improve the lives of people today.

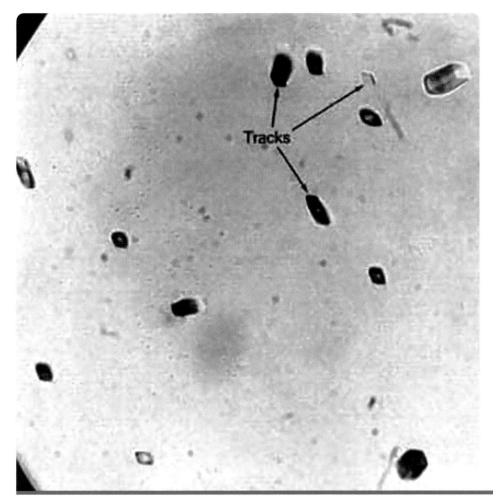

Tracks

MICA SCARRED BY URANIUM FISSION TRACK

Fragments emitted by the fission of uranium-238 leave trails of damage called fission tracks. Because the tracks are relatively large (about 1 to 15 micrometers), counting can sometimes be done by using an optical microscope. How does counting the fission tracks reveal the age of the material?

Half-Life

Use the half-life equations for absolute dating to solve the problems below.

Carbon-14 (^{14}C), which has a half-life of approximately 5,730 years, decays into nitrogen-14 (^{14}N). The following data table shows how the amount of ^{14}C in a certain plant changes over time. Use this information to answer questions 1 & 2.

	After 1 half-life	After 2 half-lives	After 3 half-lives	After 4 half-lives
% of ^{14}C in plant	50	25	12.5	6.25

1. How long will the plant have been dead after 2 half-lives have passed?

2. How long will the plant have been dead when 87.5% of its ^{14}C has become ^{14}N?

Rubidium-87 (Rb-87), which has a half-life of approximately 50 billion years, decays into strontium-87 (Sr-87). The following data table shows how the amount of Rb-87 in a certain rock changes over time. Use this information to answer questions 3 & 4.

	After 0.02 half-lives	After 0.04 half-lives	After 0.06 half-lives	After 0.08 half-lives
% of Rb-87 in rock	98.623	97.265	95.926	94.606

3. Approximately what percentage of Rb-87 will remain in the rock when it is 2 billion years old?

4. Approximately what percentage of the rock will be Sr-87 when the rock is 3 billion years old?

Potassium-40 (K-40), which has a half-life of approximately 1.3 billion years, decays into argon-40 (Ar-40). The following data table shows how the amount of K-40 in a certain rock changes over time. Use this information to answer question 5.

	After 1 half-life	After 2 half-lives	After 3 half-lives
% of K-40 in rock	50	25	12.5

5. What percentage of the rock will be Ar-40 when the rock is 2.6 billion years old?

Scientists analyzed two samples of rock taken from the moon during an Apollo moon landing. The first rock was a highland breccia. This highland breccia was 95.266% Rb-87. The second rock was a meteorite determined to contain 5.394% Sr-87.

Rubidium-87 (Rb-87), which has a half-life of approximately 50 billion years, decays into strontium-87 (Sr-87). Use this information, and the information to answer questions 6-8.

6. What is the approximate age of the highland breccia found on the moon?

7. What is the approximate age of the meteorite found on the moon?

8. Compare the age of the highland breccia to the meteorite.

Wave Characteristics

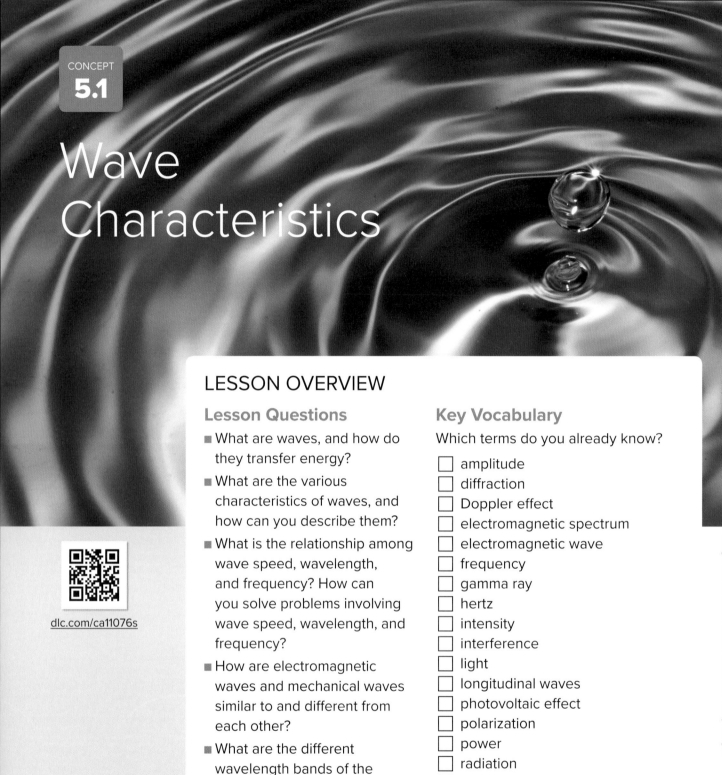

LESSON OVERVIEW

Lesson Questions

- What are waves, and how do they transfer energy?
- What are the various characteristics of waves, and how can you describe them?
- What is the relationship among wave speed, wavelength, and frequency? How can you solve problems involving wave speed, wavelength, and frequency?
- How are electromagnetic waves and mechanical waves similar to and different from each other?
- What are the different wavelength bands of the electromagnetic spectrum?
- How can I calculate the energy of electromagnetic radiation?
- How can you describe the energy, power, and intensity of a mechanical wave?
- What is the Doppler effect, and how does it relate to the frequency of a wave?

Key Vocabulary

Which terms do you already know?

- ☐ amplitude
- ☐ diffraction
- ☐ Doppler effect
- ☐ electromagnetic spectrum
- ☐ electromagnetic wave
- ☐ frequency
- ☐ gamma ray
- ☐ hertz
- ☐ intensity
- ☐ interference
- ☐ light
- ☐ longitudinal waves
- ☐ photovoltaic effect
- ☐ polarization
- ☐ power
- ☐ radiation
- ☐ radio wave
- ☐ reduction electromagnetic spectrum
- ☐ reflection
- ☐ refraction
- ☐ resonance
- ☐ speed
- ☐ speed of light (c)
- ☐ transverse waves

Lesson Questions continued

- How does the speed of a wave relate to the medium through which it travels?
- How can you describe reflection, refraction, polarization, interference, diffraction, and resonance?
- What are some medical or industrial applications of different electromagnetic and mechanical waves?

Lesson Objectives

By the end of the lesson, you should be able to:

- Understand the characteristics of waves and how waves transfer energy.
- Describe wave characteristics, including wavelength, wave period, amplitude, frequency, and wave speed.
- Explain the relationships among wave speed, wavelength, and frequency.
- Solve problems involving wave speed, frequency, and wavelength.
- Compare electromagnetic waves and mechanical waves.
- Describe how the speed of a wave varies, depending on the medium through which it passes.
- Model the different wavelength bands within the electromagnetic spectrum.
- Explain the Doppler effect in terms of apparent frequency.
- Describe wave behaviors, including reflection, refraction, polarization, interference, diffraction, and resonance.
- Investigate medical or industrial applications that rely on the characteristics of different types of waves.

Key Vocabulary continued

- ☐ wave
- ☐ wavelength
- ☐ wave speed
- ☐ x-ray

Investigating Wave Characteristics

dlc.com/ca11077s

What do you think of when you hear the term *wave*? If you have ever been to a beach, you probably think of the waves that roll in from a body of water and break on the shore. This common example of waves may be quite familiar, but it definitely is not the only example of waves.

CHARACTERISTICS OF WAVES

Every wave has certain characteristics that make it a wave. What characteristics of waves do you see in this photo?

EXPLAIN QUESTION

What are the relationships among the frequency, wavelength, and speed of waves traveling in a specific medium?

What Are Waves, and How Do They Transfer Energy?

Definition of a Wave

Crowds of people do "the **wave**." What are some properties of this phenomenon? It starts when people in one location stand up and sit down in their seats. When they do this, the people next to them then move up and down, and so on. Through this process, the "up and down" motion of people appears to be transmitted across a vast region in an arena. This wave motion is actually quite similar to waves in physics.

Some waves move through matter. The matter that a wave moves through is called the medium of the wave. A traveling wave is a disturbance that moves through space and time, transferring energy without transferring matter. Think of a disturbance as the up and down motion of a particle, similar to the up and down motion of people in the seats of an arena. The motion and characteristics of a wave are described according to many properties, as will be discussed in this lesson.

MAKING WAVES

Fans at a soccer stadium do "the wave." Why is this pattern considered to be a wave?

How Waves Transfer Energy

Waves originate from an initial disturbance, or oscillation, that provides some energy to the system. As the wave moves, it transmits the energy from the initial disturbance across a region of space. How does it transmit this energy?

Consider the motion of a water wave. The particles in a body of water such as the ocean oscillate in a circular motion near the surface of the water. This motion is typically caused by wind moving across the ocean surface, causing the water particles to move both left and right across the surface as well as up and down. As the particles oscillate, they disturb the particles around them, causing those particles to oscillate also. To an observer standing on the beach, it appears that a large body of water known as an ocean wave is moving toward the beach, where it eventually crashes. In actuality, only the energy of water particle oscillations is transmitted toward the beach. Said differently, the water particles are not actually moved toward the beach as ocean waves crash; only the energy of the particles is transferred.

WAVES ON A BEACH

A cresting wave transfers energy to a sandy beach. How can that energy change the beach?

In general, as particles in a medium oscillate or vibrate, they transfer the energy of this oscillation to particles around them, and this process continues to transmit the energy of an oscillation to particles across a distance. Through this process, a wave "propagates" through a medium. In this way, waves transfer energy without transferring matter.

When particles oscillate in a direction perpendicular to the direction that the wave propagates, the wave is a transverse wave. This is the most familiar type of wave. However, sometimes the particles in a wave oscillate in the same direction that the wave propagates. These waves are called **longitudinal waves**. Sound waves and seismic "P-waves" are examples of longitudinal waves. They are occasionally known as pressure waves or compression waves.

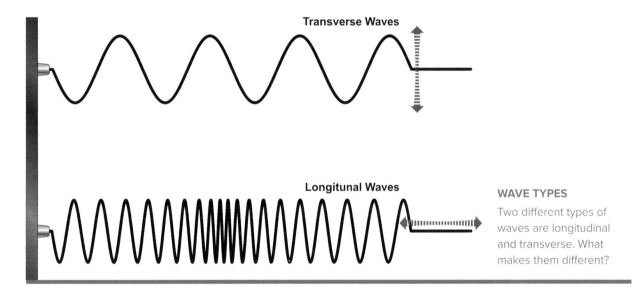

Transverse Waves

Longitunal Waves

WAVE TYPES
Two different types of waves are longitudinal and transverse. What makes them different?

What Are the Various Characteristics of Waves, and How Can You Describe Them?

Characteristics of Waves

A periodic **wave** is a wave that follows a repeating pattern as it propagates through space. That is, the oscillating pattern repeats at regular intervals of time. This repeating motion is also known as periodic motion.

A good way to understand periodic waves is to consider the motion of a spring that is moved up and down. When the spring is at rest, it is at an equilibrium position. When it is moved up and down, it gains some energy. If this motion continues, the spring will oscillate back and forth about the equilibrium point. If the oscillation is plotted against time, the result is the graph of a periodic wave. The maximum position of the spring as it moves up is called the peak and the minimum position is called the trough.

One characteristic of the periodic wave is the **wavelength**. This is the distance over which the wave completes one full oscillation. To determine this distance, choose a location of the wave at some point in its cycle. For example, choose the peak value of the wave. Then, observe the next oscillation of the wave and find the same location of the wave in this cycle. For example, observe the next peak value of the wave. The distance between these two identical parts of the wave in consecutive cycles is the wavelength. Since wavelength is a measure of distance, it is expressed in units of meters and is usually denoted by the Greek symbol λ.

PARTS OF A WAVE

Waves have a crest and a trough, and the distance of one full wave cycle is called the wavelength. How can you show the wavelength of a wave?

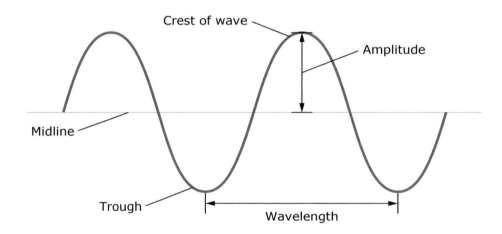

Crest of wave

Amplitude

Midline

Trough

Wavelength

Similar to the wavelength is the wave period (or just "period") of a wave. The wave period is the time it takes for a wave to complete one full oscillation. The period is a measure in "seconds per cycle," so it is expressed in units of seconds and is represented by the symbol T.

The **frequency** of a wave is the inverse of the period. While the period is the time it takes for the wave to complete one full oscillation, the frequency is the number of oscillations that a wave makes in one second. Frequency is measured in "cycles per second," which has units of 1/s. This unit, 1/s, is referred to as **hertz** (Hz). Frequency is often denoted by the symbol *f*. The following equations demonstrate the relationship between the period, *T*, and the frequency, *f*, of a wave:

$$f = \frac{1}{T} \text{ and } T = \frac{1}{f}$$

The **amplitude** of a transverse wave is the maximum distance that the wave travels from its equilibrium position. Think of the amplitude as the "height" of the wave. Since amplitude is a measure of distance, it is expressed in units of meters and is typically denoted by the symbol *A*.

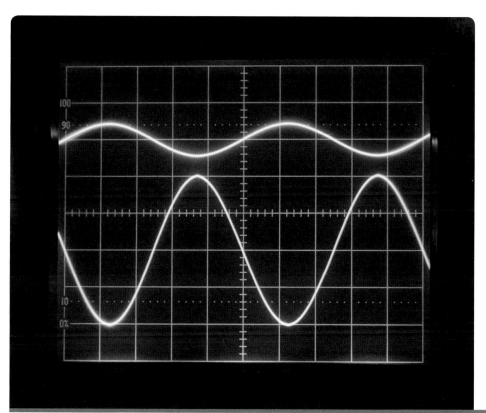

AMPLITUDE

The amplitude of a transverse wave is the "height" of the wave. How does amplitude differ in these two waves?

The **wave speed** is the **speed** at which the wave propagates through space. Like any other measure of speed, wave speed has units of meters per second, and it is typically expressed by the symbol v. The speed at which a wave travels depends upon the nature of the medium that it is passing through. For example, electromagnetic waves travel fastest in a vacuum but slower and sometimes not at all through matter. All mechanical waves require matter for their transmission. The parameters of the medium through which they travel determine their speed. For example the speed of sound depends upon the elasticity of the medium. Elastic substances maintain and spring back into shape when they are deformed by a force. For example iron will rapidly return to its shape. Inelastic substances such as soft clay, on the other hand, deform easily when a force is applied to them and may not return to their original shape. Inelastic or rigid materials have atoms or molecules with strong attractive forces, and as a rule the weaker these forces are in a medium, the slower mechanical waves will travel through them. This means that the phase of a substance can have a big impact on wave speed. You may recall that the forces holding particles together in gases are much weaker than those in liquids, which in turn are weaker than those in solids.

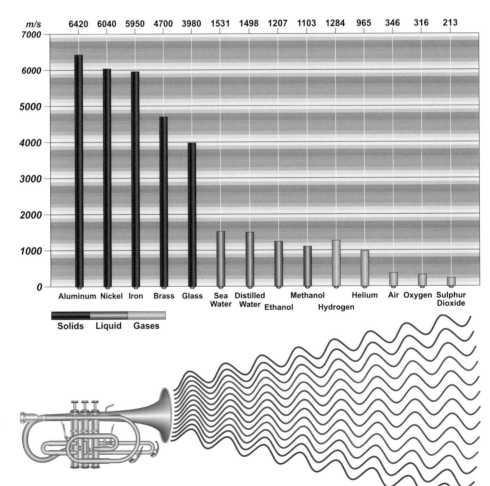

SPEED OF SOUND

Sound travels at different speeds through different materials. What properties of a material determine the speed of sound through it?

© Discovery Education | www.discoveryeducation.com ● Image: Fouad A. Saad / Shutterstock

If we use sound as an example of a mechanical wave, then we would expect it to travel slower in gases, such as air, than in liquid water or solid iron. At 45°C, the speed of sound is 343.4 meters per second in air, compared with 1,482 meters per second in water and 4,910 meters per second in iron. Notice that we gave the temperature at which the sound was measured.

Inertial properties also change the speed of a wave. Inertial properties are the characteristics that make something resistant to change or motion. One inertial property you are already familiar with is the property of density (mass/volume). Generally the greater the density the slower the waves will travel. This may seem counter intuitive, but in a single phase of matter mechanical waves travel slower at high densities and faster at low densities. Normally density decreases with temperature—the higher the temperature the lower the density. So sound for example travels slower in cold air than in warm air. This is why the speed of sound in any medium is usually accompanied by a measure of the temperature. The density-wave speed relationship also accounts for the difference in wave speed in different gases. For example sound travels about 3 times faster in helium because helium is less dense than air.

What Is the Relationship among Wave Speed, Wavelength, and Frequency? How Can You Solve Problems Involving Wave Speed, Wavelength, and Frequency?

Wave Speed, Wavelength, and Frequency

Think back to the definition of **speed** from kinematics. Recall that average speed is a measure of the distance, d, something travels in period of time, t: The speed is given by:

$$v = \frac{d}{t}$$

How can this principle be applied to waves? The distance a **wave** travels in one oscillation is the **wavelength**, λ. The time it takes to complete one full oscillation is the period, T. Applying the principle from kinematics:

$$v = \frac{d}{t} = \frac{\lambda}{T}$$

Now, the period T is the inverse of **frequency**. That is,

$$f = \frac{1}{T}$$

Substitute for f in the equation relating wavelength and period:

$$v = \frac{\lambda}{T} = \lambda\left(\frac{1}{T}\right) = \lambda f$$

This gives us an important relationship between **wave speed**, wavelength, and frequency. It shows that the wave speed is equal to the wavelength of the wave multiplied by its frequency, giving the equation $v = \lambda f$.

Problems Involving Wave Speed, Wavelength, and Frequency

It is important not to confuse frequency and wave speed. The wave speed, or speed of a wave, is distance traveled in a given amount of time. In contrast, the frequency is the number of cycles repeated in a given amount of time.

The wave speed, wavelength, and frequency are related by the following equation:

$$v = \lambda f$$

This relationship is used to solve problems of wave motion. For example, if the wavelength and frequency of the wave are known, wave speed can be calculated.

Alternatively, if wavelength and wave speed are known, the frequency can be calculated by rearranging the equation $\lambda f = v$ to get $f = \frac{v}{\lambda}$ by dividing through by λ.

Similarly, if wave speed and frequency are known, the wavelength can be calculated by rearranging the equation $\lambda f = v$ to get $\lambda = \frac{v}{f}$ by dividing through by f.

Problems Involving Wave Speed, Wavelength, and Frequency: Sample Problem 1

A sound wave traveling through a body of freshwater is measured to have a frequency of 440.0 Hz (corresponding to the musical note: "A") and a wavelength of 3.368 m.

(a) What is its speed in the water?

(b) If the water conditions are held constant, all sound waves will travel at the same speed through water. Use this fact to calculate the wavelength of a 240.0 Hz sound wave (corresponding to "middle C" on a keyboard) traveling through water.

Solution:

(a) The following information is given:

$$f = 440.0 \text{ Hz}$$
$$\lambda = 3.368 \text{ m}$$

Use the relationship $v = \lambda f$ to solve for wave speed v. Substituting the known quantities yields:

$$v = \lambda f$$
$$= (3.368 \text{ m})(440.0 \text{ Hz})$$
$$= 1482 \text{ m/s}$$

Thus, the speed of the sound wave in water is 1,482 m/s.

(b) Assume that another sound wave will travel at the same speed through fresh water as the wave analyzed in part (a). Thus, the following information is known about the next wave:

$$f = 240.0 \text{ Hz}$$
$$v = 1482 \text{ m/s}$$

Solve for wavelength, λ. Since $v = \lambda f$, it follows that:

$$\lambda = \frac{v}{f}$$

Plugging in the known quantities gives:

$$\lambda = \frac{v}{f}$$

$$= \frac{1,482 \text{ m/s}}{240.0 \text{ Hz}}$$

$$= 6.175 \text{ m}$$

Thus, the wavelength of the 240.0 Hz wave is 6.175 m.

Problems Involving Wave Speed, Wavelength, and Frequency: Sample Problem 2

The speed of a **light** wave in air is approximately 2.99×10^8 m/s. If a light wave is measured to have a wavelength of 657 nm, what is its frequency?

Solution:

The wavelength of light is given as 657 nm. First, convert this quantity to meters. Recall that $1 \text{ m} = 10^9$ nm.

$$657 \text{ nm} \left(\frac{1 \text{ m}}{10^9 \text{ nm}} \right) = 6.57 \times 10^{-7} \text{ m}$$

Thus, the following information about the light wave is known:

$$\lambda = 6.57 \times 10^{-7} \text{ m}$$

$$v = 2.99 \times 10^8 \text{ m/s}$$

We want to solve for frequency, f. We can use the following equation $v = f\lambda$. Divide through by λ to get

$$f = \frac{v}{\lambda}$$

We can plug in the known quantities to solve for f:

$$f = \frac{v}{\lambda}$$

$$= \frac{(2.99 \times 10^8 \text{ m/s})}{(6.57 \times 10^{-7} \text{ m})}$$

$$= 4.55 \times 10^{14} \text{ Hz}$$

Thus, the frequency of the light wave is 4.55×10^{14} Hz, or 455 terahertz (THz). This frequency of light falls within the range of red (visible) light waves.

How Are Electromagnetic Waves and Mechanical Waves Similar to and Different from Each Other?

Mechanical Waves and Electromagnetic Waves

Mechanical waves are propagated by the oscillations of particles in a medium. For example, when a guitar string is plucked, it disturbs the particles in the air around it, causing them to vibrate. These vibrating air particles then cause the particles around them to vibrate and so on. Sound waves can be transmitted by the particles in different media such as air molecules, water, and solid objects.

Sound waves, ocean waves, and seismic waves are all examples of mechanical waves propagated by vibrating particles.

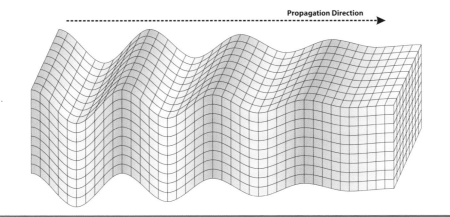

Propagation Direction

MECHANICAL WAVES

Mechanical waves move particles. How do we experience mechanical waves?

Mechanical waves may be transverse, longitudinal, or a combination of both. **Transverse waves**, such as tension waves or shear waves, move particles in directions perpendicular to the **wave** motion. **Longitudinal waves**, such as sound waves, move particles in directions parallel to the wave motion. Deep-water ocean waves (as opposed to ripples, which are transverse) are waves affected by gravity and the weather. If they reach the surface, they act as circular waves, a combination of both mechanical wave types. All mechanical waves move at speeds that are a function of the properties of the medium through which they are moving.

Electromagnetic waves are transmitted by oscillations within photons, which are particles of **light**. A photon is composed of an electric field and a magnetic field. As the photon propagates through space, the electric and magnetic fields of the photon oscillate. Photons are massless particles. That is, they are not matter.

Electromagnetic waves are propagated through fields and therefore don't require a medium. They can travel in either a vacuum or through matter. Electromagnetic waves are transverse waves and travel at the **speed** of light in a vacuum.

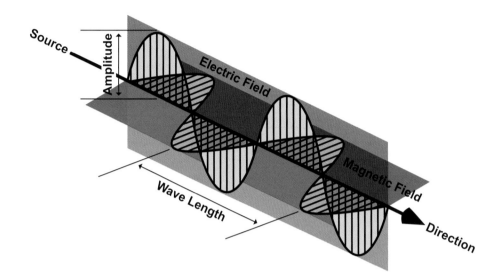

ELECTROMAGNETIC WAVES

Electromagnetic waves travel at the speed of light. They are transverse oscillations of electric and magnetic fields. Can electromagnetic waves travel in the absence of a medium?

Comparing Electromagnetic Waves and Mechanical Waves

Electromagnetic and mechanical waves are similar in some ways. Both types of waves propagate with periodic motion, meaning they can be characterized by the properties of **wavelength**, **frequency**, period, **wave speed**, and **amplitude**. However, these two types of waves are different in important ways.

First off, electromagnetic waves are not oscillations of matter; they are oscillations of photons, which are massless particles that are carriers of the electromagnetic force. Because of this, electromagnetic waves do not require a medium through which to travel. In fact, they can travel through a vacuum, such as outer space. Mechanical waves, on the other hand, can only be transmitted through matter. If there is no matter, these waves cannot propagate. For this reason, sound waves and other mechanical waves cannot travel through a vacuum, such as outer space.

Second, electromagnetic waves are transverse waves, while mechanical waves can be either transverse or longitudinal waves. For example, a sound wave is a longitudinal wave because the particles that transmit a sound wave oscillate back and forth in the same direction that the wave propagates. In contrast to this, an **electromagnetic wave** is transverse since electric and magnetic fields oscillate perpendicular to the direction in which the wave propagates.

Wave-Particle Duality

Electromagnetic radiation such as light can appear to act like waves, like particles, or both. For example, light can interfere and diffract, both of which are properties of all waves. On the other hand, light can also act like a stream of particles or photons, ejecting single electrons from target atoms, an interaction known as the photoelectric effect. This ambiguity is known as the "wave-particle duality" of light.

Both models are actually correct. Light acts like both a wave and a stream of particles. Depending on how an experiment is set up, it can reveal light's wave-like nature or its particle-like nature and sometimes both. In fact, the duality goes both ways. Solid matter can act like a wave! Electrons and other "particles" (such as atoms) have associated wavelengths and can exhibit wave-like behaviors. However, on the scale of everyday objects, these wavelengths are insignificant.

One of the ways scientists resolve the wave-particle duality is to view wave-like properties in terms of statistical effects. A diffraction pattern, for example, can emerge over time as a cumulative effect of multiple single-photon events.

What Are the Different Wavelength Bands of the Electromagnetic Spectrum?

The Electromagnetic Spectrum

Electromagnetic radiation occurs when electric and magnetic fields interact.

Even when electric and magnetic fields are static, they create observable effects. These might include the static electricity you sometimes feel when taking a shirt out of the dryer or the magnetic force holding a magnetized bumper sticker to a car. However, when electric and magnetic fields move near or through one another, that interaction creates electromagnetic waves.

Since electric and magnetic forces do not need a medium in which to propagate, electromagnetic waves can travel through a vacuum. No medium is necessary. Remember, this is a crucial difference between electromagnetic waves and mechanical waves. Mechanical waves can't propagate without a medium.

Electromagnetic energy can be described by **frequency, wavelength,** or energy, which are all interrelated. Because the **speed** of **light** in a vacuum, *c*, is constant, the wavelength and the frequency of electromagnetic waves have an inverse relationship, $c = \lambda f$. As the wavelength increases, frequency decreases, and vice versa. Low-energy electromagnetic radiation has longer wavelengths, corresponding to lower frequencies. High-energy electromagnetic radiation has shorter wavelengths, corresponding to higher frequencies.

THE ELECTROMAGNETIC SPECTRUM

The electromagnetic spectrum is the range of electromagnetic waves with any wavelength. What types of waves make up the electromagnetic spectrum?

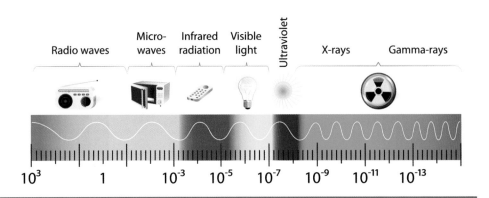

Different Wavelength Bands of the Electromagnetic Spectrum

From lowest energy (longest wavelength) to highest energy (shortest wavelength), the seven groupings along the spectrum are radio waves, microwaves, infrared, visible light, ultraviolet, x-rays, and gamma rays. The visible range of the spectrum is just a tiny portion of the entire **electromagnetic spectrum**.

Radio and microwaves are usually described by frequency (units of **hertz**); ultraviolet, infrared, and visible light by wavelength (units of meters); and x-rays and gamma rays by energy (units of electron-volts). Though referred to by different names—light, electromagnetic radiation, or rays—all electromagnetic energy is made up of the same kind of waves. The convention of using different units for different parts of the spectrum is simply a convenience that has to do with using numbers that aren't too big or too small. The spectrum doesn't actually have distinct breaks.

Radio waves have the longest wavelength and lowest frequency (and thus lowest energy) of all electromagnetic waves. The wavelength range of radio waves is from thousands of kilometers to meters. Wavelengths in this range are used primarily to transmit radio, television, mobile phone, and other satellite signals (such as GPS navigational information) through the air. Because they have the lowest energy of all electromagnetic waves, radio waves can pass through the human body without harm.

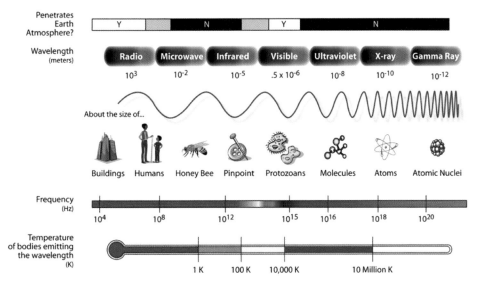

THE ELECTROMAGNETIC SPECTRUM

Observe the many properties of the different wavelengths. Why do you think some waves can penetrate Earth's atmosphere while others cannot?

Microwaves have the next shortest wavelength, ranging from meters to millimeters in length. Most people have heard of microwave ovens, which emit microwaves inside a closed chamber. The microwaves pass back and forth through the food millions of times. The microwaves cause water molecules in the food to rotate faster and faster and transfer this rotational energy to nearby molecules. The energy from the microwaves gets transferred to the molecules in the food and is converted into thermal energy, or heat. This increases the temperature of the food. Microwaves are constantly bombarding Earth, but because they only pass through us once instead of millions of times as in a microwave oven, they do not cause harm to living things.

Infrared rays are next in the electromagnetic spectrum. Their wavelengths range from about 1 millimeter (1 mm) to around 740 nanometers (740 nm). These rays are typically associated with radiated thermal energy such as thermal energy from the sun or a space heater. These rays are mostly associated with thermal energy because their particular wavelengths cause most particles around us to vibrate. These vibrations arise because molecular bonds aren't rigid. Instead, the chemical bonds act like springs, reacting to energy inputs. Energy from the infrared rays increases the **intensity** of vibration or rotation of molecules in various materials. The resultant molecular movements indicate an increased level of thermal energy, which, in most cases, corresponds to a higher temperature.

Visible light is the next shortest wavelength, ranging from 380 nm to 740 nm. Although it comprises a relatively small portion of the total electromagnetic spectrum, visible light is probably the most familiar type of **electromagnetic wave**, for this is the range of wavelength the human eye can detect. The wavelengths of visible light are absorbed and reflected by different materials, which we perceive as different colors. From longest to shortest wavelengths, these colors are classified as red, orange, yellow, green, blue, indigo, and violet. (One acronym for remembering this order is ROY G. BIV.) Red waves have the lowest energy, while blue, indigo, and violet waves have the highest energies in this range. When materials absorb visible light, they can heat up as electromagnetic energy is transferred to the material. However, the energy levels in visible light generally aren't high enough to ionize atoms or strip away electrons. Ionization can be harmful for living tissue.

Ultraviolet (UV) rays have shorter wavelengths than does visible light, ranging from 380 nm to 10 nm. Ultraviolet rays are the highest energy waves radiated in large quantities from the sun. Near-UV radiation, with energies just higher than visible light, is strongly absorbed by the surface layer of human skin. These absorbed rays can cause sunburn and, over time, skin cancer. This is why people use sunglasses and sunscreen as protection from these damaging rays.

ULTRAVIOLET

Ultraviolet rays are invisible. Why does this radiation pose a threat to the skin?

X-rays have even shorter wavelengths and higher energies than do UV rays. X-rays range from 10 nm to 0.01 nm in wavelength. The energy of x-rays is too high to be absorbed by most atoms. Instead, x-rays tend to knock electrons out of atoms, which can cause mutations and cancer in body cells. The common phrase "**x-ray** vision" refers to the ability to see through objects, such as walls or humans. This is related to the fact that x-rays can pass through many materials, including most of the tissues in the human body. When x-rays interact with materials, including the human body, they create ionizing effects, meaning the x-rays strip away electrons. Repeated exposure to ionizing radiation can change the chemical balance of cells, in some cases causing cancer. By the same token, if doctors can concentrate radiation on a few cancerous cells, they can help people get better.

Gamma rays have the shortest wavelengths (less than 10 picometers or 0.01 nm) and highest energies of the entire electromagnetic spectrum. These high-energy waves radiate from the nucleus of an atom during radioactive decay. Like x-rays, gamma rays are ionizing, meaning they knock electrons out of atoms. The high energies of gamma rays can cause serious damage to the human body.

When matter absorbs electromagnetic radiation, the energy from the waves affects the material at a molecular level. Lower energy waves, like microwaves, induce molecules to rotate. Slightly higher energy rays, such as infrared, cause molecules to vibrate. Both rotation and vibration of molecules result in the transfer of thermal energy, or heating. Higher energy radiation, such as some visible light and UV, causes energy transitions within molecules and even greater heating effects. The highest energy radiation, such as x-rays and gamma rays, immediately strip away electrons, changing the chemical nature of matter. For healthy living tissue, absorbing high-energy radiation can be very dangerous, even fatal.

SPACE TELESCOPE

Telescopes allow us to view the electromagnetic spectrum emitted or altered by objects in space. Why would telescopes designed to detect X-rays and gamma rays be placed into space outside Earth's atmosphere?

How Can I Calculate the Energy of Electromagnetic Radiation?

Speed of Electromagnetic Waves

In a vacuum, the **speed** of **light** is assigned the symbol of c. This speed has the value of 2.9979×10^8 m/s. All wavelengths of light, from radio waves to gamma rays, travel at the same speed. Even though these forms of **radiation** have the same speed, they don't have the same energy.

Waves have peaks and valleys or troughs, and the distance from peak to peak or valley to valley is the **wavelength**. The wavelength is abbreviated as the symbol λ.

The number of peaks (or valleys) that pass by a given point in a certain time period is the **wave's frequency**. The frequency is abbreviated as the symbol f.

Multiplying wavelength, which has distance units such as meters, by frequency, which has the units such as cycles per second, or **hertz** (Hz), results in the wave's speed. Therefore:

$$speed = \lambda f$$

For an **electromagnetic wave** in a vacuum, this equals c, or 2.9979×10^8 m/s, so:

$$c = f\lambda$$

Notice the units for c are distance over time, which is similar to miles per hour that we might use to describe how fast a car is going. The speed of light has similar units—except light travels at about 700 hundred million miles per hour!

Calculating the Energy of a Wave

A wave's energy is described by the formula:

$$E = hf$$

Where E is the amount of energy, f is the frequency, and h is a constant called Planck's constant that describes the linear relationship between energy and frequency. In a mathematical sense, Plank's constant is the slope of the line formed when the relationship between energy and frequency is plotted.

As the formula shows, the energy of an electromagnetic wave depends on its frequency. Energy is directly proportional to frequency. As frequency increases, energy increases. As frequency decreases, energy decreases. Lower frequency radio waves have less energy than higher frequency gamma rays.

Frequency and wavelength are linked, though, so that means energy and wavelength are also linked. However, whereas energy is directly proportional to frequency, energy is inversely proportional to wavelength. This means it has an inverse relationship. As wavelength increases, energy decreases. As wavelength decreases, energy increases.

This relationship is reflected mathematically as:

$$E = hf = \frac{hc}{\lambda}$$

To calculate the energy of a wave, you need to know either its wavelength or its frequency. (To ponder: Why is knowing the speed not enough information?)

For electromagnetic waves, high-energy gamma rays can have 10 million trillion times the energy of low-energy radio waves.

How Can You Describe the Energy, Power, and Intensity of a Mechanical Wave?

Energy, Power, and Intensity of Mechanical Waves

What does it mean for waves to transmit energy? Recall that energy is defined as the ability to do work. Recall also that work is the force applied to an object through a distance. When thinking about the energy of mechanical waves, such as ocean waves, think about how much work the **wave** could do on an object. That is, how much force would the wave exert on an object to move it through a particular distance?

Remember that the "height" of a wave is known as the **amplitude** of the wave. It turns out that the energy of a mechanical wave is proportional to the square of the wave's amplitude. Consider an ocean wave. It is intuitively clear that the bigger the wave, the more force it exerts on objects through a distance. In other words, the bigger the wave (that is, the greater the amplitude of the wave), the more energy it has. We can express this mathematically in the following way:

$$E \propto A^2$$

Here, E is the energy of the wave, A is the amplitude of the wave, and

$$E \propto A^2$$

indicates that E is proportional to

$$A^2$$

Recall that *power* is the amount of energy delivered to, or work done on, an object in a particular amount of time. Similarly, the power of a wave is defined as the rate at which the wave transmits energy in an interval of time:

$$P = \frac{\Delta E}{\Delta t}$$

Another measure related to the energy and power of a wave is called the **intensity** of the wave. Intensity, I, is defined as the amount of energy that is transmitted through an area of space in a period of time. In other words, it is the power delivered by a wave through an area:

$$I = \frac{\Delta E}{(\text{area}) \times \Delta t} = \frac{P}{\text{area}}$$

Because power is given in units of watts and area has units of square meters, intensity has units of watts per square meter, or W/m^2.

The intensity of a sound wave is related to the loudness of a sound that we hear. There is an inverse square relationship between intensity and distance from the source. The intensity decreases as the wave spreads out from its source. This is why music will be very loud directly in front of a speaker at a concert, but it will sound much quieter standing in the back of an auditorium.

Energy, Power, and Intensity of Mechanical Waves: Sample Problem 1

An ocean wave has an amplitude of 1.0 m.

(a) What happens to the energy of the wave if the amplitude doubles to 2.0 m?

(b) What happens to the energy of the wave if the amplitude decreases to 0.5 m?

WAVES HIT A ROCKY SHORE

Imagine that the winds, tides, and waves are not as strong as shown in this image. How would the properties of the weaker waves differ from the stronger ones?

Solution:

(a) Call the original amplitude of the wave A_1 and the original energy of the wave E_1. Then,

$$E_1 \propto A_1^2$$

Now, let A_2 be the amplitude of the wave after the energy has doubled and E_2 be the corresponding energy. Then,

$$E_2 \propto A_2^2$$
$$E_2 \propto (2A_1)^2$$

$$E_2 \propto 4A_1^2$$
$$E_2 \propto 4E_1$$

When the amplitude doubles, the energy quadruples.

(b) The amplitude of the wave, 0.5 m, is half the original amplitude of 1.0 m. Let A_3 be the amplitude of the wave after the energy has halved and E_3 be the corresponding energy.

$$E_2 \propto A_3^2$$

$$E_3 \propto \left(\frac{1}{2} A_1\right)^2$$

$$E_3 \propto \frac{1}{4} A_1^2$$

$$E_3 \propto \frac{1}{4} E_1$$

When the amplitude is halved, the energy is quartered.

Energy, Power, and Intensity of Mechanical Waves: Sample Problem 2

A sound originates from a single speaker near the center of a stage. The speaker produces a 60.0-W sound wave. What happens to the intensity of the sound if the distance of a listener doubles from 10.0 to 20.0 m?

SPEAKERS

Imagine yourself at a concert. What happens to the intensity of the sound waves as you change your position?

© Discovery Education | www.discoveryeducation.com ● Image: Pixabay

Solution:

Call the distance from the source d and the intensity of the sound wave I. The intensity of the sound waves satisfies an inverse square relation:

$$I \propto \frac{1}{d^2}$$

Now, let d_1 be the original distance 10.0 m and d_2 the doubled distance 20.0 m. Let the original intensity of the sound wave be I_1 and let the intensity at distance d_2 be I_2. Then,

$$I_2 \propto \frac{1}{d_2^2}$$

$$I_2 \propto \frac{1}{(2d_1)^2}$$

$$I_2 \propto \frac{1}{4d_1^2}$$

$$I_2 \propto \frac{1}{4}I_1$$

When the distance doubles, the intensity quarters.

What Is the Doppler Effect, and How Does It Relate to the Frequency of a Wave?

The Doppler Effect

An ambulance siren will rise in pitch as it moves closer, and then as it passes its pitch will lower. This is a common example of the **Doppler effect**. The Doppler effect is a phenomenon observed when waves originate from a source that is in motion relative to the observer/listener of the **wave**. This effect results in a change in the perceived **frequency** of the wave.

To understand how the Doppler effect occurs, consider again the example of the ambulance. If the ambulance were at rest, it would emit sound waves at a specific frequency. Recall that the frequency of the sound wave is the number of oscillations that the sound wave completes in one second. The pitch of the sound wave is related to the frequency of the siren that a person hears.

Now, consider the case where the ambulance begins moving toward a person standing beside the street. The siren's sound waves are still emitted at their original frequency, but the person on the street will hear more oscillations per second because the sound waves are compressed closer to one another as the sound source moves forward. This makes the apparent **wavelength** of the sound waves shorter and, because the **speed** of sound remains constant for the medium (air) and its conditions, the apparent frequency must be higher. Thus, the pitch of a sound is heard to increase when the sound source moves toward an observer.

Next, consider the case where the ambulance moves away from the person on the street. Again, the sound waves are emitted at their original frequency, but as the ambulance moves away from the observer, the sound waves traveling behind the ambulance are spread farther apart. This makes the apparent wavelength of the sound waves longer and, consequently, the apparent frequency must be lower. Thus, the pitch of the sound is heard to decrease when the sound source moves away from an observer.

Doppler Effect

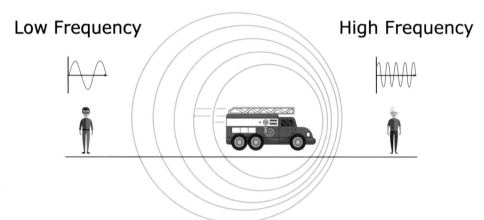

DOPPLER EFFECT
The Doppler effect occurs in moving sources of sound. Under what conditions does the observer hear a sound of shorter wavelength?

Just as the Doppler effect causes a change in the apparent pitch of sound waves, a similar mechanism causes a change in the apparent color of light **waves**. Light waves emitted by moving objects in outer space exhibit the same behaviors as the sound waves in the ambulance scenarios. When objects in outer space emit light and move toward Earth, the light appears bluer because the frequency of the light wave appears to increase. When objects move away from Earth, the light appears to be redder because the frequency of the light wave appears to decrease. This phenomenon is called, respectively, the "blueshift" and "redshift" of light.

How Does the Speed of a Wave Relate to the Medium through Which It Travels?

Wave Speed through Different Media

Mechanical and electromagnetic waves travel at different speeds when they pass through different media. For mechanical waves, the **speed** difference is related to the distance between particles in the medium. For example, the particles in a gas, such as air, are spread far apart from one another. As a result, it takes longer for a vibrating air molecule to transmit a vibration to the molecule nearest to it. In contrast, the particles in liquids, such as water, and solids, such as the ground, are packed more tightly together. Therefore, these particles can transmit vibrations to one another more easily, and thus more rapidly, allowing the mechanical **wave** to travel at a faster speed. In fact, mechanical waves, such as sound waves, travel the fastest through solids. This is why people can hear a train approaching when they press their ear to a solid railroad track, even though the sound of the train cannot yet be heard through the air.

Electromagnetic waves travel at the speed of **light** through a vacuum. This is the fastest speed that a light wave can travel (and, according to modern physics, it is faster than any object with mass can travel). However, when electromagnetic waves travel through a medium such as air, water, or glass, the waves will change speed because of various properties particular to the medium. This phenomenon is actually the reason light waves refract, or bend, when they pass from one medium to another. Light always travels more slowly through a material than it does through a vacuum.

How Can You Describe Reflection, Refraction, Polarization, Interference, Diffraction, and Resonance?

Reflection and Refraction

Reflection occurs when a **wave** strikes a boundary between two media and bounces back into the medium from which it came. When **light** strikes the surface of an object, some light is absorbed and some light is reflected. The **frequency** of the reflected light is the same as the incident light, which represents the color that we associate with that object. When light reflects off a mirror, a duplicated image can be seen. Similarly, when sound waves reflect off a wall, an echo can be heard. Sound reflects efficiently from hard surfaces such as tiled floors and walls. This is why the sound of footsteps and voices is quite reverberant, or well reflected, in tiled rooms, such as museums or bathrooms.

Refraction is the bending of a wave as the wave changes **speed**. This typically occurs when the wave passes from one medium to another. The bending of the wave occurs when the wave passes into a new medium at an angle. When this happens, the front edge of the wave will begin to travel at a new speed while the back edge is still traveling at the old speed. This causes the wave to bend, changing directions. Light, for example, will refract when it passes through a prism. During this process, light passes from air to glass and then back to air again. It refracts because light travels at different speeds through air and through glass. White light consists of different colors of light. Each frequency of light will refract a different amount when it passes through glass. Thus, white light will separate into component colors when it refracts through a glass prism.

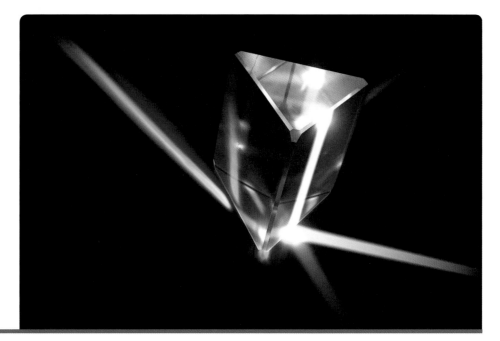

REFRACTION

Refraction causes white light to separate into a rainbow of colors when it passes through a glass prism. If violet light refracts the most, what color light refracts the least?

Polarization

The **polarization** of a wave refers to the orientation of the oscillations of a transverse wave with respect to the direction in which the wave travels. For example, light is a transverse wave. The polarization of a light wave refers to the direction in which the electric and magnetic fields oscillate. **Transverse waves** can be linearly polarized, which means that the waves oscillate in a single plane as they travel. Transverse waves can also be circularly or elliptically polarized, which means that the wave oscillations rotate as the waves travel.

Polarization is an important concept in the description of light waves because light can be filtered according to its polarization. Light that travels to Earth from the sun is not polarized, which means that the electric and magnetic fields oscillate in many directions. Light can be filtered when it passes through a material that permits only certain polarizations of light to pass through. For example, certain sunglasses are made of materials that transmit only vertically polarized light. Thus, when randomly polarized light from the sun passes through a polarizing sunglass lens, only a fraction of the light can pass through. This helps reduce the brightness of the sun's rays, thereby reducing damage to a person's eyes.

POLARIZING LIGHT
This sunglasses lens polarizes light. Why do polarizing lenses reduce glare from reflected light?

Interference and Diffraction

When two waves traveling through a medium intersect with one another, the amplitudes of each wave add together. This is called wave **interference**. It may also be referred to as superposition. An example of this is when an incoming wave encounters its reflection. The interference between the two waves occurs consistently at the same points, which makes those points appear to be standing still. This pattern is called standing-wave pattern.

To understand the effects of interference, it is important to define the phase of a wave. The phase refers to the fraction of a wave cycle that has elapsed relative to the start of the wave. Some waves are said to be "out of phase," such as when one wave starts and a second wave begins after the first wave has already completed some portion of its oscillation. That is, the two waves are out of alignment by some fraction of a wave cycle, and the amount of this difference in this alignment is called the phase.

The phase of waves is important when two or more waves interfere with one another. For example, two waves that start from the same point in their wave cycle are "in phase." If these waves interfere with one another, the amplitudes of each wave will add together fully, forming a wave that has twice the **amplitude** of each original wave. However, if two identical waves are "out of phase" by a half period, the waves will perfectly cancel each other out when they interfere with one another.

Diffraction occurs when a wave encounters an obstacle or passes through a small opening or slit. As waves pass through the slit, they bend and spread out radially. This often occurs when water waves with large wavelengths strike a barrier with a narrow opening in it. The emerging waves form a semicircular ripple pattern. If the opening is large compared to the **wavelength**, little or no diffraction occurs.

DIFFRACTION

Water waves diffract when passing through an opening in a breakwater along a shoreline. How could you observe diffraction in light waves?

If a wave encounters a barrier with multiple narrow openings, it will diffract at each of those openings. These diffracted waves will then interfere with one another. For example, if light strikes a barrier with two small slits, the light will diffract through the slits and then interfere on the other side of the slits. This will form what is known as an interference pattern beyond the slits. The pattern will have bright and dark spots or lines corresponding to the places where the diffracted waves interfered.

Resonance

Resonance is the tendency of an object or system to vibrate at a natural frequency called the resonant frequency. This frequency is determined by the particular characteristics of that object. When objects begin to vibrate or oscillate at their resonant frequency, they will vibrate at a greater amplitude than they would at other frequencies.

Resonance explains how many musical instruments produce sound. Consider a trombone, which is a brass instrument with many curved chambers filled with air. A musician vibrates his or her lips into the trombone's mouthpiece, producing many different frequencies of sound waves. When one of these frequencies is a resonant frequency of the trombone, the air in the chambers of the trombone begins to vibrate with a large amplitude. This produces a loud sound. Most musical instruments have numerous resonant frequencies at which they will vibrate with large amplitude. These are known as the "harmonics" of the instrument, and they produce different pitches.

What Are Some Technological Applications of Electromagnetic and Mechanical Waves?

Applications of Electromagnetic and Mechanical Waves: Medical Uses

There are many applications of waves in medicine. Ultrasound refers to the range of high-**frequency** sound waves that humans cannot hear. These mechanical waves are higher than 20,000 Hz. Ultrasound frequencies higher than 10 MHz are typically used in medical applications. In these applications, sound waves are transmitted through a person's body, where they reflect off of internal organs. Technological devices can determine the time it takes for the ultrasound waves to reflect back to the surface of a person's body. This information is then used to construct a detailed image of things inside the human body such as a developing fetus or the arteries around the heart.

The energy of x-rays, which are high-energy electromagnetic waves, is also useful in medical applications. As discussed earlier, x-rays pass through most of the tissues in the human body. However, x-rays are absorbed by the atoms in bones, meaning they do not transmit through bones. This principle allows doctors to produce "negative" images of the human skeleton on **x-ray** film. An x-ray image will appear black in all the places where x-rays passed through the body, and it will appear white in the places where x-rays were absorbed by bones. The result is a white image depicting the structure of the bones. Doctors can use the x-ray image to diagnose skeletal problems such as broken bones.

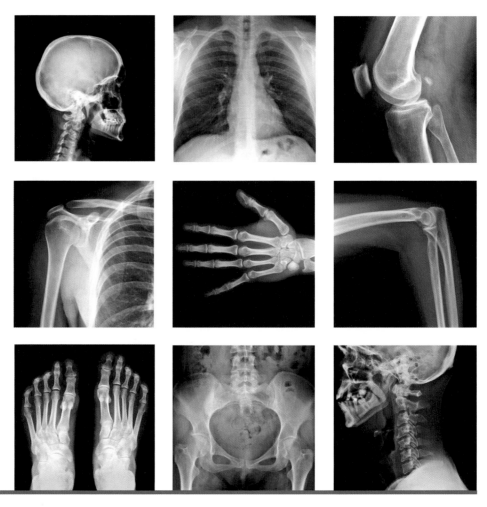

X-RAYS

Since the late nineteenth century, physicians have used X-rays to diagnose many internal conditions. How do X-rays allow imaging of internal structures?

Gamma rays are also used in medicine. Gamma rays are the highest energy waves in the **electromagnetic spectrum**. The high energy of gamma rays can be quite hazardous. However, when focused carefully, gamma rays can help destroy defective cells in human bodies. For example, gamma rays are used to destroy cancer cells and tumors in sick patients.

Applications of Electromagnetic Waves: Digitization

Every day, we use devices that depend on electromagnetic waves—cell phones, TV remotes, computers, light bulbs, GPS units, etc. We use electromagnetic radiation to keep tabs on the planet, too. Satellites take pictures of Earth from space at different wavelengths and store, send, or analyze images. Digitizing information, whether it's an image of the early universe taken by the Hubble Space Telescope or a word processing file on your computer, depends on the application of electromagnetic waves.

Digitization converts information into discrete data "bits" that computers and other processors can interpret and manipulate. Almost any kind of input can be digitized, including text, pictures, sound, music, and video. Converting from analog to digital formats involves sampling and "quantizing" a continuous variable signal so it becomes a fixed series of digital inputs instead.

Digital data is easy to store, organize, and transfer. When you send digital files, the information is being converted into electromagnetic wave pulses and transmitted anywhere in the world—and even beyond. Scientists exchange digital data from satellites, the International Space Station, and even the rovers on Mars.

Applications of Electromagnetic Waves: Photovoltaics

When an electron in a material is hit by a photon, it can absorb the photon's energy. For certain materials, especially metals, the incoming photons cause electrons to jump to a higher energy state where they flow more easily. When electrons move, they create a current. Therefore, incoming light can cause electricity to flow within and across these materials. This is called the photovoltaic effect.

The photovoltaic effect is related to the photoelectric effect. In the photoelectric effect, when a material absorbs very high-energy electromagnetic radiation, the energy of the photons can knock electrons totally away from their atoms. This effect usually occurs only with higher energy radiation such as ultraviolet, x-rays, and gamma rays. The difference is that, for the photovoltaic effect, the electrons get "energized" to a higher level, but they aren't completely stripped away from their atoms.

The discovery of the photovoltaic effect was a big surprise. Scientists found that only certain photon energy levels would have an effect. If the photons were too low energy, nothing would happen, no matter the **intensity** or number of photons. The photon energies didn't seem to "add." Instead, at a certain energy level of incoming photons, called a threshold energy, electrons would absorb the energy and be ejected. Even one photon at or above the threshold energy level would have an impact, while a million, billion, or trillion photons just below the threshold would have no effect at all.

This surprising result led scientists to a new understanding of light waves as having particle-like qualities and being quantized into discrete chunks, or photons. It was Albert Einstein who helped resolve the mystery by using Planck's constant and proposing that a photon's energy is related to its frequency by the equation $E = hv$.

PHOTOVOLTAIC PANELS

Photovoltaics absorb light energy from the sun that can then be used in many applications. What qualities must light have for photovoltaics to work?

When the material being hit by incoming radiation can conduct a controlled current, the material can be used to create a PV cell, or a photovoltaic cell. This is what makes it possible to turn sunlight, or solar **power**, into electricity. So-called solar cells are used to power a wide range of objects and systems, including calculators, cars, orbiting satellites, and even electrical grids in places without generators.

Consider the Explain Question

What are the relationships among the frequency, wavelength, and speed of waves traveling in a specific medium?

dlc.com/ca11078s

Go online to complete the scientific explanation.

Check Your Understanding

Two students are holding a spring. One student shakes the spring up and down. A wave travels along the spring to the second student. What is the type of wave modeled?

dlc.com/ca11079s

STEM in Action

Applying Wave Characteristics

The various characteristics and behaviors of waves allow scientists to learn a great deal about the nature of things in the universe.

Some scientists study a phenomenon called cosmic microwave background (CMB) **radiation**. This radiation is a distribution of electromagnetic waves in the microwave range. It exists faintly in all observable parts of outer space. Scientists believe that this radiation is **light** left over from an early stage of the formation of the universe and that it provides evidence for the Big Bang. Current evidence indicates that the universe is expanding. Thus, scientists must also apply their understanding of the **Doppler effect** to determine how the observed **wavelength** and **frequency** of this radiation may have changed. The study of this background radiation has led some scientists to conclude that the universe is flat, as opposed to being curved. They also conclude that it is expanding outward.

THE EDGE OF THE UNIVERSE?

Microwave background radiation may help scientists understand the large-scale structure of the universe by mapping anomalies such as the one indicated by the circle. What do the different colors in the image represent?

Scientists have developed sophisticated telescopes that measure X-rays and gamma rays in outer space. The purpose of observing these waves is to learn more about the behavior of distant stars and other potential sources of high-energy waves in the universe. This information will help scientists understand more about the distribution of matter in the universe as well as how high-energy particles behave.

STEM and Wave Characteristics

Many earthquakes occur daily, and most of them cause little, if any, damage. However, strong earthquakes cause considerable loss of life and property, so the study of earthquakes is an important area of science. The study of earthquakes is called seismology, and a seismologist is a scientist that studies seismology. One of the most important tools of a seismologist is a seismometer. A seismometer is a device engineered to measure the motion of seismic waves that result from a disturbance in the ground, such as an earthquake or large explosion. These devices gather information about the motion of seismic waves, such as their **wave speed** and frequency. When many seismometers are used in series, they can gather large-scale information about an earthquake. Seismologists can take information from an array of seismometers and can determine the precise location of an earthquake.

Seismologists also use seismometers to gather information about the internal structure of Earth. This process is called **reflection** seismology. In this process, an explosion is detonated at Earth's surface, causing seismic waves to travel inward toward the internal layers of Earth. When these waves strike boundaries or obstructions, they reflect back toward Earth's surface. Seismometers can detect the time it takes these waves to reflect. Seismologists then use this information to predict the existence of structures or resources underground, such as coal, water, or layers of bedrock.

Just like seismologists study the movement of waves through solid parts of Earth, certain oceanographers study the movement of waves through bodies of water by using sonar. Sonar is the process by which sound waves are emitted, reflected from a surface, and detected by a device. Submarines often use sonar to navigate through hazardous areas and to communicate with other underwater vessels. Sonar can also be used to determine the depth of a region of water in the ocean. Because it is difficult for scientists to gain direct access to the ocean floor, sonar can be used to map its topography, or shape. Sound waves are emitted toward the ocean floor. The waves reflect off the floor and return to the surface. Because oceanographers know the **speed** at which sound waves travel in water, they can determine the distance that the **wave** traveled. This allows them to generate detailed maps of the shape of the ocean floor.

Calculating the Energy of Electromagnetic Waves

Use the wavelength-frequency equation or Planck's Wave Equations to solve the following problems.

For your reference:
h = Planck's constant = 6.626 x 10^{-34} J•s
c = speed of light = 3 x 10^8 m/sec

1. A ray of light has a frequency of 7.9 x 10^{14} cycles per second (Hz). What is its energy?

2. The light from a laser has a wavelength of 500 nm. What is the energy of one photon?

3. What happens to a wave's energy if its frequency is doubled?

4. What is the energy of light with a wavelength of 662 nm?

5. A photon's energy is 8.0×10^{-19} J. What is its frequency?

Wave Speed, Wavelength, and Frequency #1

Use wave equations to solve the problems below.

1. A sound wave traveling through a certain fresh water lake has a frequency of 349.2 Hz and a wavelength of 4.25 m.

   a. What is the speed of a sound wave in this water?

   b. If the water conditions are held constant, all sound waves will travel at the same speed through water. Use this fact to calculate the wavelength of a sound wave with a frequency of 415.3 Hz.

2. A sound wave travels through a steel railroad track with a frequency of 493.9 Hz and a wavelength of 10.64 m.

   a. What is the speed of the sound in the railroad track?

   b. In the same steel track at the same temperature, what is the wavelength of a sound wave with a frequency of 1046.5 Hz?

3. A cello plays a C# note with a frequency of 277.2 Hz. If the speed of sound in air is 343 m/s, what is the wavelength of this note?

4. A trombone plays a C_3 note. If the speed of sound in air is 343 m/s and the wavelength of this note is 2.62 m, what is the frequency of this C_3 note?

Wave Speed, Wavelength, and Frequency #2

Use wave equations to solve these problems.

1. It is determined that a certain light wave has a wavelength of 3.012×10^{-12} m. The light travels at 2.99×10^8 m/s. What is the frequency of the light wave?

2. It is determined that a certain wave of infrared light has a wavelength of 8.45 μm. (denotes "micro", or 10^{-6}.) Given that $c = 2.99 \times 10^8$ m/s, what is the frequency of this infrared wave?

3. A certain AM radio wave has a frequency of 1.12×10^6 Hz. Given that radio waves travel at 2.99×10^8 m/s, what is the wavelength of this radio wave?

4. A certain FM radio wave has a frequency of 1.31 × 10⁸ Hz.

a. Given that radio waves travel at 2.99 × 10⁸ m/s, what is the wavelength of this FM radio wave?

b. Waves with long wavelengths generally travel farther. Given the calculations in this activity, which is better in transmitting signals far distances: AM radio waves or FM radio waves?

Energy, Power, and Intensity of Mechanical Waves #1

Use wave equations to solve the following problems.

1. A wave on a small lake has an amplitude of 0.1 meters. What happens to the energy of the wave by doubling its height to 0.2 meters?

2. A seismic wave has an amplitude of 0.012 meters. If the amplitude of this wave reduces to 0.006 meters, what happens to the energy associated with this wave?

3. The amplitude of a transversal wave in a slinky toy triples. What happens to the energy of the wave in the toy?

4. The amplitude of a longitudinal wave in a slinky toy increases by a factor of five. What happens to the energy of the wave of the toy?

Energy, Power, and Intensity of Mechanical Waves #2

Use wave equations to solve the following problems.

1. A student sitting 2 meters from the bell of her classroom decides it is too loud. The following day, she sits in a chair that is 4 meters from the bell. How does the intensity of the noise compare?

2. On the third day, the student sits 6 meters from the bell. What happens to the intensity of the sound that she hears the third day compared to the first day?

3. On the fourth day, the student sits 1 meter from the bell.

   a. What happens to the intensity of the sound that she hears on the fourth day as compared to the first day?

   b. What is the intensity of sound she hears on the fourth day as compared to the third day?

4. A saxophone player plays at a distance of 4.2 meters from the microphone. However, the sound is too soft, and the director wants the sound to be 9 times more intense. At what distance from the microphone should the saxophone player stand?

CONCEPT
5.2

Reflection and Refraction

dlc.com/ca11080s

LESSON OVERVIEW

Lesson Questions

■ What is reflection, and how can you describe the image formed when light reflects off a plane mirror?

■ What is refraction, and how does a thin convex lens refract light?

■ How does the focal length of a lens relate to the location of an image and the magnification of an image?

Lesson Objectives

By the end of the lesson, you should be able to:

■ Predict the types of images formed by reflection from a plane mirror and by refraction through a thin convex lens.

■ Relate the focal length of a lens to the location and magnification of an image.

■ Model the use of reflecting and refracting devices to solve specific real-world problems.

Key Vocabulary

Which terms do you already know?

☐ focal length
☐ real image
☐ refraction
☐ refractive index

Thinking about Reflection and Refraction

Look down into a pool of water on a sunny day, and you will probably see a reflection. What causes a reflection? Why don't all surfaces produce reflections?

dlc.com/ca11081s

EXPLAIN QUESTION

How does light from a headlamp use a lens and a mirror to produce a narrow beam?

WASHINGTON MONUMENT

An image of the Washington Monument is seen in the Lincoln Memorial Reflecting Pool. How would this reflection differ when the weather is windy?

What Is Reflection, and How Can You Describe the Image Formed When Light Reflects Off a Plane Mirror?

Reflection

Reflection is the process by which a wave strikes a surface (or boundary) between two media and is redirected back, possibly even in the direction from which it originated. Any type of wave can be reflected, including light waves and sound waves.

PERFECT REFLECTION

A still body of water, whether a puddle, pond, or lake, will always reflect its surroundings. What geometrical rules govern this mirror-like reflection?

Light waves can be reflected when they travel from one medium to another, such as from air to glass, from air to water, and even from air to our skin. Some surfaces absorb an amount of the light waves that strike them and reflect the rest of the waves. For example, white surfaces reflect the light waves that strike them, while black surfaces absorb those waves. (This explains why black surfaces heat up faster than white surfaces.) A colored object, such as green grass, will absorb all frequencies of light except for the green frequencies. It thus reflects green light, making it appear to be the color green.

Other surfaces, such as mirrors, will reflect all the light waves that strike them, causing the light to change direction. Any surfaces or boundaries that absorb or reflect all the light that strikes them are considered opaque. This means that it is not possible to see through them.

Plane Mirrors and Images

A plane mirror is a flat surface that reflects light that strikes it. A common plane mirror is the mirror in a bathroom that hangs flat against the wall. Curved mirrors, in contrast, are not flat and will not behave the same as plane mirrors. For example, when you observe yourself in a curved mirror at a circus or funhouse, your body appears to be distorted.

When people see objects, their brain assumes that light has traveled in a straight-line path from the object to their eyes. This path is called the line of sight. People do indeed see light that has traveled along a straight-line path when light travels directly from an object to their eyes. However, when light strikes a mirror first, it changes direction, but the brain perceives the light as though it originated along a straight-line path from an object. This principle is what creates the illusion of an image that exists behind a mirror.

To understand how people see things in mirrors, recall that all objects absorb and reflect light. For example, when light strikes a red apple, the apple absorbs all the frequencies of light except for red. The red frequencies of light are then reflected away from the object. If this light strikes a person's eye directly, the person will see the red apple. However, if this light strikes a plane mirror first, the light will be reflected into a new direction. If the redirected light then strikes a person's eye, the person will observe an image of the apple that appears to exist "on the other side" of the mirror.

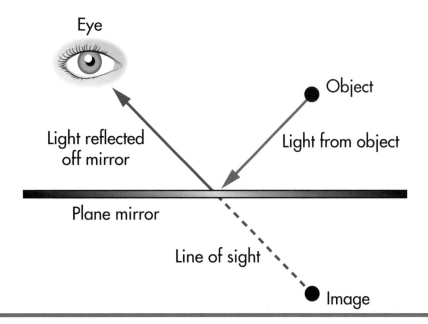

PLANE MIRROR

When light traveling from an object strikes a plane mirror, the light is reflected in a new direction. How do the properties of a mirror affect the image you see as a reflection?

The Law of Reflection

In order to describe the properties of an image in a mirror, we must discuss the law of reflection. Consider a ray of light that approaches a plane mirror. This ray is called the incident ray. To analyze how the incident ray will reflect when it strikes the mirror, draw a line perpendicular to the surface of the mirror. This is called the normal line. Measure the angle between the incident ray and the normal line. This is called the angle of incidence. Next, observe the path of the light that reflects off the plane mirror. This is called the reflected ray. The angle between the reflected ray and the normal line is called the angle of reflection.

The law of reflection states that the angle of incidence is congruent to the angle of reflection ($\angle i = \angle r$).

The properties of a reflected image can be described and predicted using the principles of reflection.

REFLECTION ANGLES

The law of reflection states that when a light ray strikes a plane mirror, the angle of incidence is equal to the angle of reflection. How is this principle useful in describing an image seen in the mirror?

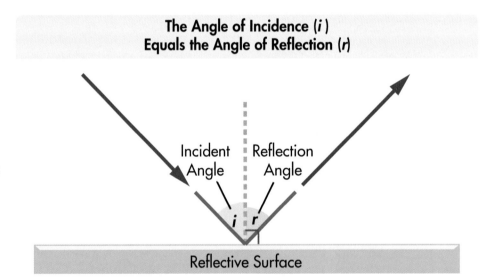

The Angle of Incidence (*i*) Equals the Angle of Reflection (*r*)

Incident Angle

Reflection Angle

i *r*

Reflective Surface

Types of Reflection and Properties of Reflected Images

The Law of Reflection is universal, so why can't we see images in all objects we look at? Why does a metallic silver painted car not produce an image, whereas a silver mirror does? Whether a surface produces an image depends upon the smoothness of the surface. If the surface is not perfectly smooth light parallel rays striking it will be reflected off at different angles. Each ray will still follow the law of reflection, but this angle will vary from point to point. The reflected rays are scattered and therefore an image is not observed. This type of reflection is called diffuse reflection. On a smooth surface such as a mirror, parallel light rays will all be reflected at the same angle. This is called regular reflection. Regular reflection produces images within a mirror.

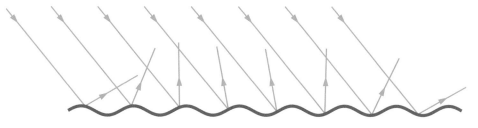

DIFFUSE REFLECTION

We cannot see an image from light reflected off a rough surface. How do the angles of reflection explain this observation?

An image produced by a plane mirror can have different properties. First, the image may appear in different locations in the mirror, depending on the location of the actual object in front of it and the location of the observer.

Similarly, if an object is moved close to the front of a mirror, the image will also appear close to the mirror. In fact, the distance between an object and a mirror is always equal to the apparent distance between the mirror and the image.

Another property of images in plane mirrors is that they are the exact size and shape of the objects placed in front of them. That is, the images of objects are not distorted, enlarged, or reduced. If this were not the case, then it would be very difficult to fix your hair in front of a mirror in the morning.

Images in plane mirrors are reversed front to back. It is a misconception that plane mirrors reverse images left to right.

Curved Mirrors

There are two types of curved mirrors, concave mirrors and convex mirrors. In concave mirrors the reflecting surface dips inward (like a cave). These types of mirrors are widely used as reflectors (in flashlights and headlights) and reflecting telescopes. The reflective surfaces of convex mirrors bulge outward. Fish eye mirrors, commonly used in stores as anti-theft devices, are an example of convex mirrors.

LIGHTING UP THE ROAD AHEAD

The lens of a vehicle's headlight allows the beam to be focused on certain areas on the road. How are the optical components of the lens engineered to focus the beam?

Concave mirrors are sometimes referred to as converging mirrors because rays striking them reflect off the mirror in convergent paths. Concave mirrors can form a variety of images, depending on the position of the object in relation to the focal point and the center of curvature of the mirror:

- An object far away (at infinity) from the mirror forms a **real image** at the focal point.
- An object closer to the mirror, just beyond the center of curvature, forms an image between the center of curvature and the focal point. The image is real, inverted, and reduced.
- An object placed between the center of curvature and the focal point forms an image beyond the center of curvature. This image is real, inverted, and magnified.
- An object placed between the focal point and the mirror will produce a virtual image (behind the mirror). The image will be magnified and upright.

Convex mirrors are sometimes referred to as diverging mirrors because rays striking them reflect off them at diverging angles. They produce only virtual images (behind the mirror) that are upright and smaller than the object.

CURVED MIRRORS DISTORT IMAGES

Chicago's silvery "Bean" is a city landmark. Why does the Bean's reflective surface distort the image of the surrounding cityscape?

What Is Refraction, and How Does a Thin Convex Lens Refract Light?

Refraction

Refraction is the process by which a wave changes direction when it enters a medium through which it travels at a different speed. For example, light waves refract, or bend slightly, as they travel from air to water. When objects are viewed in water from the surface, the objects appear to be a different size or shape than they would appear if they were viewed in air.

Refraction occurs when light changes speed as it travels into a new medium. If a wave of light strikes a boundary at an angle, the part of the light wave that strikes the boundary first will begin to move more quickly or slowly, while the rest of the wave travels on at the original speed. Once the rest of the light wave hits the boundary, it begins traveling at the slower or faster speed, but the light ray has bent due to the difference in speed from one medium to another.

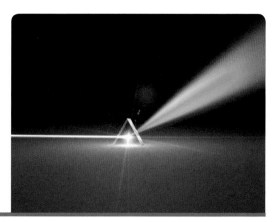

REFRACTION

The transparent glass of a prism refracts light. What properties of the incident ray and emergent ray result in refraction?

As discussed earlier, some boundaries between media will reflect and/or absorb light rays. In addition, some boundaries will allow light to transmit, or pass through, from one medium to another. When the majority of light rays transmit through the boundary of a new medium, the medium is said to be transparent. This means it is possible to see through it. Water, air, and clear glass are transparent media. When light transmits faintly through a material it is translucent. Many thin materials, such as tissue paper and stained glass, are considered translucent.

Light typically refracts whenever it transmits from one medium to another. The angle through which the light refracts is called the angle of refraction. The size of this deflection depends on the refractive indices of the two media. The **refractive index** of a substance is the ratio of the speed of light in a vacuum to the speed of light in the substance.

Light travels at different speeds in different transparent substances or media. For example in a vacuum and air light travels at around 300,000 km/s, but slows down to around 200,000 km/s in glass. The refractive index of glass is therefore 300,000/200,000 or 1.5. In water light travels at about 225,000 km/s. The refractive index of water is therefore 300,000/225,000 or 1.33.

Convex Lenses and Refraction

A convex lens, or converging lens, is a thin, curved piece of glass that is wider in the middle than at the top and bottom. When parallel rays of light strike the glass lens, they refract, changing their path. Each ray of light refracts toward the center line beyond the lens. This location is called the focal point of the lens. For this reason, a convex lens is often called a converging lens because all the rays of light moving through it converge to a single location. The distance from the lens to the focal point is called the **focal length**.

A good example of a convex lens is the lens located inside the eyeball of many organisms. When incoming rays of light strike the lens, they are refracted and focused onto a single location at the back of the eye, called the retina. The retina can be thought of as the focal point of the eye's lens.

Occasionally, the lens of the human eye does not focus light properly, causing blurred vision. To correct this, people use eye glasses that redirect light rays before they strike their eyes, allowing light to focus properly once it passes through the lenses of their eyes.

Concave Lenses and Refraction

A concave lens, or diverging lens, is a thin, curved piece of glass that is narrower in the middle than at its top and bottom. When parallel rays of light strike the glass lens, they refract, changing their path. Each ray of light refracts away from the center line beyond the lens. For this reason, a concave lens is often called a diverging lens because all the rays of light moving through it diverge.

There is still the notion of a focal length of a concave lens. Just as it was for a convex lens, the focal point is the point where parallel incident light rays appear to converge. Light rays emerging from a concave lens appear to be coming from a point before the lens.

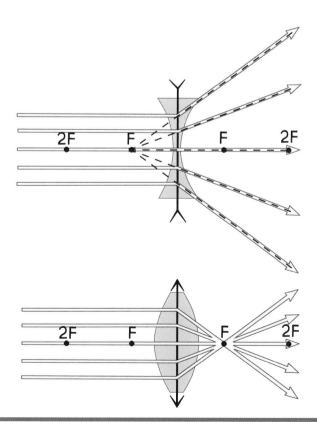

FOCAL LENGTH

Convex and concave lenses both have focal lengths. What is the difference in the direction of light rays relative to the focal length in the two types of lenses?

How Does the Focal Length of a Lens Relate to the Location of an Image and the Magnification of an Image?

Focal Length and Image Location

When an object is placed in front of a convex lens, an image of the object forms. Unlike the image formed by a plane mirror, the distance of the image from a lens will change depending on a few variables.

Consider a lens with a **focal length** f. An object is placed in front of the lens at a location d_1 from the lens. The distance of an image from a lens, d_2, is given by the following formula:

$$\frac{1}{d_1} + \frac{1}{d_2} = \frac{1}{f}$$

The focal length is positive for convex lenses and negative for concave lenses.

Images are classified as real or virtual based on the position of formation of an image. Real images are formed when the lens bends the light waves, so they converge. In this case, an image is really formed, and this image appears on the opposite side of the lens from the origin of the light rays. In contrast, virtual images are the positions where light appears to have converged on the same side of the lens as the origin of the light rays.

Real images appear when objects are placed beyond the focal length of a convex lens. Virtual images appear when objects are placed within the focal length of a convex lens. Concave mirrors produce only virtual images.

Focal Length and Image Location: Sample Problem

A convex lens has a focal length of 15.0 cm. If an object is placed at a location 25.0 cm in front of the lens, where will the image of the object form?

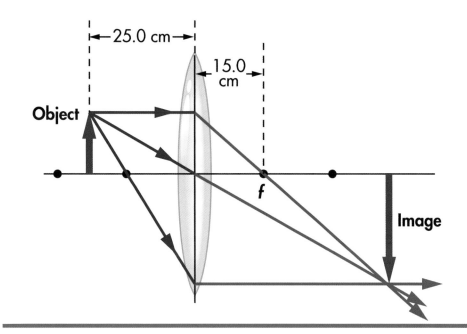

SAMPLE PROBLEM

Examine the relationship between the focal length and object placement. How is the resulting image's location related to location of the object?

Solution:

The focal length of the lens is 15.0 cm, and the distance from the object to the lens is 25.0 cm. Thus,

$$f = 15.0 \text{ cm}$$
$$d_1 = 25.0 \text{ cm}$$

Solve for the distance between the image and the lens, d_2, by using the following equation:

$$\frac{1}{d_1} + \frac{1}{d_2} = \frac{1}{f}$$

Next, solve for d_2:

$$\frac{1}{d_2} = \frac{1}{f} - \frac{1}{d_1}$$

$$\frac{1}{d_2} = \frac{d}{d_1 f} - \frac{f}{d_1 f}$$

$$\frac{1}{d_2} = \frac{d_1 - f}{d_1 f}$$

$$d_2 = \frac{d_1 f}{d_1 - f}$$

Finally, substitute the known values for f and d_1:

$$d_2 = \frac{d_1 f}{d_1 - f}$$

$$= \frac{(25.0 \text{ cm})(15.0 \text{ cm})}{(25.0 \text{ cm}) - (15.0 \text{ cm})}$$

$$= 37.5 \text{ cm}$$

The image will appear 37.5 cm beyond the lens.

Magnification and Convex Lenses

Observe the image formed by the convex lens in the previous example. One important property of the image is that it has a size different from that of the original object. When an image formed by a lens is of a different size from that of the original object, the lens magnifies the object.

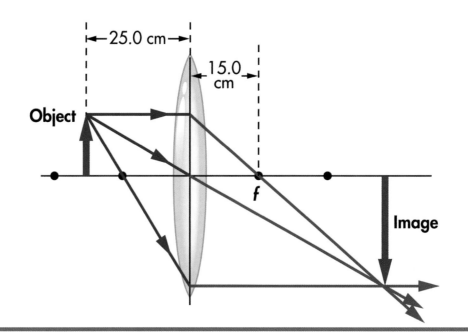

CONVEX LENS

Compare the size of the original object with its image after refraction through a convex lens. How do the properties of the lens explain the difference?

The degree to which a lens magnifies an object depends on the focal length of the lens and the distance between the object and the lens. You can observe this if you hold a magnifying glass over text on a page in a book. When the magnifying glass is placed directly onto the page, the text does not appear to be much larger. However, as you lift the magnifying glass away from the text, the image of the text becomes larger.

A microscope uses the magnifying properties of lenses to enlarge small items, allowing us to examine the details of extremely small objects and substances.

Consider the Explain Question

How does light from a headlamp use a lens and a mirror to produce a narrow beam?

Go online to complete the scientific exwplanation.

dlc.com/ca11082s

Check for Understanding

Go online to check your understanding of this concept's key ideas.

dlc.com/ca11083s

STEM in Action

Applying Reflection and Refraction

Mirrors and lenses are used in many applications in daily life, from makeup mirrors to eyeglasses. They are also used in a wide range of technologies and other applications. Lenses in microscopes, for example, can be used by a doctor or a surgeon to see tiny objects better. Some doctors also use lenses in high-definition digital cameras, called laparoscopic cameras, to see inside the body, either for diagnosis or during minimally invasive surgery. These tiny cameras use lenses and fiber optics to transmit images from inside the body to an external computer monitor. Depending on the work being done, laparoscopic cameras employ different lens types, including zoom or interchangeable fixed-focus lenses. Some types of laparoscopic cameras use a prism located in the camera head. Since different wavelengths of light refract different amounts, the prism can split the incoming image into red, green, and blue components by refracting the different colors at different angles. The three components of the light beam are directed to three CCD (charge-coupled devices) silicon chips that are sensitive to the intensity of the light, producing very high-quality images, much like those in high-end video cameras.

MAGNIFYING GLASS

A convex lens focuses other wavelengths of light as well as visible light. How can this principle be used to start a campfire?

At other times, X-rays are used to look inside the body. X-rays are electromagnetic waves that have wavelengths shorter than those of visible light. X-rays pass straight through low-density materials. This means they are difficult to manipulate using conventional lenses. For this reason, specialized curved mirrors are often used in X-ray machines instead of lenses. Most X-ray mirrors use gold or other rare metals as a reflective layer, making them very expensive. With added computer software, X-rays are used in computed tomography (CT) and computerized axial tomography (CAT) scans. In CT or CAT scans, X-rays show a series of cross-section views of the body. These cross-section images are compiled by the software to produce a three- dimensional image of the body's interior.

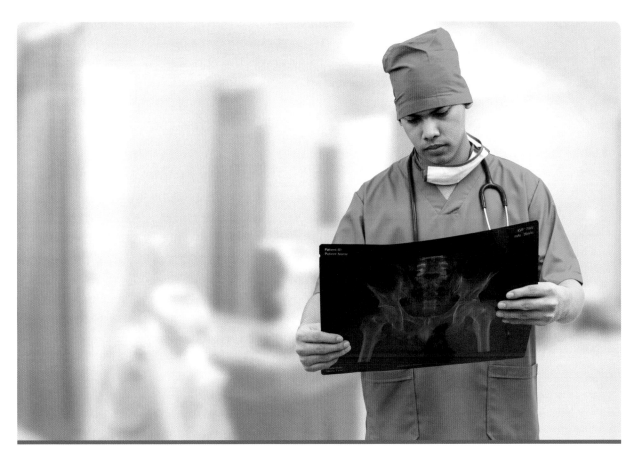

X-RAYS

Physicians use X-rays to diagnose conditions inside the body. How are X-rays manipulated to produce the images?

X-rays have other important uses as well. Because X-rays have much shorter wavelengths than visible light, they can form much more detailed images of very small objects. This ability makes X-rays particularly useful in producing silicon computer chips. The smaller and more detailed images the X-rays produce can be used to place more circuits on a chip. To enable this production, scientists have created special metal "lenses." These devices are made of aluminum blocks with microscopic holes drilled through them, perpendicular to the direction of an X-ray beam that moves through the aluminum. Aluminum is used because it is mostly opaque to X-rays, but the holes in the block leave sections of aluminum that are thin enough for the X- rays to pass through it. Some aluminum lenses can focus an X-ray beam to a spot a few millionths of a centimeter in diameter. An aluminum lens works by using differences in refractive indexes between aluminum and air. As the X-ray beam repeatedly passes from the air in a hole to a thin strip of aluminum, and then into air again, the curvature of the air-aluminum interface focuses the beam, much as light is focused as it passes into and out of a concave glass lens. The X-ray lens revolutionized the production of nanoscale chips.

STEM and Reflection and Refraction

Lenses can be used in various ways to correct vision. Eyeglasses are lenses worn in front of the eyes, and contact lenses are worn directly on the eyes. Abnormalities in the shape of the eye are a common reason for vision correction. A person with nearsightedness (myopia) can see objects close to the eye clearly, but objects at a distance appear blurry. A concave lens is used to correct the vision of a nearsighted person. A person with farsightedness (hyperopia) can see distant objects clearly, but objects close to the eye appear blurry. A convex lens is used to correct the vision of a farsighted person.

Eyeglass lenses are the product of a scientific technology that employs physics, biology, and math. Optometrists and ophthalmologists use sophisticated tools to examine the shape and functioning of the cornea, iris, pupil, lens, and retina (back wall of the eye). They measure how far light has to travel from your lens to your retina. Although the lens of the eye can change shape to adjust to the distance of the object you want to see, sometimes it isn't able to adjust sufficiently to provide clear vision.

A person's vision is blurry if the eye isn't able to focus the light that enters it directly onto light-sensitive cells located on the retina. The optic nerve attached to the retina takes the image information to the brain, enabling the person to see. When the focal point of the light is in front of the retina, the person is nearsighted. When the focal point of the light is beyond the retina, the person is farsighted. In both instances, the image seen by the person is blurry. Optometrists calculate the exact shape of the eyeglass or contact lens that will focus a clear image onto the retina, engineering an artificial device that will work with the eye to produce clearer images of objects.

Lenses are also being used to develop artificial eyes that can enable blind people to see. Just as a functioning human eye does, the artificial eye would use a lens to focus beams of light onto an artificial retina at the back of the eye. The artificial retina would consist of digital sensors that would detect the light and transmit this information to the brain.

Focal Length and Image Location

Use principles of optics to solve the problems below.

1. A particular convex lens has a focal length of 0.22 m. An object is placed at a location 0.34 m in front of the lens. Where will the image of the object form?

2. A particular convex lens has a focal length of 25.5 cm. An object is placed at a location 45.2 cm in front of the lens. Where will the image of the object form?

3. An object is placed 27 cm in front of a convex lens. An image forms 67 cm beyond the lens. What is the focal length of the lens?

4. An object is placed 35 cm in front of a convex lens. An image forms 87 cm beyond the lens. What is the focal length of the lens?

5. A particular convex lens has a focal length of 0.242 m. An object is placed at a location of 48.2 cm in front of the lens. Where will the image of the object form?

Seismic Waves

dlc.com/ca11084s

LESSON OVERVIEW

Lesson Questions

- What are the three main types of seismic waves, and how do they compare to one another?

- How do scientists measure earthquakes?

- What is the difference between earthquake intensity and magnitude? How do seismic waves provide evidence for Earth's interior structure?

Lesson Objectives

By the end of the lesson, you should be able to:

- Compare the three types of seismic waves (P, S, and surface). Explain how earthquakes are measured.

- Compare the concepts of intensity and magnitude.

- Explain how seismic waves provide evidence for Earth's interior structure.

Key Vocabulary

Which terms do you already know?

- [ ] asthenosphere
- [ ] earthquake
- [ ] epicenter
- [ ] fault
- [ ] focus (earthquake)
- [ ] frequency
- [ ] inner core
- [ ] intensity
- [ ] longitudinal waves
- [ ] magnitude
- [ ] mantle
- [ ] modified Mercalli intensity scale
- [ ] outer core
- [ ] P wave
- [ ] Richter scale
- [ ] seismic wave
- [ ] seismogram
- [ ] seismograph
- [ ] seismology
- [ ] shadow zone
- [ ] strain
- [ ] surface wave
- [ ] S wave
- [ ] wavelength
- [ ] wave period

Introducing Seismic Waves

In 1985, a massive earthquake hit Mexico City, killing approximately 9,000 people. The source of this destruction was the movement of tectonic plates, specifically at their boundaries, over 600 km away, which released tremendous amounts of energy. How does the earth moving, especially when originating hundreds of kilometers away, generate such a major natural disaster?

dlc.com/ca11085s

EXPLAIN QUESTION

| What kinds of waves do earthquakes produce, how are they measured, and what evidence do they provide about Earth's interior?

A BROKEN ROAD

An earthquake turns a straight highway into a rising and dipping wave of asphalt. What clues can this severely broken road reveal about the seismic wave that passed through Earth at this point?

What Are the Three Main Types of Seismic Waves, and How Do They Compare to One Another?

Seismic Waves

FAULT BLOCK MOUNTAINS

The Grand Tetons are an example of a mountain range formed by fault blocks: Earth's crust cracked, or faulted, because of swelling within it. What caused the earthquake in this case?

Earthquakes release energy that travels through solid ground in the form of seismic waves. Where does the energy come from? Potential energy builds up as a result of stress on rocks along cracks in Earth's crust called faults. The stress occurs because pieces of Earth's lithosphere called tectonic plates are in constant motion. This motion causes rock on either side of a **fault** to deform, or show **strain**. Eventually, the stress becomes so great that rock breaks, moving suddenly along the fault. When rock breaks, the stress is released, along with the stored potential energy. Seismic waves carry this released energy through solid ground.

Earthquakes generate several different types of seismic waves. Some seismic waves travel through Earth's interior. Geologists refer to these as body waves because they move through bodies of rock. Other seismic waves, called surface waves, travel along the surface of the ground.

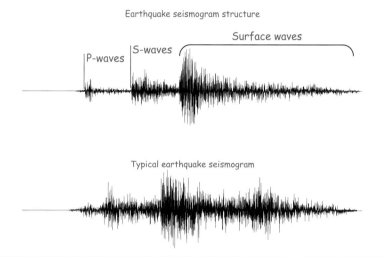

Earthquake seismogram structure

P-waves | S-waves | Surface waves

Typical earthquake seismogram

THREE TIMES THE DANGER

Earthquakes strike more than once with primary, secondary, and surface waves.

P Waves

P waves, or primary waves, are one of two types of body waves. P waves are compressional seismic waves, also called **longitudinal waves**. Compressional waves cause matter to expand and contract as they pass through. This produces a back-and-forth motion of rock particles that is parallel to the direction of the **P wave**. Picture a spring toy held in place on both ends. Then squeeze several loops together and release them. The energy travels down the spring toy to the other end and sets up a back-and-forth movement of energy. This is how compressional waves transfer energy.

P waves are the fastest **seismic wave**. In addition to moving through solid ground, they can also move through liquids and gases. P waves are the first waves felt or recorded at a distance from the location of movement along the fault.

S Waves

S waves, or secondary waves, are another type of body wave produced during an **earthquake**. S waves are a type of transverse, or shear, wave. Transverse waves move matter perpendicular to the direction the wave is traveling. The motion of rock particles is up and down or side to side, depending on the orientation of the wave. Unlike P waves, S waves move through solids only—they cannot move through liquids or gases.

S waves are the second-fastest seismic wave. So, they arrive after P waves some distance from the fault.

Surface Waves

Surface waves move only along Earth's surface, not through its interior. The movement of surface waves is similar to ripples on the surface of a pond. Surface waves are the slowest seismic wave and therefore the last to arrive at a distance from the fault. However, surface waves can do a lot of damage because they affect the ground surface as well as all the structures that people build.

How Do Scientists Measure Earthquakes?

The Focus and Epicenter

The first step in measuring an **earthquake** is determining its precise location. The focus, or hypocenter, of an earthquake is the point where the rock breaks along a **fault**. Typically, this occurs at some depth beneath the ground. Another useful measurement is the **epicenter**, or the spot on Earth's surface directly above the focus. News reports of an earthquake often mention the location of the epicenter. This is useful information because shaking is generally most severe at the epicenter of an earthquake and gradually diminishes with distance from the epicenter.

EPICENTER

The epicenter of an earthquake is at Earth's surface, directly above the focus. Where does the focus lie?

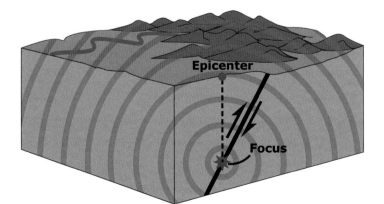

© Discovery Education | www.discoveryeducation.com

Measuring Seismic Waves

The study of seismic waves, or **seismology**, provides information about the location and severity of an earthquake. A **seismograph** is a tool that produces a visual record of ground movements. A simple seismograph consists of a weighted pen that hangs over a tray supporting spooled paper. The paper continually moves beneath the pen. When the ground is still, the pen traces a straight line along the moving paper. When the ground shakes, the paper tray shakes with it, but the weighted pen's inertia keeps it relatively still. The shaking of the paper as it moves past the pen produces a tracing of the wave motion. The recording of the wave motion produced by a seismograph is called a **seismogram**. Modern seismographs use electronics to make their recordings.

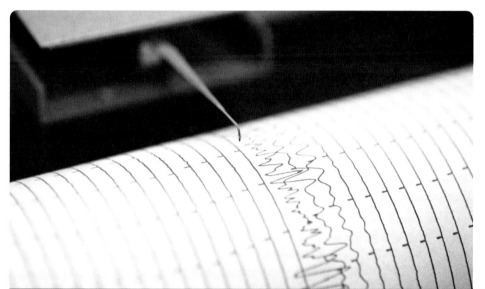

SEISMOGRAPH

A seismograph is the instrument used to determine the arrival time of an earthquake's seismic waves. How does the seismograph work?

A seismogram contains information about the exact time each of the different seismic waves arrives at the ground beneath the instrument. The amplitude of the waves on the seismogram provides information about the severity of the shaking, which is a function of the amount of energy released by the earthquake, or its **magnitude**.

Using Seismograms to Determine the Epicenter

Seismologists can determine the exact location of an earthquake's epicenter using seismograms recorded at different locations on Earth. Because P waves travel faster than S waves, the difference in time between the arrival of P waves and S waves increases with distance from the epicenter. The difference between the arrival times of the two waves increases at a known rate, which allows seismologists to determine a location's distance from the epicenter.

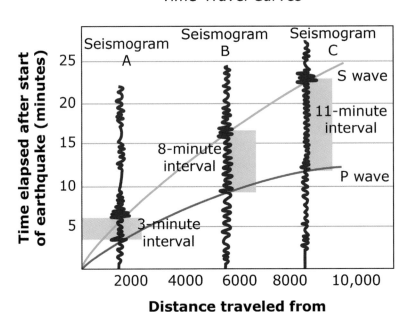

Locating Earthquake Epicenter

Time-Travel Curves

DISTANCE FROM THE EPICENTER

The time difference between the arrival of P waves and S waves increases at a known rate with distance from the epicenter. What does a longer interval indicate?

A single seismogram does not tell what direction the earthquake came from, only how far it was from the seismograph. The epicenter could be anywhere along a circle with a radius equal to the distance from the seismograph. It takes three seismograms recorded in different locations to determine the exact location of the epicenter. On a map, a circle is drawn around each seismograph's position, the radius being the distance from the seismograph to the epicenter. The epicenter is the point of intersection of all three circles.

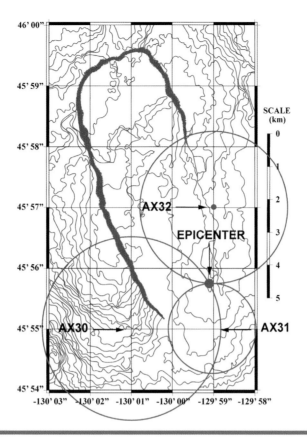

46' 00"

45' 59"

45' 58"

45' 57"

45' 56"

45' 55"

45' 54"

AX32

EPICENTER

AX30

AX31

-130' 03"   -130' 02"   -130' 01"   -130' 00"   -129' 59"   -129' 58"

EPICENTER

In this diagram, circles are drawn around three seismographs located at points AX30, AX31, and AX32. The radius of each circle is the distance to the epicenter determined by the difference between the arrival times of the P waves and S waves. How do the centers of each circle relate to the earthquake's focus?

What Is the Difference between Earthquake Intensity and Magnitude?

Quantifying the Severity of Earthquakes

The most familiar scale used to quantify the severity of earthquakes is the **Richter scale**. The Richter scale and the newer Moment **Magnitude** scale are logarithmic scales that provide information about the energy released during an **earthquake**. Each number on a logarithmic scale is actually a power of 10. So, a magnitude of 1 is equivalent to 10^1, or 10. A magnitude of 3 is equivalent to 10^3, or 1000. This allows the scale to represent a very wide range of values. Logarithmic scales are useful for describing earthquakes because earthquakes range widely from tiny movements that people cannot even feel to massive temblors that destroy structures for miles around.

The numbers on the Richter scale represent the logarithms of the wave heights on seismograms. Each whole number increase of magnitude on the Richter scale represents the release of about 32 times more energy. Why isn't it 10 times more? The answer to that question is complicated, but has to do with converting the amplitudes of waves on a **seismogram** to the energy released by an earthquake.

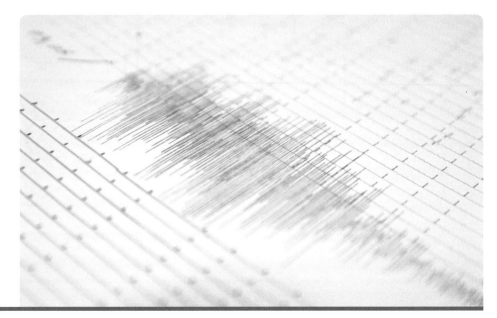

MAGNITUDE

Seismograms provide evidence for the intensity of a specific earthquake. What units do scientists use to measure the intensity of an earthquake?

Quantifying the Severity of Earthquakes: Sample Problem

Calculate the difference in energy released by a magnitude 3 earthquake and a magnitude 7 earthquake.

Solution:

Each whole number increase in magnitude represents about 32 times more energy. The difference between 7 and 3 is four whole numbers. So, we can estimate the difference in energy released by a magnitude 3 earthquake and a magnitude 7 earthquake by multiplying 32 four times:

$$32^4 = 32 \times 32 \times 32 \times 32 = 1,048,576 \text{ or } 1.0 \times 10^6$$

A magnitude 7 earthquake releases about one million times more energy than a magnitude 3 earthquake.

Earthquake Intensity

Intensity is a measure of earthquake severity that quantifies the impact in human terms. Intensity gives information about the amount of shaking and damage on the ground. Seismologists quantify intensity using the **Modified Mercalli Intensity scale**.

The numbers on the Modified Mercalli Intensity scale represent the reactions of people and damage to structures. The following is an abbreviated version of the scale:

Scale Number	Intensity	Effects	Richter Scale Equivalent
I	Instrumental	• Detected only by seismographs	<4.2
II	Feeble	• Some people feel it	
III	Slight	• Similar to a truck passing by • Can be felt by people resting	
IV	Moderate	• Can be felt by people walking	
V	Slightly strong	• Church bells ring • Sleeping persons awake	<4.8
VI	Strong	• Trees sway • Objects fall off shelves	<5.4
VII	Very strong	• Walls crack • Plaster falls	<6.1
VIII	Destructive	• Drivers lose control of vehicles • Masonry fractures • Poorly constructed buildings are damaged	
IX	Ruinous	• Some buildings collapse • Pipes break • Ground cracks open	<6.9
X	Distastrous	• Multiple cracks in ground • Many buildings destroyed • Landslides widespread	<7.3
XI	Very disastrous	• Most buildings and bridges collapse • Roads and railways destroyed • Pipes and cables broken	<8.1
XII	Catastrophic	• Total destruction • Trees fall • Ground rises and falls in waves	>8.1

THE MODIFIED MERCALLI INTENSITY SCALE

The Modified Mercalli Intensity scale measures the impact of an earthquake. Have you ever felt an earthquake? What scale number would you give that experience?

How Do Seismic Waves Provide Evidence for Earth's Interior Structure?

Using Seismic Waves to Study Earth's Interior

Some of the characteristics of seismic waves make them useful for studying the conditions deep inside Earth. First, body waves pass through Earth's interior. Second, the speed at which the waves travel depends on the conditions of the materials they are passing through. The speed of seismic waves increases with increasing density of the rock. S waves are stopped completely when they reach liquid.

After traveling through the body of the planet, P waves and S waves from significant earthquakes are recorded by seismographs located around Earth's surface. By analyzing the arrival times of the seismic waves and the distances the waves traveled from the **earthquake** focus to the seismographs, scientists can estimate the density of materials the waves traveled through. Density changes with the type of minerals in rock and the pressure that the rock is under. This information helps geologists construct models for the composition and structure of Earth's interior layers.

Shadow Zones

When they first began recording seismic waves, seismologists noticed that body waves don't reach certain regions of Earth following an earthquake. The regions where body waves aren't detected are called shadow zones. S waves have a large **shadow zone** that extends from roughly 105° to 180° in both directions from the focus of a particular earthquake. Because S waves don't travel through liquid, geologists infer that the shadow zone is the result of a liquid layer deep inside Earth.

Geologists can estimate the depth of liquid layers by analyzing shadow zones. The large **S wave** shadow zone results from the liquid **outer core**.

P waves do travel through liquid. However, their speed changes and the waves are deflected, forming a smaller shadow zone for P waves. Similarly, as P waves pass through the liquid outer core, their speed changes again and their paths are deflected at larger angles. Based on these observations, scientists inferred the existence of a solid inner core within the liquid outer core.

Consider the Explain Question

What kinds of waves do earthquakes produce, how are they measured, and what evidence do they provide about Earth's interior?

dlc.com/ca11086s

Go online to complete the scientific explanation.

Check for Understanding

How can scientists use data from body waves to study Earth's interior?

dlc.com/ca11087s

STEM in Action

Applying Seismic Waves

Deep within Earth, massive slabs of rock grind past each other. The energy released is enormous, and travels in seismic waves through layers of Earth until it reaches the surface. The ground is cleaved and the surface shakes, causing everything on it to break apart and fall. People and animals lose their balance and are thrown to the ground. Confusion and panic lead to even more destruction. Can measuring the amplitude and **frequency** of seismic waves help predict earthquakes?

When a major **earthquake** strikes near a populated area, the results can be devastating. The 7.0-**magnitude** earthquake that rocked Haiti in 2010 caused hundreds of thousands of deaths and major injuries. Deaths and injuries do not happen just because of ground shaking, though. They occur when buildings, bridges, and other structures collapse. In some cases even greater damage occurs after the first event; powerful aftershocks can cause buildings to collapse from damage that was not visible after the first tremor, making even apparently sturdy buildings unsafe. How do architects and engineers apply information about seismic waves to structural design?

COLLAPSED CHURCH
Many structures did not survive the 2010 Haiti earthquake and its major aftershocks. What poses the greatest risks during an earthquake: the quake itself, or its effect on objects at Earth's surface?

Earthquake-resistant engineering has been implemented in developed countries such as Japan and the United States for many decades. As a result, far fewer people are killed when major earthquakes strike these countries, compared with less-developed countries. For example, when the 6.9-magnitude Loma Prieta earthquake hit near San Francisco, California, in 1989, only 63 people died. When a large earthquake hit San Francisco when it was less developed, back in 1906, thousands of people were killed; scientists estimate its magnitude was between 7.7 and 8.3.

STEM and Seismic Waves

Geologists use knowledge of seismic waves to analyze movements of Earth's crust and conditions in Earth's interior. Seismologists, city planners, and architects use the same information to predict earthquakes and prepare emergency plans and designs to protect the public. Seismologists use technologies such as seismographs, seismometers, and computers to record the seismic waves produced by earthquakes. How do instruments that detect and measure seismic waves benefit people?

A seismometer is a device that translates ground shaking into signals that can be transmitted to a remote computer. Seismologists set up earthquake monitoring networks along active **fault** lines by burying multiple seismometers in the ground.

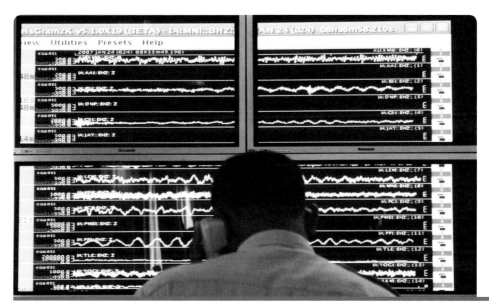

MONITORING EARTHQUAKE AFTERSHOCKS

Even if an earthquake does minimal damage, seismic waves still roll through Earth as aftershocks. Why would seismologists want to monitor these waves?

The seismometers send their signals to computers that analyze the information about ground shaking. Seismologists use this information and their knowledge of physics, geology, and mathematics to determine the movements and **strain** along the fault. These networks can also help predict earthquakes, allowing the people in targeted areas sufficient time to launch safety measures.

Using physical and computer models, architects and engineers apply knowledge of seismic waves to build safer structures. These models simulate the shaking that occurs during major earthquakes and reveal weaknesses in structures that must be reinforced. Architects and engineers develop fixes using a combination of mathematical calculations and trial and error. City planners use knowledge of seismic waves and geology to develop guidelines for building in earthquake zones. Rescue personnel use the same information to focus search-and-rescue operations after major earthquakes.

Quantifying the Severity of Earthquakes

Use your knowledge of earthquake magnitude to solve the problems below.

1. Calculate the difference in energy released by a magnitude 5 earthquake and a magnitude 7 earthquake.

2. Earthquake A has a magnitude of 3. What magnitude earthquake would release 810,000 times more energy than earthquake A?

3. Joules are a unit of energy. Because earthquakes result from a sudden release of energy in Earth's crust, the amount of energy released by an earthquake can be estimated based on the magnitude of the earthquake. An earthquake with a magnitude of 1 releases about 1.99526×10^6 joules of energy. Approximately how many joules of energy does a magnitude 4 earthquake release? Write your answer in scientific notation. (Hint: Each whole number increase in magnitude on the Richter scale represents an increase of about how many times more energy?)

4. What magnitude earthquake releases approximately 50 trillion joules of energy?

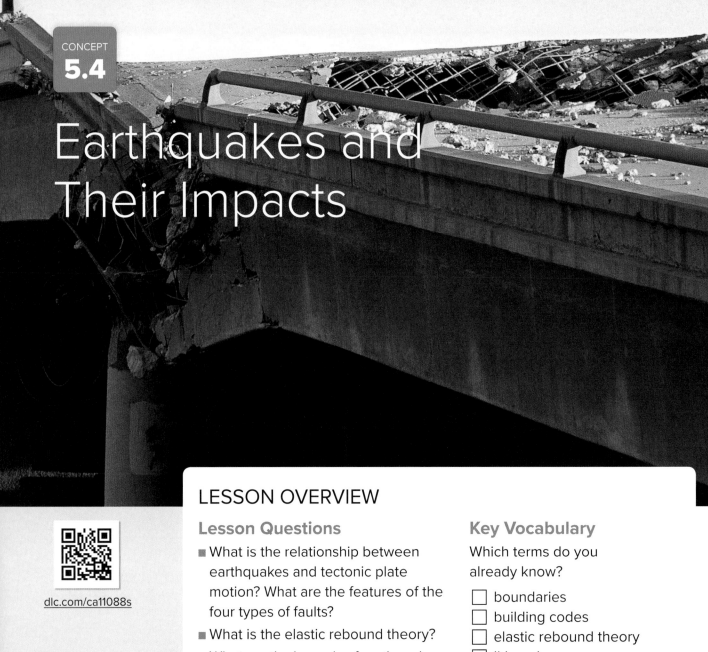

Earthquakes and Their Impacts

LESSON OVERVIEW

Lesson Questions

- What is the relationship between earthquakes and tectonic plate motion? What are the features of the four types of faults?
- What is the elastic rebound theory?
- What are the hazards of earthquakes, and how can people prepare for them?

Lesson Objectives

By the end of the lesson, you should be able to:

- Explain the relationship between earthquakes and tectonic plate motion.
- Explain elastic rebound theory.
- Explain the hazards of earthquakes, and how can people prepare for them.
- Explain what a tsunami is and how one is formed.

Key Vocabulary

Which terms do you already know?

- ☐ boundaries
- ☐ building codes
- ☐ elastic rebound theory
- ☐ lithosphere
- ☐ magnetic field
- ☐ normal
- ☐ reverse fault
- ☐ seismic activity
- ☐ strike-slip fault
- ☐ tectonic plate
- ☐ thrust fault
- ☐ tsunami

dlc.com/ca11088s

Image: Joseph Sohm / Shutterstock

Exploring Earthquakes and Their Impacts

Even if you live in a region of the world that is far from an earthquake-prone area, you'll see images of earthquake damage in the news. Can you recall the names of the places you have seen in such news stories?

dlc.com/ca11089s

EXPLAIN QUESTION

| Why do most earthquakes occur in certain places on Earth's surface?

EARTHQUAKE DAMAGE

A resident surveys the damage to a home after the 2010 Haiti earthquake. Why are earthquake safety procedures emphasized more in some areas than in others?

What Is the Relationship between Earthquakes and Tectonic Plate Motion?

Plates and Plate Boundaries

Earth's lithosphere is not one solid piece but is separated into tectonic plates that constantly are moving together, apart, and past one another. This phenomenon can be described by the theory of **plate tectonics**. There are three major types of tectonic plate boundaries:

- Convergent boundaries are found in locations where two tectonic plates move toward each other. When two plates of **continental crust** come together, they collide and push against each other. When a plate of continental crust and a plate of **oceanic crust** come together, or two plates of oceanic crust come together, **subduction** occurs. Oceanic plates are denser and sit lower on the asthenosphere than continental plates, so oceanic plates always will subduct below continental plates when they converge. If at any point two oceanic plates collide, the denser of the two will subduct beneath the other.

PLATE BOUNDARIES

Tectonic plates interact at plate boundaries. At what type of boundary do plates slide past each other?

- Divergent boundaries are found where two tectonic plates move away from each other.

- Transform boundaries are found where two adjacent tectonic plates slide in parallel motion past each other in opposite directions.

© Discovery Education | www.discoveryeducation.com ● Image: USGS

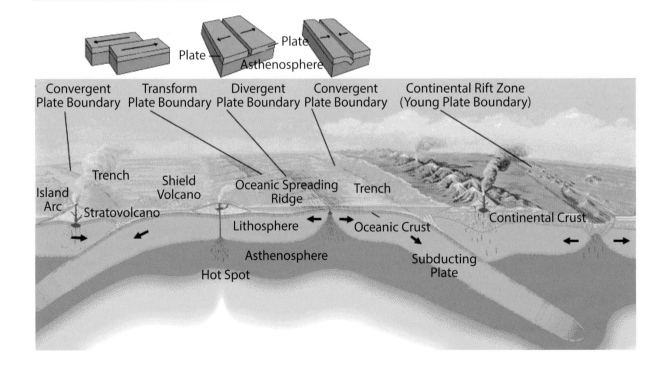

Convergent Plate Boundary · Transform Plate Boundary · Divergent Plate Boundary · Convergent Plate Boundary · Continental Rift Zone (Young Plate Boundary)

Plate · Plate · Asthenosphere

Island Arc · Trench · Stratovolcano · Shield Volcano · Oceanic Spreading Ridge · Trench · Lithosphere · Oceanic Crust · Continental Crust · Asthenosphere · Hot Spot · Subducting Plate

Earthquakes and Plate Tectonics

Tectonic plates do not have smooth edges, so they grind against each other as they move past each other. This can cause a great deal of **pressure** to build at transform boundaries. Tremendous pressure also builds when two plates push against each other at convergent boundaries. When this this pressure becomes too great, it is released in the form of an **earthquake**. Due to this continuous cycle of pressure building and releasing, earthquakes occur most frequently along tectonic plate boundaries.

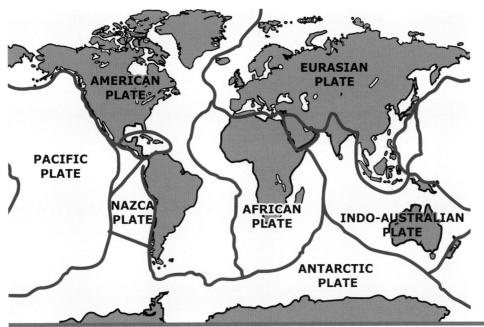

EARTH'S TECTONIC PLATES

The major tectonic plates are named for the continents or oceans they contain. How do tectonic plates interact at different kinds of boundaries?

Pressure also can cause the crust to break farther into the plates, forming faults. Faults are cracks in a body of rock that the rock can move along. Although rocks usually are held in place by friction, with enough pressure, the rocks will move. The breakage of rock to form a **fault**, as well as the movement of rocks along a preexisting fault, results from a sudden release of pressure. This sudden movement of rock as a result of the release of pressure is called an earthquake.

Plate tectonics is the driving force behind this buildup and release of pressure. Earthquakes are caused by movement and displacement of rock along plate boundaries and faults.

What Are the Four Types of Faults?

Faults

When **pressure** builds along tectonic plate boundaries, rocks farther inside the plates can crack. This results in a **fault**. This fault consists of a fracture in the crust (called the fault plane) in which two blocks of rock (or fault blocks) move relative to each other. These two fault blocks are referred to as the **hanging wall** and the **footwall**. The hanging wall is the fault block that is above the fault plane. The footwall is the fault block that is below the fault plane.

There are four major types of faults characterized by the way the hanging wall and the footwall move relative to each other. These four major faults are called normal, reverse, thrust, and strike-slip.

FAULT LINE

Fault lines can drastically alter the landscape in an area. What type of fault line caused the canyon in this image?

Normal Faults

In a **normal fault**, the hanging wall moves down relative to the footwall. A normal fault results from tension and **extension**, or the **stress** on rocks caused by the pulling apart of fault blocks or plates at a **divergent boundary**.

Reverse Faults

In a **reverse fault**, the hanging wall moves up relative to the footwall at an angle of 45 degrees or greater. Reverse faults result from **compression**, the stress on rocks caused by the squeezing together of fault blocks or plates at a **convergent boundary**. Reverse faults commonly occur at reactivated normal faults when the direction of pressure changes from extension to compression.

Thrust Faults

A **thrust fault** is a low-angle (45 degrees or less) reverse fault. Like reverse faults, thrust faults are caused by compression. However, the fault blocks in a thrust fault move at shallower angles. Normal, reverse, and thrust faults are known collectively as dip-slip faults.

Remember that fault blocks are not perfectly smooth, so no single measurement along the fault will capture the exact angle of movement.

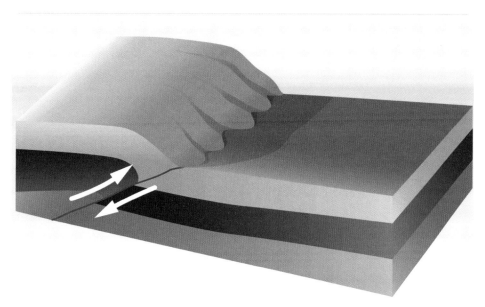

THRUST FAULT

Thrust faults are similar to reverse faults. In which direction do the hanging wall and footwall move at a thrust fault?

Strike-Slip Faults

In a **strike-slip fault**, the fault blocks move past each other horizontally. This is similar to what happens at a transform plate boundary. Just as at a **transform boundary**, the fault blocks do not have smooth edges. This causes them to grind against each other as they move horizontally in opposite directions. Pressure builds until the fault blocks finally slip, releasing the pressure and causing an **earthquake**.

HAITI'S FAULT LINES

A strike-slip fault line runs across the country of Haiti. Movement at this fault line caused a devastating earthquake there in 2010. Why are earthquakes more likely in Haiti than in Brazil, or in Japan than in Russia?

What Is the Elastic Rebound Theory?

Elastic Rebound Theory

While **fault** blocks are held in place by friction, over time, **stress** can build up along a fault. This stress is so great that it can result in rocks bending until they reach their breaking point. It also can cause fault blocks to shift where the rocks were broken by a previous release of stress. Earthquakes are caused when stress that has accumulated along a fault is released suddenly, eliminating the **pressure** that had been causing the rocks to bend. Without this pressure, the rocks can return to their original state.

This phenomenon is described by the **elastic rebound** theory. This occurs when rock along a fault moves suddenly and then snaps back to its original shape. This is similar to the way a rubber band will become deformed when it is stretched, then break and snap back to its original shape when the stress becomes too great.

What Are the Hazards of Earthquakes, and How Can People Prepare for Them?

What Happens during an Earthquake?

The shaking of **Earth**'s surface during an **earthquake** causes most of the damage and loss of life that people typically associate with these events. Buildings, bridges, and other structures can collapse, especially if they have not been designed to withstand earthquakes. As Earth's crust shakes, terrain that supports mountainsides can become unstable. Rocks can be jarred loose from mountainsides and lead to landslides that threaten people and structures. Additionally, earthquakes that happen under water can displace huge volumes of water. This can result in flooding of nearby coasts.

Earthquake Hazard Map

Because earthquakes can be so dangerous, people have invested many resources into preparing for them. This is especially important in areas where earthquakes are more likely to occur. Unlike tornadoes and hurricanes, earthquakes are not seasonal, and they do not occur over a relatively predictable cycle. Geologists have worked for decades to understand where earthquakes occur in order to prepare populations in susceptible areas.

An earthquake hazard map illustrates the seismic activity in a region. In this particular map, a region of high seismic hazard is prone to large, destructive earthquakes.

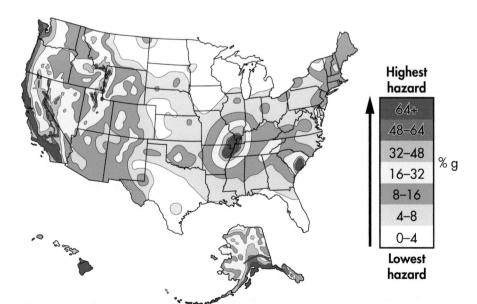

Highest hazard

64+
48–64
32–48
16–32
8–16
4–8
0–4

% g

Lowest hazard

HAZARD MAP

This map is based on historical seismic activity and our current knowledge of plate tectonics. What seismic activity patterns do you notice in the United States?

According to this map, regions in the western United States, Alaska, and Hawaii have a high earthquake risk. An area's seismic risk is related to where it is located in relation to tectonic plate boundaries. Alaska and the northwestern United States are along **subduction** zones. In these regions, one tectonic plate dives beneath another. The southwestern coast of the United States is located along a **transform boundary**. Here, two plates grind past one another.

TECTONIC ACTIVITY

The theory of plate tectonics predicts that earthquakes are more common along or near plate boundaries. How is this map of global earthquake frequency evidence in support of the theory?

05-04-2017

Some high-risk areas are far from plate boundaries. Hawaii is located in the middle of the Pacific plate, but it consists of a series of active volcanoes. The seismic activity in Hawaii is related to volcanism.

Other areas may be high risk because of the existence of ancient plate boundaries and faults. **Plate tectonics** slowly forms and destroys continents. Ancient boundaries are no longer active—that is, tectonic plates are no longer moving at these locations. Around New Madrid, Missouri, the ancient faults formed more than 750 million years ago, when an ancient supercontinent began to drift apart. Today, the faults are hidden beneath 30 to 60 meters of river sediments. Although the two sides of the **fault** are not currently moving relative to each other, the region remains less stable than regions without fault lines. Therefore, earthquakes are more likely to occur there.

Regions far from current and ancient tectonic plate boundaries also experience earthquakes. However, earthquakes in these regions are generally less frequent and much weaker. Some earthquakes can be caused by human activities, such as pumping water underground or damming a river. Thus, no region has zero earthquake risk.

Building Codes

If a region is in an area of high seismic hazard, buildings need to be designed with earthquakes in mind. Structures that cannot adequately absorb or dissipate seismic energy may crack or even collapse. Engineers try to solve this problem by using different design techniques and materials that reduce the risk of severe damage or collapse in the event of an earthquake.

Engineers design buildings to accommodate the seismic waves that cause Earth's crust to shake. For example, very tall buildings, like skyscrapers, are constructed to sway. Even though it may feel uncomfortable, the swaying motion helps the building absorb shocks during an earthquake. In addition, structures are designed to withstand the side-to-side change in weight imposed during shaking. To reduce the overall weight of the building, many structures use a light roof. Also, engineers reinforce floors with the building frame to ensure the floors do not shake loose.

Architects and engineers also consider the materials used to construct the building. Materials are selected for strength, durability, and flexibility. Engineers and architects also have to consider the substrate underneath the building. The shaking from earthquakes can alter the strength and stability of soils, in a process called liquefaction, which is particularly common in sandy and silty soils. During liquefaction, the soil moves like a fluid and can no longer support structures. This creates tilting or collapsing risks.

EARTHQUAKE DAMAGE

Building codes impose structural requirements to protect buildings from collapsing during natural disasters. Who is responsible for enforcing building codes?

Knowing the importance of these practices, engineers adhere to building codes, or safety standards established by the government. Seismic building codes do not require buildings to be completely earthquake proof, but the codes ensure the building will withstand the quake with as little damage as possible. This approach increases the chances that people in the buildings will survive earthquakes and evacuate safely.

Technologies improve as our understanding of how to protect structures from earthquakes increases. Consequently, newer buildings are generally safer than older buildings. Older buildings that are deemed unsafe may be demolished and replaced with buildings that adhere to more up-to-date codes. Architects and engineers also retrofit older buildings by bolting the foundation, improving how the frame is connected. A retrofit often includes strengthening the crimping wall, or the short, wood-framed wall in the sub-area crawl space. If the crimping wall collapses during an earthquake, the first floor of a building often drops to the ground, undermining the stability of the building. Engineers also add braces to the shear walls, the vertical wooden frame of the structure, to prevent tipping or overturning during an earthquake.

Preparing for an Earthquake

Earthquakes are unsettling and scary. Planning takes some of the uncertainty out of the situation.

An effective emergency plan should cover the following:

1. Learn about earthquake risk in the area from a local chapter of the American Red Cross. They can provide information on the prevalence of earthquake risk in a given area.

2. Find out how citizens are alerted to an emergency in the area. Alerts may be transmitted through the television, by fire alarms, or church bells. Of course, in the event of earthquake, you may feel it before you hear about it—especially if you're near the epicenter.

3. Determine the location of the closest emergency shelter and know how to get there. If you have pets, find out whether or not the shelter will allow animals.

4. If you are concerned about an elderly relative, family member, or neighbor, ask if special services are available for the elderly.

5. Purchase insurance that will protect your family members and personal property from loss in the event of an earthquake.

Create a disaster plan: Discuss with your family what might happen in the event of an earthquake. The plan should be a team effort, and it should delegate responsibilities to all family members who can participate.

1. Post emergency telephone numbers in a location where all family members can find and use them.

2. Teach children of all ages how to call 911.

3. Identify safe locations in the home in case of an earthquake.

4. Educate all family members on where to locate and how to turn off the water, gas, and electricity at main switches in the home.

5. Ensure that all family members know not only the location of the fire extinguishers in the home, but also how to operate them.

6. Designate a location to meet that is easy for all family members to reach and is close to the parent's workplace or the children's school. Make sure everyone in your family has the address and phone number of the location.

Prepare the home: Earthquakes cause the ground to rupture and shake. This can dislodge items in the home. There are some simple steps you can take to limit the damage and injuries that may result from shaking during an earthquake. If you live in an earthquake-prone area like the West Coast of the United States, it is important to securely fasten wall shelves, large furniture, pictures, and mirrors. Place heavy objects on lower shelves. Mirrors and picture frames should be positioned away from beds, couches, or other locations where a person might sit, so shattering glass won't injure them.

Develop a communication plan: During an earthquake, telephone service may be limited. Designate an out-of-state member of the family or a friend to be an emergency contact. This person should not be affected by the disaster. He or she should have all of the phone numbers and email addresses of each family member.

Prepare an emergency kit: During an earthquake, many services may be disrupted. An emergency kit should be well-stocked with the following items to sustain a family for a few days, and preferably up to two weeks. Store these items in a section of your home that will be safely accessible in the event of an earthquake.

1. Water: Estimate one gallon of water per person per day.
2. Food: Pack non-perishable food items.
3. Medicine: Include any medicines that family members need on a daily basis, as well as vitamin, mineral, and protein supplements to ensure adequate nutrition.
4. First aid kit: This kit should include a first aid book, scissors, thermometer, sunscreen, pocketknife, needle and thread, bandages, and splinting material.
5. Pet supplies: Remember that pets will also need to eat. Make sure there is adequate pet food and water in the emergency kit.
6. Cooking supplies: Pack a can opener, camp stove, and gas canisters.
7. Common supplies: Pack candles, matches, flashlights, and extra batteries.
8. Hygiene: Pack soap. In case water is limited, pack alcohol-based hand gels and wipes as well.
9. Means of communication: After an earthquake you may be without electricity or even cellular service, so a battery- or solar-powered radio will allow you to stay informed of the hazards and sources of assistance in your area.

SHOPPING CART

Every family's emergency plan should involve stocking up on necessary supplies, such as water. What are other components of an emergency plan?

What to Do During an Earthquake

Practicing a disaster plan is essential because it makes a response more natural, which helps during a moment of crisis. When a disaster strikes, remain calm and move through your disaster plan. The first step is finding a safe location to wait out the disaster.

If you are outdoors:

Remain outside, but move away from buildings, streetlights, and utility poles.

If you are in a vehicle:

Come to a stop as soon as safely possible.

- Avoid stopping near buildings, trees, utility poles, and overpasses. Even after the shaking has stopped, these structures may be unstable and could collapse or fall.
- Avoid downed power lines as the wires may still be conducting electricity. If you touch them, you could be electrocuted.
- Once the shaking has stopped, return to the road but avoid bridges, ramps, and roads that have sustained damage.

If you are indoors:

During an earthquake, stay indoors until the shaking has stopped.

- Take cover under a sturdy table and hold on to the table's legs until the shaking stops.
- In the absence of a table, move to the corner of a building and shield your face from debris and glass.
- Avoid glass windows, light fixtures, or objects that could become displaced and fall.
- Only a load-bearing doorframe is safe to stand under, but a doorframe should be used as a last resort only.
- Avoid getting into an elevator.

STEPS

There are some simple steps that can help you survive an earthquake. What additional steps could you take to protect yourself from an earthquake if you were indoors?

© Discovery Education | www.discoveryeducation.com • Image: Center for Disease Control

What Is a Tsunami, and How Does One Form?

On Friday, March 11, 2011, a magnitude 9.0 **earthquake** occurred approximately 70 kilometers off the Oshika Peninsula of Tohoku, Japan. The earthquake took place under the sea, about 30 km below the sea floor. It was the most powerful earthquake in recorded history. The earthquake originated in an area where the Pacific Plate subducts under the plate that carries the islands of Japan. The break, about 500 km long, caused a large area of seafloor to rise many meters. The moving seafloor triggered a giant wave—a tsunami.

Despite a very efficient warning and evacuation system, the tsunami killed about 20,000 people. As it swept inland, it destroyed or damaged over a million buildings. The tsunami also damaged bridges, roads, and airports, severely disrupting all communications and interrupting power supplies. At the Fukushima Daiichi Nuclear Power Plant, the raging flood waters caused three nuclear reactors to catch fire after hydrogen gas inside them exploded, and people living near the plant had to be evacuated. Although this earthquake and tsunami were not the deadliest on record, they were the most expensive in history, with an estimated cost of about US $235 billion.

Tsunami Formation

Water waves form when a force pushes or pulls the water, and then energy travels through the water. The water rises and falls as waves move through it. Use the diagram below to remind you about the different parts of a wave.

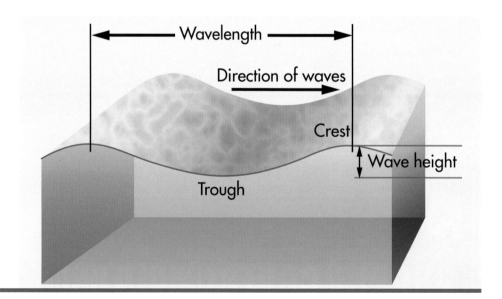

PARTS OF A WAVE

Wavelength is the distance between two wave crests. How is wave height calculated?

Most water waves are generated by the wind or by the gravitational pull of the moon and sun. A tsunami, however, is a series of waves produced when an earthquake, a massive landslide of rocks or soil, a volcanic eruption, or a meteorite impact, transfers energy to the ocean. A tsunami is a shallow-water wave, which is defined as a wave that has a wavelength at least 11 times the depth of the water beneath it. These usually occur in relatively shallow water. However, if a wave is long enough, it is considered shallow water no matter where it is located. In the deepest part of the ocean, a tsunami wave can exceed 500 km in length and reach speeds up to 890 km/h.

In the middle of the ocean, a tsunami wave can pass unnoticed. As the tsunami wave approaches the coastline, the wave begins to interact with the ocean floor, causing the wavelength to decrease and the wave height to quickly increase. As a result, the wave produces a wall of water that can rapidly flood the low-lying regions of the coast. One reason that tsunami waves are so dangerous is because they initially appear as relatively harmless, albeit fast-moving, tides. An initial rapid influx of water up the shore is an indicator of an approaching, much larger wave. Draw-down describes a scenario when a wave trough hits the shoreline before the crest. When draw-down happens, the sea level appears to drop rapidly just before the wave strikes the shore. The wave of water washing onshore may last from five to 30 minutes. Once the initial wave passes, a succession of waves will arrive every five to 90 minutes, depending on the period of the tsunami wave. The largest wave in the tsunami set is often not the first wave but the third to eighth wave.

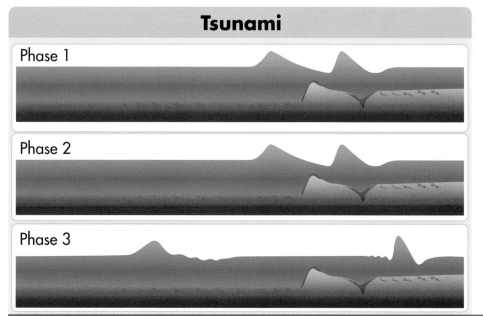

Tsunami

Phase 1

Phase 2

Phase 3

TSUNAMI FORMATION

During an undersea earthquake, Earth's crust shifts suddenly and displaces water. How does this movement initiate a tsunami?

Tsunami Warning

Because tsunamis, like earthquakes, cannot be predicted, it is imperative that communities be prepared. The threat of a tsunami striking the coastline of the United States is very real. During the past 200 years, at least 24 tsunamis have caused damage to the United States and its territories. When major earthquakes occur with a magnitude large enough to warrant concern, the Tsunami Warning Centers, located in Hawaii and Alaska, notify authorities and others.

The objectives of the Tsunami Warning Centers are to determine the location and size of an earthquake, to determine the potential of tsunami wave generation, to predict tsunami wave arrival times and locations, and to dispatch warnings to the population in the immediate hazard zone. Earthquakes that generate tsunamis usually occur close enough to the coast that waves arrive within one or two hours. A person along the coastline following an earthquake should take important steps to avoid being harmed in the event of a tsunami.

- Look for evacuation signs.
- Head toward higher ground.
- Listen for official warnings.
- Remain on higher ground until you hear it is safe to leave.
- Look for others who may need assistance and make room for them.

WARNING SIGN

This sign indicates that the beach may be prone to a tsunami. What actions should someone take when a tsunami is imminent?

Not all powerful earthquakes produce tsunami waves. The notices posted after a large earthquake are precautionary measures. They may be canceled when the threat is deemed unlikely.

Consider the Explain Question

> **Why do most earthquakes occur in certain places on Earth's surface?**

Go online to complete the scientific explanation.

dlc.com/ca11090s

Check for Understanding

> **How does a tsunami wave form and move through the ocean?**

dlc.com/ca11091s

STEM in Action

Causes of Earthquakes and Their Impacts

By tracking the areas where earthquakes and volcanic eruptions have occurred throughout history, scientists can see a pattern. This pattern allows scientists to determine the boundaries of tectonic plates. This information can also be used to determine where earthquakes may happen again.

CROSSING THE BOUNDARY

This road sign near Bakersfield, California, lets travelers know when they are crossing onto the North American plate. How did scientists determine where the boundary was? Would you be able to tell it was a boundary without the sign?

But knowing where an **earthquake** might occur is only one factor in predicting a quake. Conditions along the **fault** line, or fault plane, have a significant effect on the magnitude of an earthquake. Faults differ. At some faults, two solid blocks of rock meet, while at others, smaller pieces of rock are trapped in the boundary.

A team of scientists near Bakersfield, California, drilled down into a fault zone to measure the slippage and sample the material in the fault.

The geologists subject samples of material from the fault zone to earthquake-like strains under laboratory conditions. By doing so, they are able to model, observe, and measure how the material responds during an earthquake. The results of these tests provide data for modeling the movements of the fault during an actual earthquake. The movement along this particular fault is gradual. Other laboratory tests, however, use rock surfaces that do not contain a layer of pebbles and clay. These tests model the conditions at fault zones with much greater friction.

STEM and Causes of Earthquakes and Their Impacts

A seismologist is a geologist who specializes in the study of vibrations in **Earth**'s interior—known as seismic waves—and earthquakes. Seismic waves are waves of energy that travel through Earth's interior due to an earthquake, an explosion, or other tectonic forces. Seismologists can measure these waves using an instrument called a **seismograph** or seismometer.

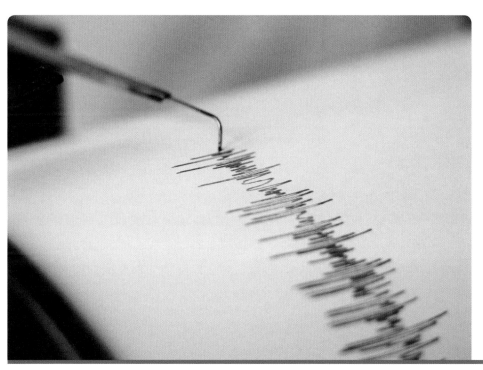

THE RICHTER SCALE

Seismologists measure the strength of earthquakes using the Richter scale. Every whole number on the Richter scale represents earthquake waves that are 10 times the amplitude of the previous number. The energy released by the earthquake is about 32 times the previous number on the scale. How does the Richter number relate to the impact of an earthquake?

Shear wave velocity, or the speed at which a shear wave passes through an Earth material, reveals information about the material's texture, or stiffness. Soil stiffness is an important factor in determining the amount of shaking a building will undergo during an earthquake. But seismographs are expensive, and geologists cannot wait around for seismic waves in order to evaluate the stiffness of a soil. Fortunately, geophones are much less expensive than seismographs, and a series of geophones can be used to detect the arrival time of a shear wave as it travels through soil, away from its starting point. Producing low-energy shear waves for testing is inexpensive, too; all it takes is a sledgehammer.

Seismologists use a range of technologies, from a simple measuring tape and sledgehammer to more complex geophones and a computer. The map generated from their data can be used to help predict which parts of the city may require special building designs in order to reduce the risk of destruction during the next earthquake. New building projects in earthquake-prone areas can also benefit from shear wave velocity soil analysis. Whether the waves are from an earthquake or a sledgehammer, they help reveal properties of the materials within Earth.

Understanding the Universe

LESSON OVERVIEW

Lesson Question

- What evidence do scientists use to explain the nature and origin of the universe?

Lesson Objective

By the end of the lesson, you should be able to:

- Understand the evidence that explains the nature and origin of the universe.

Key Vocabulary

Which terms do you already know?

- [ ] astrophysics
- [ ] big bang theory
- [ ] blue shift
- [ ] cosmic background radiation
- [ ] cosmology
- [ ] Earth
- [ ] electromagnetic radiation
- [ ] electromagnetic spectrum
- [ ] frequency
- [ ] galaxy
- [ ] hypothesis
- [ ] light year
- [ ] Milky Way galaxy
- [ ] red shift
- [ ] remote sensing
- [ ] steady state theory
- [ ] theory
- [ ] wavelength

dlc.com/ca11092s

Investigating and Understanding the Universe

dlc.com/ca11093s

Have you ever looked up at the stars and wondered how they came to be? Or where the moon came from? Or why the sun rises and sets? Maybe you have wondered what is out there in the universe. For centuries, scientists have asked themselves the same questions.

DUST CLOUDS IN SPACE

Dust clouds are just one type of object scientists study in the universe. What information does studying dust clouds provide scientists?

EXPLAIN QUESTION

How has technology been used to collect evidence that verifies the scientific theory of the big bang?

What Evidence Do Scientists Use to Explain the Nature and Origin of the Universe?

The Origins of the Universe

Scientists estimate that the universe is about 13.7 billion years old. This is much older than **Earth**. Earth is approximately 4.6 billion years old. The universe is also much older than the solar system to which Earth belongs.

Scientists cannot make direct observations of most astronomical objects. Instead, they must study the light from these distant objects to gain an understanding about them. Scientists then can use this information from the objects' light to better understand the origin of the universe. Advances in technology over the last century have allowed astronomers to make observations of fainter and more distant objects across the entire **electromagnetic spectrum**. These observations have yielded evidence about the origin of the universe. With this evidence, scientists developed a theory to explain the initial formation of the universe. Scientific theories are ways of explaining why things happen in the natural world. They begin with a hypothesis, or an idea of how scientists think something works. Scientists then collect data to test the hypotheses. Scientific theories are thought to be correct until new information suggests alternative theories. Scientists always check theories by collecting more observations and by experimenting.

LOWELL OBSERVATORY, ARIZONA

The telescope in this dome gathers data from visible light and infrared radiation. The data is used to create images using digital technology. How do the designs of modern telescopes help them collect data from space?

Sometimes, new observations cause a theory to be reshaped or modified to match the new evidence. The theory of how the universe came to be is explained by the big bang theory. The big bang theory was first proposed in 1927. Today, the **big bang theory** is generally accepted because many observations and experimental results support it. However, details about the theory are still being debated.

The Big Bang Theory

Less than a century ago, the universe was thought to be static and infinite. The **steady state theory** held that the universe had always existed in its current state, with a constant average density. However, in the 1920s, American astronomer Edwin Hubble discovered that the universe was in fact expanding. This showed the steady state theory to be invalid. The big bang theory eventually took its place as the generally accepted theory to explain the origin of the universe.

The big bang theory states that the universe formed during a single event in which all matter and energy suddenly expanded from an extremely small point. This point, called a singularity, is thought to have been infinitesimal, infinitely dense, and infinitely hot. It is thought to have been smaller than a single atom and made of pure energy. One of the biggest mysteries of the universe is how the entire universe inflated at an extremely high rate from a point smaller than a single atom to the size of a baseball, almost instantaneously. This mystery continues to plague scientists, but the laws of physics do allow for such an event.

To measure the age of the universe, scientists exploit the fact that light travels at a known finite speed. Scientists express distances in the universe in units called light-years. A light-year is a measure of distance in space equal to the distance that light travels in one year. One light-year equals about 9.46×10^{12} km. Because objects in space are many light-years away, the light and other **electromagnetic radiation** that an observer on Earth detects actually originated many years ago. An observer is literally seeing into the past. This means that if scientists look back in time far enough, they can make observations about earlier states of the universe. By determining the rate at which the universe is expanding, scientists can work backward to determine the age of the universe: approximately 13.7 billion years.

© Discovery Education | www.discoveryeducation.com • Image: pixelparticle / Shutterstock

THE BIG BANG

The big bang theory states the universe expanded from a singularity, and continues to expand. What evidence supports the predictions of the theory?

The Universe Following the Big Bang

During the initial expansion of the big bang, the laws of physics came into effect. Science assumes that the universe works as a single system and the interactions of mass and energy are governed by the same principles everywhere. The theories and laws we develop from observations on Earth can be used to explain the formation of the universe. Our understanding of gravity is a good example of this. Scientists say the exact amount of gravity necessary to produce the universe existed in the singularity. Too little gravity, and nothing would exist because matter never would have formed. Too much gravity, and nothing but a series of black holes would have formed. Because just enough gravity existed, some of the tremendous energy of the big bang converted to matter in the form of electrons and other subatomic particles.

All objects in the universe are made of matter that developed during the first fractions of a second following the big bang. The law of conservation of energy states that energy can neither be created nor destroyed, but only changed from one form to another. The theory of relativity states $E = mc^2$, which means energy is equal to mass times the speed of light squared. That means that matter can be changed into energy, and energy changed into matter. Scientists use these two laws to explain how the energy from the expansion of a singularity can form the matter in the universe. After the initial expansion, the universe was a hot soup of electrons and other subatomic particles. As the universe slowed and cooled in the first second of expansion, protons and neutrons formed. Within the first three minutes of expansion, matter was still too hot to form atoms. The universe was a dense cloud of protons, neutrons, and electrons from which no light could escape.

Mass exists in two opposing forms called antimatter and matter. For example, an antielectron (also called a positron) has a positive electric charge. An antiproton has a negative charge. Matter and antimatter annihilate each other when they come into contact. This contact releases energy. For anything to exist in the universe, there had to be more matter than antimatter. All objects that exist in the universe are made of this excess matter. Some have found contradictions between the law of conservation of energy and the big bang theory, since neither address where the singularity of condensed energy originated. However, the big bang theory only refers to the time after the singularity began to expand, and here the law of the conservation of energy applies.

The two most common elements in the universe are hydrogen and helium. This is because hydrogen and helium are the simplest atoms to form. Scientists think the first atoms of hydrogen began to form three minutes after the big bang. Hydrogen atoms contain only one proton, so when the universe cooled enough to form atoms, these were the first to form. As the universe cooled further, helium atoms formed. Helium atoms contain two protons. Next to form were lithium atoms, with three protons. As the cloudy soup of protons, neutrons, and electrons ordered itself into atoms, light penetrated through the universe for the first time, about 380,000 years after the big bang.

Evidence for the Big Bang Theory

Evidence that supports the big bang theory includes:

- **cosmic background radiation**
- the measureable expansion of the universe
- the relative abundances of the different elements in the universe
- the known laws of physics

Cosmic background radiation, also known as cosmic microwave background (CMB) radiation, is radiation that fills the observable universe almost uniformly. It is thought to be left over from the big bang. It was first discovered by accident in the 1960s by the physicists Arno Penzias and Robert Wilson. The COBE (Cosmic Background Explorer) satellite was launched in 1989. It gave the first clear images of cosmic background radiation. The WMAP (Wilkinson Microwave Anisotropy Probe) satellite was launched in 2001. It gave scientists a much clearer picture of CMB radiation that was nearly uniform throughout the universe. In other words, CMB radiation was made of electromagnetic waves with similar wavelengths. As a result, scientists concluded that nearly all of the light within the early universe was released at the same time. This evidence supports the big bang theory.

The small temperature variations found in the CMB represent slight density differences. These density differences illustrate variations in the distribution of mass throughout the early universe. Areas with more matter in the early universe have large clusters of galaxies today. This evidence gives further support to the big bang theory.

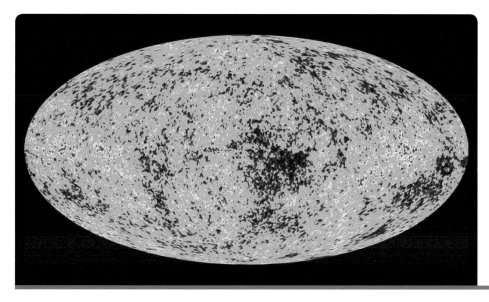

COSMIC MICROWAVE BACKGROUND RADIATION

The colors in this image show the distribution of microwave radiation throughout the universe. How could this image support the Big Bang Theory?

Scientific knowledge is based on the assumption that laws of physics operate the same today as they did in the past. Using the data collected from spectral analysis, CMB radiation, and red-shift evidence (explained later), scientists can infer conditions of the past using the laws that are now known to be true. Applying the law of the conservation of energy and the theory of relativity to observational data, scientists have developed a plausible explanation of the origin of the universe.

Hubble's Observations

The expansion of the universe can be observed and measured. Observing the expansion of the universe provides strong evidence for the big bang theory. Measuring the rate of expansion allows scientists to work backward to determine the precise age of the universe, beginning with the big bang.

In the 1920s, American astronomer Edwin Hubble made some of the first observations of the expansion of the universe employing the principles of the Doppler effect. The Doppler effect is the apparent change in the **frequency** of a wave caused by the changing distance between the observer and the object emitting the wave. When waves are moving toward an observer, they appear to be compressed, resulting in an apparent shortening of **wavelength** and an increase in frequency. When waves are moving away from an observer, the waves appear to be stretched, resulting in an apparent lengthening of wavelength and decrease in frequency.

With light waves, the apparent change in wavelength shifts the light toward different colors. Redshift is the apparent shift of light wavelengths toward the red end of the electromagnetic spectrum. Redshift happens when a luminous object is moving away from Earth. Blueshift is the apparent shift of light wavelengths toward the blue end of the electromagnetic spectrum. Blueshift happens when a luminous object is moving toward Earth. Both of these phenomena can be explained by the Doppler effect.

If the universe is expanding, one would expect most objects in the universe to have a redshift, meaning they are moving away from Earth. Hubble observed the redshift of most galaxies in the universe, which is evidence for the expansion of the universe. Scientists apply the rate of expansion backward to estimate the moment of the big bang.

REDSHIFT MODEL

Scientists observe redshift of light due to the universe's expansion. How is the distance of an object related to its redshift?

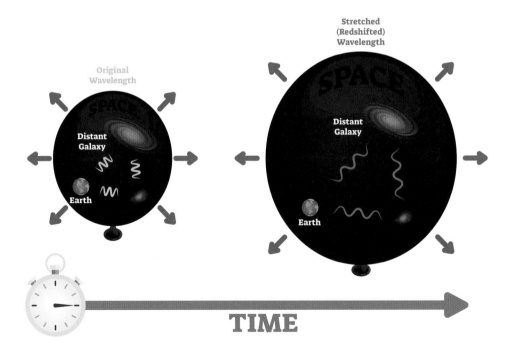

Original Wavelength

Stretched (Redshifted) Wavelength

Distant Galaxy

Distant Galaxy

Earth

Earth

TIME

More Evidence for the Big Bang Theory

The relative abundance of elements in the universe and the known laws of physics provide additional evidence for the big bang theory. The two most common elements in the universe are hydrogen and helium. In fact, hydrogen and helium may compose more than 98 percent of the ordinary matter in the universe. The next most common element in the universe is lithium. Recall that hydrogen, helium, and lithium atoms contain, respectively, one, two, and three protons. They are the three simplest elements, and so they would have been the first to form out of the soupy mix of free protons and neutrons produced by the big bang. The fact that most of the matter in the universe consists of these three simple elements is further evidence for the big bang theory.

The remaining elements on the periodic table were made much later than hydrogen, helium, and lithium. Irregularities in the density of the early universe allowed gravity to exert an uneven pull on the matter in the universe. This uneven pull of gravity allowed hydrogen gas molecules to come together. Countless collisions between these hydrogen atoms generated tremendous heat. Eventually, they ignited to form the first stars. The universe's early stars formed the first galaxies, including the **Milky Way galaxy**. The Milky Way is thought to be one of the oldest galaxies in the universe, about 13 billion years old. Today, the universe is composed of billions of galaxies. Stars and galaxies now contain most of the visible mass of the universe.

DISTANT GALAXIES

Galaxies have different shapes and often contain billions of stars. What do you think the odds are another galaxy contains a planet similar to Earth?

Stars are fueled by a process called nuclear fusion. Fusion is a nuclear reaction in which the nuclei of certain light elements, particularly hydrogen, combine with atoms with larger nuclei. This process is accompanied by an enormous release of energy. The nucleus of a hydrogen atom contains one proton. During nuclear fusion, hydrogen nuclei fuse together to form helium atoms with nuclei that contain two protons. These heavier atoms sink toward the core of a star. They fuse into new atoms of heavier elements with more and more protons in their nuclei. The heavier elements continue to sink toward the core of the star. The nuclear fusion process continues until iron is formed. Iron does not give off energy through nuclear fusion. When most of the elements in the star have fused into iron, the star runs out of fuel. Then, the star becomes more and more dense until it explodes into a supernova. This explosion spreads the star's elements throughout the universe. The energy from the explosion causes more fusion, producing even heavier elements. The deaths of the first stars gave birth to the elements of the universe.

The processes that first began immediately after the big bang continued, and they are still occurring today. About five billion years ago, gas began to coalesce to form a star known as the sun. Dust and gas coalesced around this star 4.6 billion years ago to form a very special planet known as Earth. Nuclear fusion is still happening in the sun and in countless other stars, and the universe is still expanding.

Consider the Explain Question

How has technology been used to collect evidence that verifies the scientific theory of the big bang?

Go online to complete the scientific explanation.

dlc.com/ca11094s

Check Your Understanding

How does the big bang theory explain the origin of the universe?

dlc.com/ca11095s

 in Action

Applying Understanding the Universe

Will the universe continue to expand forever?

While scientists' current understanding of the origin of the universe is that it has been expanding since the big bang, the origins and nature of the universe are a subject of great debate and uncertainty. Proponents of the **big bang theory** admit that if the universe had a beginning, they must also allow the possibility of it having an end. Those who support that **steady state theory** think differently, arguing that the universe has always been infinite, meaning it has no beginning and, therefore, no end. The rate at which the universe is expanding is accelerating, which leads some scientists to think the universe will expand forever. What would this imply for the ultimate fate of the universe? Is it possible that the expansion of the universe could eventually slow and the universe might collapse back in on itself in a reversal of the big bang?

Professor Stephen Hawking, one of the leading researchers on the subject of the early universe and **cosmology**, has suggested a model for the behavior of the universe just after the big bang. By combining Einstein's general **theory** of relativity with quantum theory, he was able to explain some of the observations made by astronomers using the Hubble space telescope and other advanced instrumentation. Hawking suggested that, in the big bang, the universe expanded very rapidly. It expanded to trillions and trillions its size in a fraction of a second. His theory predicted that this expansion was not quite uniform. This irregular expansion would produce small variations in the intensity of the microwave background leftover from the big bang. As a result, some regions could collapse and form new galaxies and stars. The microwave background Hawking referenced has been observed and measured using satellites. It was found to have exactly the kind of variations predicted, confirming Hawking's ideas.

Professor Hawking is not the only one to study the subject of the early universe and cosmology. Another recent **hypothesis** is the presence of dark matter. By studying ratios of hydrogen to helium in space, scientists have realized that much of the mass of the universe cannot be seen. They know it must be there because mass cannot disappear, but what is it? Some astrophysicists think that as much as 27 percent of the universe could be made up of dark matter and 68 percent of the universe is composed of dark energy. They also think that empty space is not empty after all.

As scientists continue to study the rate of acceleration in the universe and learn more about dark matter and dark energy, their understanding of the origins and nature of the universe will continue to evolve.

MATTER IN SPACE

The bright spots in this image are galaxies. What do some astrophysicists think is present in the dark areas between these galaxies?

STEM and Understanding the Universe

The scientists who study the origin and evolution of the universe are called cosmologists. Cosmologists have a strong knowledge of the laws of physics, advanced mathematics, and the characteristics of the different bodies in the solar system. Using this knowledge, they collect and analyze data from satellites, telescopes, and other tools of the trade to help them develop theoretical models to explain both the history and the future of the universe. For example, scientists analyze the data gathered about cosmic microwave background radiation to connect the beginnings of the universe with the current observations. Even though scientists are dealing in theories and mathematical models, those theories have to be rooted in evidence if they are going to stand up to the scrutiny of the science community and the test of time.

One thing cosmologists study is the speed of the universe. As they measure and compare distances of objects in the universe, they have learned that the universe is expanding at a rapid rate. Cosmologists must determine how fastthe universe is expanding and speculate about what may be causing it to expand.

The universe is vast. While scientists know a lot about the universe, there is also a lot they do not know. As cosmologists study the universe, they learn more about its size, its characteristics, and the relationship between it and humans as a whole. By studying the universe, from its history through its future state, cosmologists also learn more about the future of **Earth**.

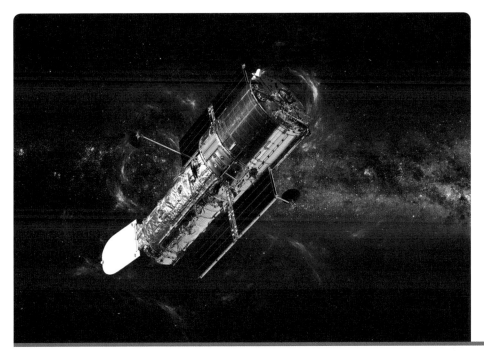

THE HUBBLE SPACE TELESCOPE

The Hubble Space Telescope has provided cosmologists with images of vastly distant galaxies. How have images from Hubble advanced our understanding of the universe?

Stars and Galaxies

CONCEPT
6.2

dlc.com/ca11096s

LESSON OVERVIEW

Lesson Questions

- What are stars?
- What are galaxies?

Lesson Objectives

By the end of the lesson, you should be able to:

- Understand the nature of stars.
- Understand the nature of galaxies.

Key Vocabulary

Which terms do you already know?

- ☐ absolute magnitude
- ☐ apparent magnitude
- ☐ atomic number
- ☐ black hole
- ☐ elliptical
- ☐ galaxy
- ☐ giant star
- ☐ Hertzspring-Russel (H-R) diagram
- ☐ Milky Way
- ☐ neutron star
- ☐ nuclear fusion
- ☐ nucleosynthesis
- ☐ planetary nebula
- ☐ pulsar
- ☐ star
- ☐ supergiant star
- ☐ white dwarf

Thinking about Stars and Galaxies

Have you ever laid outside on a dark summer night and watched the stars move across the sky? What myths or stories do you know about the night sky?

dlc.com/ca11097s

EXPLAIN QUESTION

❚ **What is the nature of stars, and how do they populate a galaxy?**

THE MILKY WAY GALAXY

On clear, dark nights, the band of gas, stars, and dust forming one arm of the Milky Way can be seen from Earth. How many of the stars in the night sky can you name?

What Are Stars?

Stars Release Energy

The sun is Earth's closest **star** and the source of energy that fuels countless living things on Earth. We depend on energy from the sun to grow plants that are at the base of most food chains. We use these plants for food, fabric, and medicines. Energy from the sun also keeps our planet at a temperature suitable for life. Solar energy drives weather, ocean currents and the water cycle. Most of the energy resources we depend on for fuel and electricity originally came from the sun's energy.

The sun is not unique among stars. All stars release huge amounts of energy. This energy radiates outward into space. Where does this energy come from? Deep in the core of a star, the nuclei of atoms join together in a process called **nuclear fusion**. Huge amounts of energy are released when nuclei fuse. This energy moves outward from the star's core until it reaches the star's surface. From there, it is released into space primarily as electromagnetic radiation.

ENERGY FROM THE SUN

Like all stars, the Sun releases huge amounts of energy through the process of nuclear fusion. In what other ways is the sun similar to or different from other stars?

Energy released by the sun travels through space and impacts Earth. Scientists measure the energy released by the sun every day. They count sunspots and observe solar flares; they use magnetometers to detect changes in magnetic fields; they monitor aurora activity to discover patterns in the amount and size of the radiation from the sun; and they analyze the full spectral range of the sun's radiation. By synthesizing this information, scientists can make predictions about the nature and ultimate fate of the sun.

Solar flares are sudden bursts of electromagnetic energy and particles from the surface or near the surface of the sun. Bigger bursts, called coronal mass ejections (CMEs), also blast high levels of energy into space. When energy and particles from CMEs hit Earth's magnetosphere, they are deflected to the poles and cause auroras. Auroras are shiny, colored light displays in the night sky. Such bursts are known to damage power stations, satellites, and radio transmissions. The size and number of the bursts forecast detrimental effects Earth may experience.

Sunspots are areas of low temperature that form on the surface of the sun. They appear dark against the background of the sun's bright disk. Scientists discovered that changing levels of energy released by the sun follows a pattern called the sunspot cycle. These cycles last about 11 years. Some are a little longer, and some are shorter. Noncyclical variations also occur, and their effects on Earth depend on the length and size of the cycles and the intervals between.

Using weather records and observed solar patterns, scientists have identified one such noncyclical variation of lower solar activity that impacted Earth for about 500 years. Starting in the 14th century, this period, referred to as the Little Ice Age, was caused by a period of low solar activity. Records from around the world during this period indicate colder than normal winters and snowfalls. Many agricultural areas experienced crop failures throughout the Little Ice Age.

SUNSPOTS

Sunspots are giant magnetic storms on the Sun. They appear in cycles that have been correlated to changes in Earth's weather patterns. In what ways do these cycles impact Earth's weather?

Stars Form Elements

When the nuclei of atoms fuse inside stars, new elements form. Remember that elements have different numbers of protons in their nuclei. The number of protons in an element is its **atomic number**. Nuclear fusion produces atoms with larger and larger atomic numbers. Unlike chemical reactions, in nuclear reactions, the number of atoms is not conserved, because atoms are joined to form new elements. For example, each hydrogen nucleus has one proton. The fusion of two hydrogen nuclei forms a helium nucleus, which has two protons. The formation of elements by nuclear fusion inside stars is called **nucleosynthesis**. Nucleosynthesis happens when the temperature inside stars is so hot that electrons are ejected from atoms. This leaves bare nuclei that move so fast, they can fuse together when they collide.

Stellar processes formed much of the matter that makes up our planet, our bodies, and all of the things around us. (Stellar means "relating to stars," just as solar means "relating to the sun.") The first three elements were formed several hundred thousand years after the big bang. These elements were hydrogen, helium, and lithium. The first stars formed from atoms of these elements. Nucleosynthesis formed the next 20 or so elements in the periodic table, up to iron (atomic number of 26). Heavier elements than these are formed during supernovae, explosive deaths of huge stars.

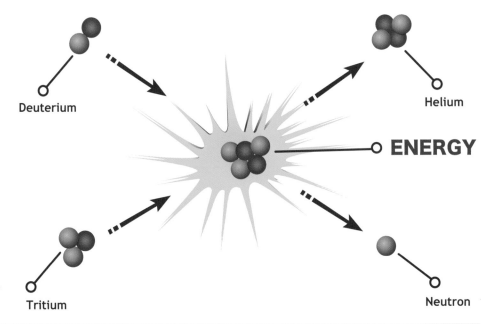

Deuterium

Helium

ENERGY

Tritium

Neutron

NUCLEAR FUSION ON A STAR

Conditions inside stars enable the fusion of elements to create heavier elements, releasing vast amounts of energy. How do the fusion of deuterium and tritium begin the process of forming other elements?

The Life Cycle of a Star

Stars go through predictable changes over time. Scientists use terms borrowed from biology to talk about these changes: birth, death, and life cycle.

Stars form from giant clouds of dust and gas in space. Gravity pulls the gases and dust particles toward one another, squeezing them into smaller and smaller spaces. As the volume of a cloud decreases, the pressure and temperature inside the cloud increases. If the mass of gases and dust is great enough, the temperature at the center will rise high enough for nuclear fusion of hydrogen to begin. This is the birth of a star.

Once nuclear fusion begins, the outward pressure from the tremendous release of energy and electrons balances the inward pressure from gravity. The volume no longer contracts but remains stable for a period of time as the star proceeds with nuclear fusion of hydrogen. This stable period of a star's life cycle, during which hydrogen fusion occurs, is called the main sequence.

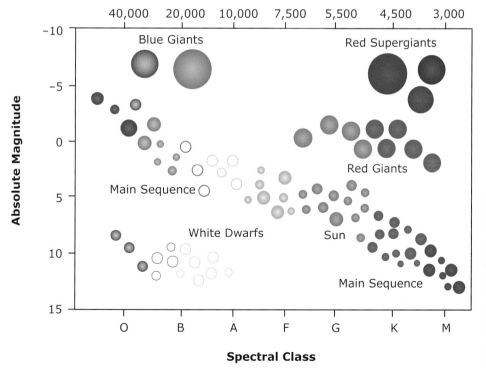

Star Magnitude, Temperature, and Spectral Class

HERTZSPRUNG-RUSSELL DIAGRAM

The Hertzsprung-Russell diagram organizes stars by their surface temperature and absolute magnitude, or brightness. How would the sun's place in the diagram change over billions of years?

Although all stars proceed through the main sequence phase, not all main-sequence stars have the same properties. Stars that begin with more material, or mass, burn hotter than those than are born with less material. What is more the initial mass of a star determines its life-history or evolution. The temperature of a star determines its color. Hotter stars appear bluer in color, whereas cooler stars appear redder. Temperature also influences the brightness of a star, though its radius and its distance from Earth also affect how bright it appears in the sky. Astronomers use the term *apparent magnitude* to describe how bright a star appears from Earth and *absolute magnitude* to describe a star's actual brightness.

Stars that begin with more mass burn through their hydrogen fuel more quickly and therefore have shorter life cycles compared to stars with less initial mass. Eventually, however, all stars use up their supplies of hydrogen, bringing an end to fusion reactions. When the pull of gravity is no longer balanced by the outward push from fusion, the core of the star begins to contract. At the same time, the outer shell of the star expands and cools. The star has now entered the **giant star** phase of its life cycle. The expanding, cooling shell typically appears red, and stars during this phase are called red giants. The core of a red giant heats as it contracts. Eventually the temperature increases enough to cause the nuclear fusion of helium, forming carbon nuclei. (The nucleus of a carbon atom contains six protons.) Giants are typically yellow-orange during the helium fusion phase.

Death of a Star

All stars evolve the same way up to the giant phase. What happens next depends on the star's initial mass. When the supply of helium runs out, the core again contracts due to unbalanced gravitational force. In lower-mass stars like our sun, fusion stops at this point because there is not enough mass to raise the pressure and temperature to fuse helium into carbon. The core shrinks and the outer layers of the star are expelled into space, forming a **planetary nebula**. The small, spent core glows white and is called a white dwarf. Over billions of years, **white dwarfs** cool to become black dwarfs.

WHITE DWARF AND PLANETARY NEBULA

A planetary nebula of ionized gas surrounds this white dwarf, the burned-out core of a lower-mass star. What will happen to this gas over time?

In stars with initial masses at least eight times greater than the sun's, gravity continues to pull carbon atoms together after helium runs out. The temperature in these supermassive stars increases enough for carbon fusion to form elements with higher atomic numbers—nitrogen, oxygen, and eventually iron. Nucleosynthesis cannot produce elements heavier than iron, so once a core is mostly iron, fusion ceases. Instantly, the core collapses under its own massive gravitational force. The temperature reaches more than 100 billion degrees. The repulsive forces between the iron nuclei blow the star's mass into space in a supernova. Elements heavier than iron form in the intense heat and pressure of a supernova explosion.

If the mass of a supermassive star is between eight and twenty times that of the sun, the remains from its supernova will form a rapidly spinning, highly magnetic **neutron star** that emits electromagnetic radiation from its magnetic poles. If a neutron star is oriented in just the right direction, astronomers can detect pulses of radiation as the star spins. Astronomers call these neutron stars pulsars.

If the mass of a supermassive star is much greater, its core collapses under its own gravity following a supernova. The gravitational collapse is so complete that no energy or matter can escape. The star collapses forever inside this mysterious **black hole**.

Stellar Evolution Overview

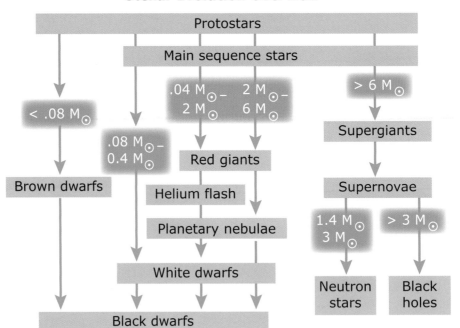

STELLAR EVOLUTION

Stellar evolution is the development of stars from their formation to their "deaths." The evolution of a star depends primarily on its mass. What fate is predicted for the sun, considering its physical features?

Studying Stars

Scientists use a variety of tools to study stars. Stars give off energy across the entire range of the electromagnetic spectrum. Scientists have developed a variety of telescopes that detect these emissions in specific ranges. These ranges include visible light, radio waves, and X-rays. Scientists use information about a star's emissions to determine the star's properties.

These properties, in turn, give information about the star's starting mass, history, and future. For example, at first glance, all stars appear white, but if you look closely, stars actually come in a range of colors, from blue to red. A star's color gives scientists information about its temperature and life cycle phase. Scientists have organized stars into classes by their color. In addition, by using a spectroscope, scientists can tell which elements make up the star. A spectroscope splits the light from a star into a spectrum using a prism. Each element has its own unique spectral pattern. Scientists compare the spectral pattern from a star to the patterns produced by known elements. Then they can determine which elements make up the star. From these studies scientists have determined that the most common elements in stars are hydrogen and helium. In fact, hydrogen and helium make up 96–99% of a star's mass.

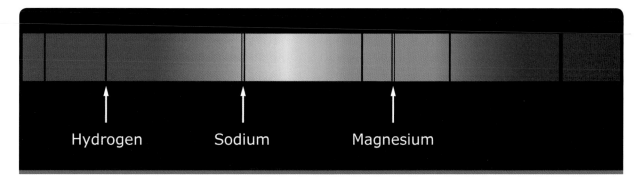

Hydrogen   Sodium   Magnesium

Color and brightness can also be used to determine the distance to a star. When electromagnetic waves are seen coming from an object moving toward you, they appear compressed. In other words, their wavelengths appear shorter. When an object is moving away from you, wavelengths appear longer. When light waves lengthen, they are said to shift to the red end of the spectrum. This is called a redshift. A blueshift, or shift toward the blue end of the spectrum, happens when light waves are seen from objects moving toward Earth. This information is very important because it allows scientists to create a map of the universe.

STAR SPECTRUM

Each star has its own absorption spectrum, with dark lines representing the spectral pattern of each element present in the star. What information does this spectrum provide to scientists about its star?

What Are Galaxies?

The Milky Way Galaxy

The appearance of the **Milky Way** in the night sky has fascinated people since the beginning of human history. The invention of telescopes allowed scientists to observe that the Milky Way is made up of stars. Advances in telescope technologies revealed fuzzy, spiral objects in the sky far beyond our **galaxy**. Some scientists began to speculate that the Milky Way was one of many "island universes."

Scientists attempted to map the Milky Way by dividing the sky into segments and counting stars. However, it wasn't until scientists started to puzzle out relationships among luminosity, **apparent magnitude**, and distance that accurate stellar maps could be made. Starting in the early 1900s, scientists began gathering the evidence to conclude that we are living in a spiral- shaped galaxy about 100,000 light-years across, containing billions of stars.

Soon afterward, telescope technology advanced to the point at which scientists could confirm the most remarkable ideas about space. In 1924, Edwin Hubble used a 100-inch telescope in California to discover that many of the fuzzy objects discovered previously were indeed distant galaxies. Like our own, these distant galaxies are made of billions of stars.

STRUCTURE OF THE MILKY WAY

The billions of stars in the Milky Way are organized in a central bulge from which a series of spiral arms emerge. What type of galaxy is this?

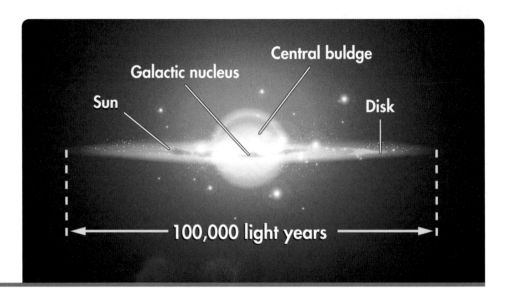

Galactic nucleus

Central buldge

Sun

Disk

100,000 light years

Types of Galaxies

After decades of tedious surveying and advances in telescope technology, scientists know that the universe is full of billions of galaxies. Scientists classify galaxies by their shapes.

Many galaxies are spiral-shaped like a pinwheel, including our own Milky Way. Some galaxies are elliptical, shaped like a sphere that has been stretched in opposing directions. Others lack a distinct geometric form. These are called irregular galaxies.

SPIRAL GALAXY TYPES

Spiral galaxies come in many types. This diagram also shows an irregular galaxy (NGC 6822, in the center of the bottom row). How is the irregular galaxy different from spiral galaxies?

Consider the Explain Question

| **What is the nature of stars, and how do they populate a galaxy?**

Go online to complete the scientific explanation.

dlc.com/ca11098s

Check Your Understanding

| **You observe two stars in the night sky. Why does the reddish star appear brighter than the bluish star?**

dlc.com/ca11099s

STEM in Action

Applying Stars and Galaxies

Astrophysics is a branch of astronomy that deals with celestial bodies. Astrophysicists study how stars form and interact with matter. Observational astrophysicists use telescopes to examine the full spectrum of electromagnetic waves emitted by stars. Theoretical astrophysicists develop hypotheses to explain the creation of stars, galaxies, and the universe. They develop models to simulate their observations, and they design missions to collect additional data to disprove or support their hypotheses. Vital to the job of an astrophysicist is the technology used to collect the evidence.

Many of the hypotheses developed by theoretical astrophysicists have been supported by data collected by the Hubble space telescope. Hubble has been orbiting Earth since 1990 and has been sending back crystal clear images of distant stars and galaxies. Technology has continued to advance, and a replacement telescope is set to be launched into orbit in a few years.

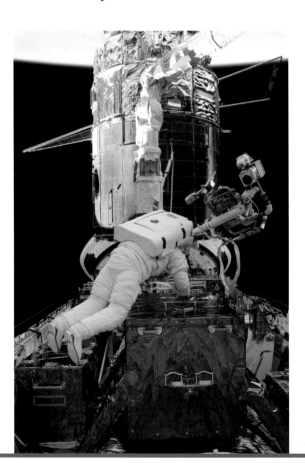

CORRECTING HUBBLE'S VISION

Astronauts install a new camera on the Hubble space telescope. What advantages does a space-based telescope have over a telescope on Earth's surface?

Conceived over twenty years ago, the James Webb space telescope is expected to find its place in orbit after a 2021 launch date. It was named after the head of NASA from 1961–68. It will house instruments to collect light information about distant stars and galaxies. The JWST is an international project involving a partnership between NASA, the European Space Agency, and the Canadian Space Agency. Unlike the Hubble telescope that currently orbits Earth, the JWST will orbit the sun 1.5 million kilometers from Earth at a point called the second Lagrange point (L2). The complicated design of technology and materials needed to operate a telescope in the harsh conditions of space is immense. While one side of the telescope will be exposed to the sun and reach temperatures of 85°C, the opposite side, facing the outer border of the solar system, will reach −233°C.

MODEL OF THE JAMES WEBB SPACE TELESCOPE

A model of the JWST is on display at the Maryland Science Center in Baltimore. How do you think engineers propose to expand the sunshield in space?

STEM and Stars and Galaxies

Not only must the materials chosen for this design be able to withstand extreme temperatures, the parts must be configured to allow for continual collection of data. Engineers have designed a tennis court sized reflective canopy to shield the telescope from intense solar radiation and thus control the operating temperature. This sunshield will be positioned to reflect excess solar radiation away from the telescope out into space.

Deploying the telescope from Earth to its position in space will be a tricky maneuver. The telescope will be launched folded up in a rocket. Once out of Earth's atmosphere, it will separate and unfold its sunshield. Using small on-board rockets, the JWST will slowly make its way to the L2 position over the course of several months. Aerospace engineers expect the telescope to be ready for operational use six months after its launch.

AEROSPACE ENGINEERS WORK ON THE JWST

Aerospace engineers work on constructing a part for the JWST. Why do you think they are wearing protective suits?

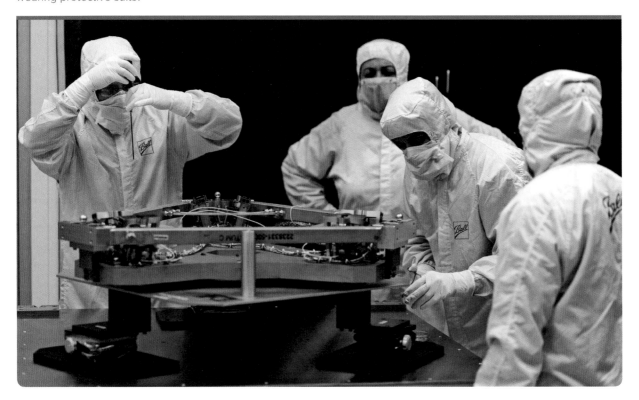

English ——————— A ——————— Español

absolute age   the age given in years, of a fossil, a rock, a feature, or an event; usually determined through radiometric dating

edad absoluta   edad de un fósil, una roca, una característica geológica o un evento expresada en años; por lo general se determina mediante datación radiométrica

absolute magnitude   the brightness that a star would have if it were 32.6 light-years from an observer

magnitud absoluta   brillo que tendría una estrella si estuviera a 32.6 años luz de un observador

absorption   a physical process in which one substance takes in a given amount of another substance

absorción   fenómeno físico en el cual una sustancia toma una cantidad dada de otra sustancia

absorption spectra   a measurement of a given sample's absorption of light as a function of wavelength/frequency; the information from this is specific to any element or compound, and can be used to identify unknown materials

espectro de absorción   medida de la luz absorbida por una muestra dada expresada como función de longitud de onda/frecuencia; este dato es específico para cada elemento o compuesto y se puede usar para identificar materiales desconocidos

acceleration   a change in velocity over time

aceleración   cambio en la velocidad en un tiempo determinado

acceleration due to gravity   the change in velocity caused by a gravitational force

aceleración de la gravedad   cambio en la velocidad causado por la fuerza gravitacional

alpha particle   a subatomic particle composed of two protons and two neutrons, represented by the symbol a

partícula alfa   partícula subatómica compuesta por dos protones y dos neutrones, se representa con el símbolo a

amplitude   the maximum displacement of a wave from its rest position; "strength" of a wave

amplitud   desplazamiento máximo de una onda desde su posición de reposo; "intensidad" de una onda

aphelion   the point in the orbit of a planet or other orbiting body where it is farthest from the sun or the body around which it revolves

afelio   punto de la órbita de un planeta, o de otro cuerpo que sigue una órbita, más alejado del sol o del cuerpo alrededor del cual orbita

apparent magnitude   the brightness of a star as it appears from Earth, irrespective of its distance

magnitud aparente   el brillo de una estrella tal como se aprecia desde la Tierra, sin tener en cuenta su distancia

asteroid   a small object made of rock or metal that originates in an orbit between Mars and Jupiter

asteroide   pequeño objeto compuesto por roca o metal que se origina en una órbita entre Marte y Júpiter

asthenosphere   The layer of soft but solid mobile rock found below the lithosphere. The asthenosphere begins about 100 km below Earth's surface and extends to a depth of about 350 km; the lower part of the upper mantle.

astenosfera   capa de roca capaz de moverse, blanda pero sólida, que se encuentra bajo la litosfera. La astenosfera comienza aproximadamente a 100 km bajo la superficie de la Tierra y se extiende hasta una profundidad de unos 350 km; parte inferior del manto superior.

astrophysics   a branch of astronomy that focuses on the physical properties of stars and other celestial bodies, as well as the physical laws of the universe

astrofísica   rama de la astronomía que se enfoca en las propiedades físicas de las estrellas y otros cuerpos celestes y en las leyes físicas del universo.

atom   the smallest unit of an element that has all the chemical properties of that element

átomo   unidad más pequeña de un elemento que tiene todas las propiedades químicas de dicho elemento

atomic nucleus   the central, densest part of the atom, which is composed of protons and neutrons

núcleo atómico   parte central y más densa del átomo, que está compuesta por protones y neutrones

atomic number   the number of protons in the nucleus of an atom

número atómico   número de protones contenidos en el núcleo de un átomo

atomic spectroscopy   Each element absorbs or emits light at specific wavelengths of light. In atomic spectroscopy, light is either passed through or emitted by a substance. A monochrometer measures the specific wavelengths of light absorbed or emitted in an attempt to identify the substance.

espectroscopia de absorción atómica   Cada elemento absorbe o emite luz a una determinada longitud de onda de luz. En la espectroscopia atómica, la luz pasa por una sustancia o es emitida por ella. Un monocrómetro mide la longitud de onda específica de la luz que se absorbe o se emite para así identificar la sustancia.

average speed   the distance traveled by an object divided by time it traveled

rapidez promedio   distancia recorrida por un objeto dividida entre el tiempo que toma el recorrido

average velocity   the displacement of an object divided by the time it traveled

velocidad promedio   desplazamiento de un objeto dividido entre el tiempo que toma el desplazamiento

axis   an imaginary line around which an object spins or revolves; also one of a number of lines used for determining coordinates

eje   línea imaginaria alrededor de la cual un objeto gira o rota; también una de las varias líneas que se usan para determinar coordenadas

beta particle a high-energy electron, denoted β; also known as a positron

partícula beta electrón de alta energía, indicado como β; también conocido como positrón

Big Bang theory the most commonly accepted scientific theory of how the universe formed; states that the universe expanded from a hot, dense initial condition at a specific point in time around 13.5 billion years ago

Teoría del Big Bang teoría científica más comúnmente aceptada sobre cómo se formó el universo; establece que el universo se expandió a partir de una condición inicial densa y cálida, en un momento específico, hace alderredor de 13.5 mil millones de años

black hole a space object with surface gravity great enough that not even light waves can escape it

agujero negro objeto espacial con una gravedad superficial tan fuerte que ni siquiera las ondas luminosas pueden escapar de él

blue shift a shift of light wavelengths towards the blue end of the electromagnetic spectrum that takes place when a light source is moving towards an observer

corrimiento al azul desplazamiento de longitudes de ondas luminosas hacia el extremo azul del espectro electromagnético que tiene lugar cuando una fuente de luz se mueve hacia la persona que la observa

celestial sphere a large, imaginary sphere centered on an observer and encompassing the sky overhead

esfera celeste gran esfera imaginaria centrada en un observador y que abarca el cielo encima de él

center of gravity the average location of the weight of a system

centro de gravedad la ubicación promedio del peso de un sistema

center of mass the average location of the mass of a system

centro de masa la ubicación promedio de la masa de un sistema

centripetal force any force that causes centripetal acceleration

fuerza centrípeta cualquier fuerza que produce aceleración centrípeta

chain reaction an event in which the products of one reaction serve as the reactants in the next; in nuclear reactions, successive fission reactions produce neutrons that split other nuclei

reacción en cadena evento en el cual los productos de una reacción sirven como reactantes en la siguiente; en las reacciones nucleares, las sucesivas reacciones de fisión producen neutrones que dividen otros núcleos

chemical potential energy amount of chemical energy stored in a substance

energía química potencial cantidad de energía química almacenada en una sustancia

closed system   a system that cannot exchange matter or energy with anything outside it

sistema cerrado   sistema que no puede intercambiar materia ni energía con nada del exterior

compression   occurs when rocks are squeezed by external forces directed toward one another to put stress on the rock, acting to decrease its volume or shorten its dimensions

compresión   ocurre cuando las rocas son apretadas unas junto a otras por fuerzas externas dirigidas hacia otras y que presionan la roca, dando como resultado una disminución de su volumen o un acortamiento de sus dimensiones

conductor   a material that allows electricity, heat or sound to pass through it easily

conductor   material que permite el paso de la electricidad, el calor o el sonido con facilidad

conservation of energy   Energy cannot be created out of nothing, nor can it be completely destroyed. Energy can only change its form.

conservación de la energía   la energía no puede crearse de la nada, o no puede ser destruida por completo. La energía solo cambia de forma.

conservation of energy   a law that states that energy is conserved in a closed system

conservación de la energía   ley que establece que en un sistema cerrado la energía se conserva

conservation of momentum   a law that states that the total momentum is conserved in a closed system

conservación del momento   ley que establece que en un sistema cerrado el momento total se conserva

continental crust   The rocks of Earth's crust that make up the base of the continents, ranging in thickness from about 35 km to 60 km under mountain ranges. Continental crust is generally less dense than oceanic crust.

corteza continental   rocas de la corteza terrestre que constituyen la base de los continentes, su espesor va desde alrededor de 35 km hasta 60 km bajo cadenas montañosas. Por lo general la corteza continental es menos densa que la corteza oceánica.

convergent boundary   a tectonic plate boundary at which two tectonic plates move toward each other, causing collisions and subduction zones

límite convergente   límite de una placa tectónica en el cual dos placas se mueven una hacia otra y producen colisiones y zonas de subducción

core   the innermost layer of Earth, comprised of the liquid outer core and solid inner core; consists mainly of iron and nickel

núcleo   capa más interna de la Tierra, consta del núcleo externo líquido y el núcleo interno sólido; constituido principalmente por hierro y níquel

cosmic background radiation   weak radiation in space that is left over from the first stages of the Big Bang that theoretically created the universe

radiación del fondo cósmico   radiación débil en el espacio que queda de las primeras etapas del Big Bang que en teoría creó el universo

cosmology the study of the origin, history, and current state of the universe, based on observation and the use of theoretical models

cosmología estudio del origen, la historia y el estado actual del universo basado en las observaciones y el uso de modelos teóricos

Coulomb's law the principle that states that the electric force between two electrically charged objects is directly proportional to the charges of the two objects and inversely proportional to the square of the distance between them

ley de Coulomb principio que establece que la fuerza eléctrica entre dos objetos eléctricamente cargados es directamente proporcional a las cargas de ambos objetos e inversamente proporcional al cuadrado de la distancia que los separa

current a measurement of the flow of electric charge passing a certain point per unit time; any flow of liquid or electric charge

corriente medida del flujo de carga eléctrica que pasa por un determinado punto por unidad de tiempo; cualquier flujo de líquido o de carga eléctrica

D

data recorded measurements or observations collecting during a scientific investigation

datos registro de mediciones u observaciones recopiladas durante una investigación científica

daughter isotope an isotope that forms from the radioactive decay of an atom; the isotope may or may not be the same element as its parent

isótopo hijo isótopo que se forma por la desintegración radiactiva de un átomo; el isótopo puede ser o no ser el mismo elemento que el isótopo padre

diffraction a change in direction of light or sound waves around objects in their paths

difracción cambio en la dirección de las ondas luminosas o sonoras alrededor de los objetos que encuentran en su camino

directly proportional a relationship between two variables in which an increase in the value of one causes an increase in the value of the other

directamente proporcional relación entre dos variables en la cual un aumento en el valor de una produce un aumento en el valor de la otra

displacement (vector) a length vector pointing from an object's starting point to its ending point

desplazamiento (vector) vector de longitud que va desde el punto de partida de un objeto hasta la posición final

displacement (water) the method to determine the volume of a solid object using the difference in water volume before and after the addition of the object

desplazamiento (agua) método para determinar el volumen de un objeto sólido usando la diferencia en el volumen del agua antes y después de introducir el objeto en ella

distance the amount of space between one point and another

distancia espacio entre dos puntos

divergent boundary a tectonic plate boundary at which two tectonic plates move away from each other

límite divergente límite de una placa tectónica en el cual dos placas tectónicas se mueven separándose una de otra

Doppler effect the effect that is produce by the lengthening or compressing of the wavelengths of electromagnetic or sound waves; caused by the movement of one object (either the waves source or the receiver) and the other object is stationary

efecto Doppler efecto producido por el estiramiento o la compresión de las longitudes de onda de ondas electromagnéticas o sonoras; es causado por el movimiento de un objeto (la fuente de las ondas o el receptor) mientras que el otro objeto permanece estacionario

E

Earth the third planet from the sun; the planet on which humans and other organisms live

Tierra tercer planeta a partir del sol; planeta en el cual vivimos los seres humanos y otros organismos

earthquake 1. sudden movement of rock within Earth's crust caused by accumulated stress along a fault 2. a sudden shaking of the ground caused by tectonic plate movement that generates seismic waves

terremoto 1. movimiento repentino de la corteza terrestre causado por la acumulación de presión a lo largo de una falla 2. sacudida repentina del suelo producida por el movimiento de una placa tectónica que genera ondas sísmicas

elastic collision a collision between two or more objects where the total amount of kinetic energy is conserved.

colisión elástica colisión entre dos o más objetos en la que se conserva la cantidad de energía cinética total

elastic potential energy the capacity to do work stored in a material or physical system that can change shape

energía potencial elástica capacidad de realizar trabajo almacenado en un material o sistema físico que puede cambiar de forma

elastic rebound the sudden release of energy caused by the fracturing of deformed rocks when they return to their original undeformed structure

recuperación de la deformación elástica súbita liberación de energía causada por las rocas fracturadas o deformadas cuando regresan a su estructura original no deformadas

electric field a set of lines that defines the motion of charged particles near each other

campo eléctrico conjunto de líneas que definen el movimiento de partículas cargadas cerca unas de otras

electric potential energy the capacity to do work arising from charge stored in a material or physical system

energía potencial eléctrica capacidad de realizar trabajo que surge de una carga almacenada en un material o sistema físico

electrical conductivity   the ability of a substance to carry an electric current

conductividad eléctrica   capacidad de una sustancia para transportar una corriente eléctrica

electromagnetic radiation   waves of electromagnetic energy of various wavelengths, ranging from gamma rays (shortest wavelengths) to radio waves (longest wavelengths)

radiación electromagnética   ondas de energía electromagnética de varias longitudes de onda, abarca desde los rayos gamma (longitudes de onda más cortas) a las ondas de radio (longitudes de onda más largas)

electromagnetic spectrum   the full range of frequencies and wavelengths of electromagnetic waves

espectro electromagnético   rango completo de frecuencias y longitudes de onda de las ondas electromagnéticas

electromagnetic wave   a wave that can transport its energy through a vacuum

onda electromagnética   onda que puede transportar su energía a través del vacío

electromagnetism   a set of forces due to stationary or moving electric charges

electromagnetismo   conjunto de fuerzas debidas a cargas estacionarias o en movimiento

electron   a negatively charged subatomic particle that exists in various energy levels outside the nucleus of an atom

electrón   partícula subatómica con carga negativa que existe en varios niveles de energía alrededor del núcleo de un átomo

element   a pure substance that cannot be broken down into simpler substances by chemical reactions and that is made up of only one type of atom

elemento   sustancia pura que no puede dividirse en sustancias más simples mediante reacciones químicas y que está constituida solo por un tipo de átomos

elliptical   shaped like an oval

elíptico   con forma ovalada

emission   release of energy or matter from components in a system

emisión   liberación de energía o materia de los componentes de un sistema

energy   the ability to do work or cause change; can be stored in chemicals found in food and released to the organism to do work

energía   capacidad de realizar trabajo o producir un cambio; puede almacenarse en sustancias químicas que se encuentran en los alimentos y liberarse al organismo para realizar trabajo

entropy   measure (abbreviated "S") of the amount of energy in a physical system that is not available to do work

entropía   medida (simbolizada "S") de la cantidad de energía en un sistema físico que no está disponible para realizar trabajo

epicenter   the location on Earth's surface that is directly above an earthquake's focus

epicentro   punto de la superficie terrestre que se encuentra directamente encima del foco de un terremoto o movimiento sísmico

equilibrium state of balance between all parts of a system

equilibrio estado de balance entre todas las partes de un sistema

equinox the twice-a-year occurrence during which Earth's axis is perpendicular (at a 90 angle) to a line joining the sun and Earth's center

equinoccio situación que se produce dos veces al año durante la cual el eje de la Tierra está en posición perpendicular (en un ángulo de 90 grados) a la línea que une el centro de la Tierra y el sol

extension occurs when rock bodies are pulled apart by external forces directed away from one another

extensión ocurre cuando los cuerpos de rocas se separan por efecto se fuerzas externas alejándose unos de otros

F

fault a crack in a body of rock along which rocks on opposite sides slide past each other

falla grieta en un cuerpo rocoso a lo largo del cual se deslizan las rocas de ambos lados, unas junto a otras

fault-block mountain a mountain that forms along normal faults due to the tilting, uplift, or dropping of large pieces of crust

montaña de bloques fallados montaña que se forma a lo largo de fallas normales debido a la inclinación, elevación o descenso de grandes trozos de corteza

fission the splitting of a nucleus of an atom into at least two other nuclei, releasing large amounts of energy

fisión división del núcleo de un átomo en al menos otros dos núcleos, liberando una gran cantidad de energía

focal length the point at which parallel light rays converge (or seem to converge) after passing through a lens

distancia focal punto en el cual un rayo paralelo converge (o parece converger) después de haber pasado a través de una lente

focus (ESS) the location beneath Earth's surface where an earthquake begins; directly beneath the epicenter

foco (ESS) lugar bajo la superficie de la Tierra donde comienza un terremoto; directamente debajo del epicentro

fold a bend in originally horizontal rock layers, caused by pressure or heat that softens the rock.

pliegue curvatura en capas rocosas que originalmente eran horizontales, causada por presión o por calor que ablanda la roca

folded mountain a mountain formed by large-scale folding and uplift

montaña de pliegue montaña formada por un plegamiento y una elevación a gran escala

footwall the block of rock that moves downward along a fault, found below the hanging wall

bloque yacente (o piso) bloque de roca que se desplaza hacia abajo a lo largo de una falla, se encuentra abajo del bloque colgante (o techo)

force an interaction between objects that causes a change to the objects' motion.

fossil the preserved remains of an organism, or traces of an organism such as a mark or print left by an animal

frame of reference an item against which the motion of an object can be measured

free body diagram a diagram showing all the forces acting on an object

frequency the number of waves that pass a given point during a specified period of time

fuerza interacción entre objetos que origina un cambio en el movimiento del objeto

fósil restos conservados de un organismo o de huellas de un organismo como marcas o huellas dejadas por un animal

marco de referencia elemento o elementos respecto a los cuales puede medirse el movimiento de un objeto

diagrama de cuerpo libre diagrama que muestra todas las fuerzas que actúan sobre un objeto

frecuencia número de ondas que pasan por un punto dado durante un periodo de tiempo específico

G

galaxy a group of solar systems, dust, and gas held together by gravity, usually revolving around a black hole

gamma ray an electromagnetic wave with a very short wavelength (typically less than 10^{-10} m) and very high energy and frequency (typically greater than 1019 Hz)

gas a state of matter without any defined volume or shape in which atoms or molecules move about freely

giant impact hypothesis the generally accepted hypothesis about the origin of Earth's moon, according to which Earth was struck by a Mars-sized body, and the debris from this impact combined in orbit around Earth to form the moon

giant star a star at the stage in its life cycle when it stops burning hydrogen, begins burning helium, and expands to a large, low-density star

galaxia grupo de sistemas solares, polvo y gas que se mantiene unido por la gravedad y que, por lo general, gira alrededor de un agujero negro

rayos gamma ondas electromagnéticas con una longitud de onda muy corta (normalmente menos de 10^{-10} m) y con energía y frecuencia muy altas (por lo general de más de 1019 Hz)

gas estado de la materia que no tiene volumen ni forma definidos en el cual los átomos o moléculas se mueven libremente

teoría del gran impacto hipótesis generalmente aceptada sobre el origen de la luna de la Tierra, según la cual la Tierra fue impactada por un cuerpo del tamaño de Marte y los restos de este impacto se unieron en una órbita alrededor de la Tierra y formaron la luna

estrella gigante estrella en la etapa de su ciclo de vida en la cual deja de quemar hidrógeno, empieza a quemar helio y se expande formando una estrella grande de poca densidad

gravitational force an attractive force that occurs between all objects that have mass

fuerza gravitacional fuerza de atracción que se produce entre todos los objetos que tienen masa

---

gravitational force an interaction between any two objects with mass that attracts them to one another; the magnitude of the gravitational force increases as the mass of the two objects increases and decreases as the distance between the objects increases

fuerza gravitacional interacción entre dos objetos cualesquiera con masa que se atraen el uno al otro; la magnitud de la fuerza gravitacional aumenta cuando aumenta la masa de los objetos y disminuye cuando aumenta la distancia entre ellos

---

gravitational potential energy energy stored due to position in a gravitational field; commonly due to Earth's gravity

energía potencial gravitacional energía almacenada debida a la ubicación en un campo gravitacional; por lo general debido a la gravedad de la Tierra

---

gravity a force that exists between any two objects that have mass and that pulls the objects together. The greater the mass of an object, the greater its gravitational pull.

gravedad fuerza entre dos objetos cualesquiera que tienen masa y que atrae uno hacia el otro. Cuanto mayor es la masa de un objeto, mayor es la atracción gravitacional.

---

gravity an attractive force present between any two masses

gravedad fuerza de atracción presente entre dos masas

H

half-life the expected time it takes for half of the atoms of a radioactive element to decay

semivida (o período de semidesintegración) tiempo que se espera que tome la desintegración de la mitad de los átomos de un elemento radiactivo

---

hanging wall the block of rock that moves upward along a fault; found above the footwall

bloque colgante (techo) bloque de roca que se desplaza hacia arriba a lo largo de una falla, se encuentra encima del bloque yacente (piso)

Hardy-Weinberg equation $p^2 + 2pq + q^2 = 1$; the frequencies of two alleles, p and q, in a population will remain stable if no selective pressures are acting on a sufficiently large population

ecuación de Hardy-Weinberg $p^2 + 2pq + q^2 = 1$; las frecuencias de dos alelos, p y q, en una población permanecerán estables si no actúan presiones selectivas en una población suficientemente grande

---

heat the transfer of thermal energy through processes such as radiation, convection, or conduction

calor transferencia de energía térmica por medio de procesos como radiación, convección o conducción

heat energy   a form of energy that transfers between particles in a substance or system through kinetic energy transfer

energía calorífica   forma de energía que se transfiere entre partículas en una sustancia o en un sistema por medio de transferencia de energía cinética

hertz   measurement of wave frequency

hercio   medida de la frecuencia de onda

Hertzspring-Russel (H-R) diagram   a diagram plotting the absolute magnitudes of stars relative to the different stages in a star's life cycle

diagrama de Hertzsprung-Russell (H-R)   diagrama en el que se representan las magnitudes absolutas de las estrellas en relación con las diferentes etapas del ciclo de vida de una estrella

hypothesis   a testable explanation for a problem or phenomena

hipótesis   explicación, que se puede poner poner a prueba, para un fenómeno o problema

I

igneous   1. one of the three major rock types, formed by the cooling and crystallization of magma or lava 2. the processes involved in the melting and cooling of magma

ígneo   1. uno de los tres principales tipos de rocas, formado por el enfriamiento y la cristalización del magma o lava 2. proceso involucrado en la fusión y enfriamiento del magma

index fossil   fossils of organisms belonging to species that existed in large numbers for a relatively short amount of geologic time; used to date the rocks in which they are found

fósil guía   fósiles de organismos pertenecientes a especies que existieron en gran número durante un tiempo geológico relativamente corto; se usan para datar la rocas en las que se hallan

induction   a distribution of electrons within a conductor caused by a varying magnetic field

inducción   distribución de los electrones dentro de un conductor originada por una variación en el campo magnético

inelastic collision   a collision between two or more objects where the total amount of kinetic energy is not conserved.

colisión inelástica   colisión entre dos o más objetos en la que no se conserva la cantidad de energía cinética total

inertia   an object's resistance to a change in motion

inercia   resistencia de un objeto a un cambio en su movimiento

inertial frame of reference   coordinate system and set of points to independently locate and orient objects in space and time

marco de referencia inercial   sistema de coordenadas y conjunto de puntos para ubicar y orientar objetos de manera independiente en el espacio y el tiempo

inner core   the solid, inner portion of Earth's core, composed of an alloy of iron, nickel, and other heavy elements; rotates within the liquid outer core

núcleo interno   parte interna y sólida de la Tierra, compuesta por una aleación de hierro, níquel y otros elementos pesados; rota dentro del núcleo externo líquido

instantaneous speed   the rate of motion of an object at a point in time

rapidez instantánea   tasa de movimiento de un objeto a un punto en el tiempo

instantaneous velocity   the rate of motion of an object traveling in a specified direction at a point in time

velocidad instantánea   tasa de movimiento de un objeto que viaja en una dirección específica a un punto en el tiempo

insulator   a material that does not readily conduct electricity or heat

aislante   material que no conduce fácilmente la electricidad o el calor

intensity   a subjective measurement of the strength of an earthquake based on the amount and type of damage, including physical, economic, and widespread emotional damage

intensidad   medida subjetiva de la fuerza de un terremoto basada en la cantidad y tipo de daños que produce, incluyendo daños físicos, económicos y emocional generalizado

interference   the effect of two or more waves traveling through the same medium

interferencia   efecto de dos o más ondas que viajan por el mismo medio

internal energy   total of the potential energies and kinetic energies of the molecules of an object

energía interna   total de las energías potenciales y cinéticas de un objeto

inversely proportional   a relationship between two variables in which an increase in the value of one causes a decrease in the value of the other

inversamente proporcional   relación entre dos variables en la cual un aumento en el valor de una produce una disminución en el valor de la otra

irreversible process   changes in properties that a system undergoes from the initial state to the final state that cannot be restored completely to the initial state

proceso irreversible   cambios en las propiedades que experimenta un sistema desde el estado inicial hasta el estado final y que no puede revertirse por completo al estado inicial

isolated system   structure or arrangement unable to interact with other structures or arrangements

sistema aislado   estructura u ordenamiento que no es capaz de interactuar con otras estructuras u ordenamientos

isotope   an atom of the same element with the same number of protons but a different number of neutrons; has the same atomic number but different atomic mass

isótopo   átomo del mismo elemento con el mismo número de protones pero diferente número de neutrones; tiene el mismo número atómico pero diferente masa atómica

J

joule   a unit of measurement of energy

julio   unidad de medida de la energía

K

kinetic energy   the energy an object has due to its motion

energía cinética   energía que tiene un objeto debido a su movimiento

kinetic friction   a resistive force between two objects moving pass each other

fricción cinética   fuerza de resistencia entre dos objetos que se mueven uno sobre el otro

L

light   a type of electromagnetic radiation, commonly referred to visible light or light which can be directly seen with the human eye

luz   tipo de radiación electromagnética; el término se usa comúnmente referido a la luz visible o luz que el ojo humano puede ver directamente

light year   the distance light travels in a vacuum in one year; about 6 trillion miles

año luz   distancia que recorre la luz en el espacio en un año; alrededor de 6 billones de millas

longitudinal waves   a wave that occurs when the particles of a medium move parallel to the direction of the wave

onda longitudinal   onda que se produce cuando las partículas de un medio se mueven en paralelo a la dirección de la onda

M

magnetic field   a set of lines that defines the motion of charged particles near a magnet

campo magnético   conjunto de líneas que definen el movimiento de partículas cargadas cerca de un imán

magnitude   size of ground movement caused by seismic waves due to energy released

magnitud   tamaño del movimiento del suelo provocado por las ondas sísmicas debido a la energía liberada

mantle   the layer of solid rock between Earth's crust and core

manto   capa de roca sólida entre la corteza y el centro de la Tierra

mass   the amount of matter in an object

masa   cantidad de materia en un objeto

mass number   the total number of neutrons and protons in an atom (also known as nucleon number)

número de masa   número total de neutrones y protones en un átomo (también conocido como número másico)

Mass-energy equivalence   the relationship that mass is a special form of energy

equivalencia entre la masa y la energía   relación en la que la masa es una forma especial de energía

matter   material that has mass and takes up some amount of space

materia   material que tiene masa y ocupa espacio

measurement   the collection of data (such as mass, volume, temperature, etc.) described by a standardized unit (such as kilogram, liter, degrees Celsius)

mediciones   conjunto de datos (como masa, volumen, temperatura, etc.) descritos en unidades estandarizadas (como kilogramo, litro, grados Celsius)

metal   a shiny, dense substance that easily conducts heat and electricity

metal   sustancia brillante y densa que conduce fácilmente el calor y la electricidad

metals   elements that give up electrons easily, are malleable and ductile, and are good electrical conductors

metales   elementos que ceden electrones con facilidad, son maleables y dúctiles, y son buenos conductores eléctricos

meteor   a streak of light in the sky that forms when a piece of rock from space burns up in Earth's atmosphere (related term: shooting star)

meteoro   reflejo de luz en el cielo que se forma cuando un trozo de roca del espacio se quema en la atmósfera de la Tierra (palabra relacionada: estrella fugaz)

meteorite   a piece of rock or metal from space that strikes Earth's surface

meteorito   trozo de roca o metal del espacio que golpea la superficie de la Tierra

mid-ocean ridge   an oceanic rift zone that consists of long mountain chains with a central rift valley; divergent boundary

dorsales centro-oceánicas   zona dorsal centro-oceánica que consta de largas cadenas montañosas con una fosa tectónica central; límite divergente

Milky Way galaxy   the galaxy containing the sun and its solar system, along with millions of other stars in a spiraling pattern, part of which can be seen as a band of "milky" diffuse light across the night sky

galaxia Vía Láctea   galaxia en la que se encuentra el sol y su sistema solar, junto con millones de otras estrellas en un patrón espiral, parte de la cual es visible como una banda de difusa luz "lechosa" en el cielo nocturno

mineral   a naturally occurring, inorganic solid with a definite chemical composition and characteristic crystalline structure

mineral   sólido inorgánico natural con una composición química definida y una estructura cristalina característica

modified Mercalli intensity scale   the scale with values from I to XII used to characterize earthquakes based on a subjective measurement of the amount and type of damage they cause, including physical, economic, and widespread emotional damage

escala de intensidad Mercalli modificada   escala con valores de I a XII que se usa para clasificar los terremotos según una medición subjetiva de la cantidad y tipo de daños que producen, incluyendo daños físicos, económicos y emocional generalizado

molecule   a group of atoms held together by chemical bonds

molécula   grupo de átomos unidos por enlaces químicos

momentum   a quantity of how much inertia a dynamic object has

motion   a change in the position of an object compared to another object (related term: move, movement)

momento   cantidad de cuánta inercia tiene un objeto dinámico

movimiento   cambio en la posición de un objeto en comparación con otro objeto (palabra relacionada: mover, desplazamiento)

N

negative charge   a charge of the same sign as that of an electron, often due to a surplus of electrons

carga negativa   carga del mismo signo que la de un electrón, con frecuencia se debe a un exceso de electrones

net force   the resulting force determined by combining all of the forces acting on an object

fuerza neta   fuerza resultante determinada por la combinación de todas las fuerzas que actúan sobre un objeto

neutrino   a subatomic particle with no electric charge and which travels at nearly the speed of light

neutrino   partícula subatómica sin carga eléctrica que viaja a casi la velocidad de la luz

neutron   a subatomic particle with no electric charge that is located within the nucleus of the atom and has a mass approximately equal to 1 amu

neutrón   partícula subatómica sin carga eléctrica que se encuentra dentro del núcleo de un átomo y tiene una masa aproximadamente igual a 1 uma

neutron star   a small-diameter, very dense star composed of neutrons held together by gravity

estrella de neutrones   estrella muy densa, de pequeño diámetro y compuesta por neutrones que se mantienen unidos por la gravedad

Newton's law of universal gravitation   the law that states that the magnitude of the gravitational force increases as the mass of the two objects increases and decreases as the distance between the objects increases

ley de la gravitación universal de Newton ley que establece que la magnitud de la fuerza gravitacional aumenta cuando la masa de los objetos aumenta y disminuye cuando la distancia entre los objetos aumenta

Newton's laws   the three fundamental laws Isaac Newton discovered governing the motion of objects

Leyes de Newton   las tres leyes fundamentales que Isaac Newton descubrió sobre el movimiento de los objetos

non-inertial frame of reference   coordinate system and set of points that depend on the location and orientation of objects in space and time

marco de referencia no inercial   sistema de coordenadas y conjunto de puntos que dependen de la ubicación y orientación de los objetos en el espacio y el tiempo

normal fault   an inclined fault in which the hanging wall slips downward relative to the footwall

falla normal   falla inclinada en la cual el bloque colgante (techo) se desplaza hacia abajo respecto al bloque yacente (piso)

nuclear fission   a reaction where the nucleus of an atom splits.

fisión nuclear   reacción el la cual el núcleo de un átomo se divide

nuclear fission   a nuclear reaction in which the nuclei of isotopes of certain heavy elements, such as uranium and plutonium, split and are divided into smaller atoms

fisión nuclear   reacción nuclear en la cual el núcleo de isótopos de ciertos elementos pesados, como el uranio y el plutonio, se separan y se dividen en átomos más pequeños

nuclear fusion   a reaction where two or more nuclei of atoms combine to form a single nucleus.

fusión nuclear   reacción en la cual dos o más núcleos de átomos se combinan para formar un solo núcleo

nuclear reaction   a reaction that occurs in the nucleus of an atom

reacción nuclear   reacción que ocurre en el núcleo de un átomo

nuclear reactor   a device where nuclear reactions are initiated and controlled

reactor nuclear   dispositivo en el cual se inician y controlan reacciones nucleares

nucleosynthesis   a system of nuclear reactions which occur in stars through which the atomic nuclei of all of the chemical elements are formed

nucleosíntesis   sistema nuclear de reacciones que ocurren en las estrellas y mediante las cuales se forman los núcleos atómicos de todos los elementos químicos

nucleus (atom)   the core of an atom where most of the mass of an atom exists; contains protons and neutrons

núcleo (del átomo)   el núcleo o centro de un átomo es donde está la mayor cantidad de masa del átomo; contiene protones y neutrones

O

observation   the act of watching over something or taking notice; in science, observations are carefully recorded as part of the scientific process

observación   acción de observar, vigilar o prestar atención a algo; en ciencia, las observaciones se registran detalladamente como parte del proceso científico

oceanic crust   the portion of Earth's crust that makes up the ocean floor and is generally denser and thinner than continental crust

corteza oceánica   parte de la corteza terrestre que conforma el fondo del océano y que por lo general es más densa y más fina que la corteza continental

open system   a system that can exchange matter and energy with outside sources

sistema abierto   sistema que puede intercambiar materia y energía con fuentes del exterior

orbit   the circular or elliptical path of an object as it revolves around another object

órbita   trayectoria circular o elíptica de un objeto que gira alrededor de otro

outer core   the liquid outer portion of Earth's core, composed primarily of iron and nickel

núcleo externo   parte exterior, líquida, del núcleo de la Tierra, compuesto principalmente por hierro y níquel

P

P wave   compressional seismic waves generated by earthquakes

ondas P   ondas sísmicas de compresión generadas por los terremotos

parent isotope   a radioactive isotope that changes into different isotopes through radioactive decay

isótopo padre (o precursor)   isótopo radioactivo que se transforma en diferentes isótopos mediante desintegración radiactiva

perihelion   the point in the orbit of a solar system body when it is closest to the sun

perihelio   punto en la órbita de un cuerpo de un sistema solar en el que se halla más cerca del sol

periodic table   a chart that scientists use to organize and classify all the different elements

tabla periódica   tabla que usan los científicos para organizar y clasificar todos los elementos

phase (lunar)   a description of the amount of illumination of the moon as seen from Earth at different points in its cycle

fase (lunar)   descripción de la cantidad de iluminación de la luna vista desde la Tierra en diferentes momentos de su ciclo

photoelectric effect   a current flows through a substance when light hits its surface; also known as the Hertz effect

efecto fotoeléctrico   corriente que fluye a través de una sustancia cuando la luz incide sobre su superficie; también se conoce como efecto de Hertz

photon   a bundle or quantum of electromagnetic energy that demonstrates particle-like behavior

fotón   haz o cuanto de energía electromagnética que muestra un comportamiento similar al de una partícula

photovoltaic effect   production of electric current in certain materials upon exposure to light

efecto fotovoltaico   producción de una corriente eléctrica en determinados materiales debida a la exposición a la luz

physical property   a characteristic that can be observed (intensive), such as texture, color, odor, melting point, boiling point, density, or measured (extensive) such as mass, length, volume, that is used to describe matter and can be observed or measured without changing its composition

propiedad física   característica que se usa para describir la materia y que puede observarse (intensiva) o medirse (extensiva) sin cambiar su composición; la textura, el color, el olor, el punto de fusión, el punto de ebullición y la densidad son características intensivas; la masa, la longitud y el volumen son características extensivas

GLOSSARY

planetary nebula   a large cloud of gas and dust in outer space ejected by an aging star near the end of its life cycle

nebulosa planetaria   gran nube de gas y polvo en el espacio exterior emitida por una estrella que está envejeciendo y se encuentra cerca del final de su ciclo de vida

plasma   A gas-like state of matter in which most of the particles are charged ions.

plasma   estado de la materia semejante al gas en el cual la mayoría de las partículas son iones cargados.

plate tectonics   the theory that describes the movement and recycling of segments of Earth's crust, called tectonic plates

tectónica de placas   teoría que describe el movimiento y reciclaje de fragmentos de corteza terrestre, llamados placas tectónicas

polarization   process of transforming unpolarized light (waves in multiple planes) to polarized light (waves in a single plane)

polarización   proceso de transformación de luz no polarizada (ondas en planos múltiples) en luz polarizada (ondas en un solo plano)

positive charge   a charge of the same sign as that of a proton, often due to a deficit of electrons

carga positiva   carga del mismo signo que la de un protón, con frecuencia se debe a un déficit de electrones

potential energy   the amount of energy that is stored in an object; energy that an object has because of its position relative to other objects

energía potencial   cantidad de energía almacenada en un objeto; energía que tiene un objeto por su posición respecto a otros objetos

potential energy   energy stored due to position or configuration

energía potencial   energía almacenada debido a la posición o configuración

power   the ratio of the amount of work done per unit of time, or the rate at which energy is transferred or transformed

potencia   relación de la cantidad de trabajo realizado por unidad de tiempo, o velocidad o ritmo en el que la energía se transfiere o se transforma

pressure   force exerted per unit area by many particles of a gas randomly striking the walls of its container

presión   fuerza ejercida por unidad de área por muchas partículas de un gas que chocan aleatoriamente contra las paredes del recipiente que lo contiene

proton   a subatomic particle with a positive charge that is located in the nucleus of an atom and has a mass of approximately 1 amu

protón   partícula subatómica con carga eléctrica positiva que se encuentra dentro del núcleo de un átomo y tiene una masa aproximada de 1 uma

pulsar   a celestial object, thought to be a rapidly rotating neutron star, which emits regular pulses of radio waves

pulsar   objeto celeste, que se cree que es una estrella de neutrones que gira rápidamente; emite pulsos regulares de ondas de radio

488 Discovery Education

Q

quantum   a discrete amount of energy proportional to the frequency of the radiation it represents (plural: quanta)

cuanto   cantidad discreta de energía proporcional a la frecuencia de la radiación que representa

quantum mechanics   a description of the dual particle-wave behavior and interactions of energy and matter; also known as quantum physics or quantum theory

mecánica cuántica   descripción del comportamiento dual onda-partícula y las interacciones de la energía y la materia; también se conoce como física cuántica o teoría cuántica

quark   a class of subatomic particles that are the building blocks of protons and neutrons

quark   tipo de partícula subatómica que constituye la base de los protones y neutrones

R

radiation   a process by which energetic electromagnetic waves move from one place to another

radiación   proceso por el cual las ondas energéticas electromagnéticas se desplazan de un lugar a otro

radio wave   a type of electromagnetic radiation with long wavelength and low energy; located next to microwaves on the electromagnetic spectrum

onda de radio   tipo de radiación electromagnética con una longitud de onda larga y baja energía; en el espectro magnético se encuentra cerca de las microondas

radioactive decay   a process by which an unstable atom loses energy by emitting ionized particles over a period of time

desintegración radiactiva   proceso por el cual un átomo inestable pierde energía al emitir partículas ionizadas durante un periodo de tiempo

radioactive isotope   an isotope with an unstable nucleus, which can spontaneously decay

isótopo radiactivo   isótopo con un núcleo inestable, el cual puede desintegrarse espontáneamente

radioactivity   the spontaneous emission of radiation, which is the process in which unstable atoms break down into smaller atoms, releasing energy

radiactividad   emisión de radiación espontánea, que es el proceso en el cual un átomo inestable se divide en átomos más pequeños y libera energía

real image   figure or likeness resulting from convergence of light rays from an object

imagen real   figura o retrato que resulta de la convergencia de los rayos de luz sobre un objeto

red shift As an object in space moves away from an observer, the wavelengths of light waves produced by the object are lengthened. Because red is among the longest wavelengths of visible light, astronomers call this phenomenon a "red shift."

corrimiento al rojo Cuando un objeto en el espacio se mueve alejándose de un observador, las longitudes de onda de las ondas luminosas que el objeto produce se alargan. Como el rojo se encuentra entre las longitudes de onda más largas de la luz visible, los astrónomos llaman a este fenómeno "corrimiento al rojo".

reduction a decrease in the oxidation state of an atom or molecule due to the gain of electrons

reducción disminución en el estado de oxidación de un átomo o una molécula debido a la ganancia de electrones

reflection a change in the direction of a wave when it hits a barrier and bounces back

reflexión cambio en la dirección de una onda cuando incide en una barrera y rebota hacia atrás

refraction a change in the direction and velocity which occurs when a seismic or electromagnetic wave travels from one material into another of different density, state, or elasticity

refracción cambio en la dirección y velocidad que se produce cuando una onda sísmica o una onda electromagnética pasan de un material a otro que tiene diferente densidad, estado o elasticidad.

refractive index ratio of speed of light in a vacuum to speed of light in a given substance

índice de refracción razón de la velocidad de la luz en un vació en relación con la velocidad de la luz en una sustancia dada

relative age the dating of events based solely upon the order in which they occurred

edad relativa datación de eventos basada solo en el orden en el que ocurrieron

remote sensing making observations of a body without making physical contact

detección remota hecho de realizar observaciones de un cuerpo sin que exista contacto físico con él

resistance a measure of the degree to which a material tries to prevent charge from flowing through it

resistencia medida del grado al cual un material intenta evitar una carga que fluye a través de él

resonance one object vibrating at the same frequency as another object forces the second object into vibrational motion

resonancia un objeto que vibra a la misma frecuencia que otro induce un movimiento de vibración en el segundo

reverse fault a fault in which the hanging wall block has moved upward relative to the footwall block

falla inversa falla en la cual el bloque colgante (techo) se ha desplazado hacia arriba respecto al bloque yacente (piso)

reversible process changes in properties that a system undergoes from an initial state to a final state that can be completely restored back to the initial state

proceso reversible cambios en las propiedades que experimenta un sistema desde un estado inicial hasta un estado final que puede revertirse por completo al estado inicial

revolution the orbiting of an object around another object

revolución movimiento por el cual un objeto gira alrededor de otro describiendo una órbita completa

revolve to move around another object along a circular path, as in an orbit (related word: revolution)

girar dar vueltas en torno a otro objeto a lo largo de una trayectoria circular, como en una órbita (palabra relacionada: revolución)

Richter scale a logarithmic scale used to measure the magnitude of an earthquake; commonly ranges from 1 to 10

escala de Richter escala logarítmica que se usa para medir la magnitud de un terremoto; por lo general abarca del 1 al 10

rock cycle a model describing the transformations of rocks from one major rock type to another

ciclo de las rocas modelo que describe las transformaciones de las rocas desde un tipo de roca principal a otro

rotate turning around on an axis; spinning (related word: rotation)

rotar girar sobre un eje; dar vueltas (palabra relacionada: rotación)

rotation the spinning of a celestial body, such as a planet, around an axis

rotación giro de un cuerpo celeste, como un planeta, alrededor de un eje

S

S wave transverse seismic waves generated by earthquakes; also called shear waves or secondary waves

onda S ondas sísmicas transversales generadas por terremotos; también se denominan ondas de cizalla u ondas secundarias

satellite any object that orbits another object

satélite cualquier objeto que orbita alrededor de otro objeto

scalar a quantity that is measured by its magnitude (amount) but has no direction

escalar cantidad que se mide según su magnitud (cantidad), pero no tiene dirección

seafloor spreading the process by which new oceanic lithosphere forms at mid-ocean ridges as tectonic plates pull away from each other

expansión del fondo oceánico proceso por el cual se forma nueva litosfera oceánica en las dorsales centro-oceánicas a medida que las placas tectónicas se separan una de otra

sedimentary   a word describing a rock or layer of rocks formed by the lithification of transported or precipitated particles

sedimentario   término que describe una roca o una capa de rocas formadas por la litificación de partículas transportadas o precipitadas

seismic wave   waves of energy that travel through Earth's interior due to an earthquake, other tectonic forces, or an explosion

onda sísmica   ondas de energía que viajan a través del interior de la Tierra debido a un terremoto, otras fuerzas tectónicas o una explosión

seismogram   the visual record produced by a seismograph, showing the arrival times and magnitudes of various seismic waves

sismograma   informe visual producido por un sismógrafo, que muestra los momentos de llegada y las magnitudes de varias ondas sísmicas

seismograph   an instrument used to detect and measure earthquake waves and other ground vibrations

sismógrafo   instrumento que se usa para detectar y medir ondas de terremotos y otras vibraciones del suelo

seismology   the study of seismic waves, earthquakes, and other ground vibrations

sismología   estudio de las ondas sísmicas, los terremotos y otras vibraciones del suelo

semiconductor   a material that has a conductivity that is between that of an insulator and a conductor; a material that conducts electricity under some conditions and not others

semiconductor   material que tiene una conductividad que se encuentra entre la de un aislante y la de un conductor; material que conduce electricidad bajo ciertas condiciones y no en otras

shadow zone   the boundaries outside of which seismic waves are not recorded

zona de sombra   límites fuera de los cuales no se registran las ondas sísmicas

shear stress   force applied to rock in two opposing directions parallel to a surface such as a fault plane

tensión tangencial   fuerza aplicada a la roca en dos direcciones opuestas paralelas a la superficie, como en un plano de falla

silicate   a mineral that contains covalently bonded silicon and oxygen

silicato   mineral que contiene sílice y oxígeno unidos por un enlace covalente

solar eclipse   the temporary blockage of sunlight by the moon as it travels between Earth and the sun

eclipse solar   bloqueo temporal de la luz del sol por parte de la luna cuando se desplaza entre la Tierra y el sol

solar system   a system of objects that revolve around a star such as the sun

sistema solar   sistema de objetos que giran alrededor de una estrella como el sol

solstice   the twice-a-year occurrence during which the sun appears at the highest point in the sky as seen from the North or South pole

solsticio   situación que se produce dos veces al año durante la cual el sol está en el punto más alto en el cielo, visto desde los polos Norte y Sur

speed the rate at which distance is traveled	**rapidez** tasa a la que se recorre una distancia
speed of light (c) the velocity of light in a vacuum, measured as approximately 300,000,000 meters per second	**velocidad de la luz (c)** la velocidad de propagación de la luz en el vacío es aproximadamente de 300,000,000 metros por segundo
star a massive ball of gas in outer space that gives off heat, light, and other forms of radiation	**estrella** gran bola de gas en el espacio exterior que emite calor, luz y otras formas de radiación
state of matter one of the four states in which matter exists – solid, liquid, gas or plasma	**estado de la materia** uno de los cuatro estados en los cuales existe la materia: sólido, líquido, gaseoso o plasma
static electricity the accumulation of electrical charges on a surface	**electricidad estática** acumulación de cargas eléctricas en una superficie
static friction a resistive force between stationary objects due to the roughness of the two surfaces in contact	**fricción estática** fuerza de resistencia entre objetos estacionarios debido a la rugosidad de las dos superficies en contacto
steady state theory a theory, no longer widely accepted, which states that the universe is and has always been constant in its average density	**teoría del estado estacionario** teoría, actualmente no aceptada por muchos, que establece que la densidad promedio del universo es y siempre ha sido constante
strain deformation of a geologic structure caused by stress	**deformación (strain)** deformación de una estructura geológica originada por la tensión
stress force that acts on rocks to cause deformation by tension, compression, or shear	**tensión** fuerza que actúa sobre las rocas y causa deformación por tensión, comprensión o tensión tangencial
strike-slip fault a fault along which blocks on opposite sides of the fault plane slide horizontally past one another in opposite directions	**falla de rumbo** falla a lo largo de la cual los bloques de lados opuestos del plano de falla se deslizan horizontalmente una junto a otra en direcciones opuestas
strong nuclear force the force that holds the nucleus of atoms together	**interacción nuclear fuerte** fuerza que mantiene juntos los átomos del núcleo
subatomic of or relating to something having dimensions smaller than that of an atom	**subatómico** perteneciente a o relacionado con algo que tiene dimensiones más pequeñas que las de un átomo

subduction   the sinking of an oceanic plate beneath a plate of lesser density at a convergent boundary

subducción   hundimiento de una placa oceánica bajo una placa de menor densidad en un límite convergente

superconductor   a material that conducts electricity with zero resistance, usually at very low temperatures

superconductor   material que conduce la electricidad con una resistencia cero, por lo general a temperaturas muy bajas

supergiant star   a star that is larger, brighter, and more massive than a giant star, being thousands of times brighter than the sun and having a relatively short lifespan

estrella supergigante   estrella que es más grande, más brillante y tiene más masa que una estrella gigante; es miles de veces más brillante que el sol y tiene una vida relativamente corta

surface wave   a seismic wave which travels along or just below Earth's surface

onda superficial   onda sísmica que viaja por la superficie de la Tierra o justo por debajo de ella

T

the laws of thermodynamics   a set of laws that describe fundamental physical properties including temperature, energy, and entropy

leyes de la termodinámica   conjunto de leyes que describen las propiedades físicas fundamentales entre las que se incluyen temperatura, energía y entropía

theory   a set of principles that explain a group of phenomena or facts

teoría   conjunto de principios que explican un grupo de fenómenos o hechos

thermal energy   energy in the form of heat

energía térmica   energía en forma de calor

thrust fault   a type of reverse fault with a fault plane that dips less than 45

falla de cabalgamiento   tipo de falla inversa con un plano de inclinación menor de 45 grados

tide   the regular fluctuation of sea water driven by the gravitational pull of the moon and sun on Earth's oceans and other large bodies of water

marea   fluctuación regular del agua del mar originada por la atracción gravitacional de la luna y el sol sobre los océanos de la Tierra y otros grandes cuerpos de agua

transform boundary   a tectonic plate boundary along which plates slide horizontally past one another in opposite directions

límite transformante   límite de placas tectónicas a lo largo de la cual las placas se deslizan horizontalmente una junto a otra en direcciones opuestas

transistor   an electronic component consisting of three terminals, the current through two of the terminals is controlled by the voltage or current applied to the third

transistor   componente electrónico que consta de tres terminales, la corriente que pasa a través de dos de los terminales está controlada por el voltaje o corriente que se aplica al tercero

transmutation the process of changing one nucleus into another

transmutación proceso por el que un núcleo se transforma en otro

transverse waves a wave that occurs when the particles of a medium are displaced perpendicularly to the direction of the wave

onda transversal onda que se produce cuando las partículas de un medio se mueven perpendicularmente a la dirección de la onda

U

uniform circular motion motion that is both circular and at constant speed

movimiento circular uniforme movimiento que tiene una trayectoria circular y una velocidad constante

V

vector a quantity with components of both magnitude and direction

vector cantidad con componente de magnitud y dirección

velocity a vector quantity that indicates both the rate at which displacement changes and the direction of motion

velocidad cantidad vectorial que indica la tasa a la que cambian el desplazamiento y la dirección del movimiento

voltage a measure of the electrical potential difference between two points

voltaje medida de la diferencia de potencial eléctrico entre dos puntos

W

wave a disturbance caused by a vibration that propagates through space and time

onda perturbación producida por una vibración que se propaga a través del espacio y del tiempo

wave period the amount of time required for two successive wave crests to pass a fixed point in space; the reciprocal of frequency

periodo de onda cantidad de tiempo necesario para que dos crestas de ondas sucesivas pasen por un punto fijo en el espacio; recíproco de frecuencia

wave speed the speed at which a wave travels, calculated by the frequency multiplied by the wavelength

velocidad de onda velocidad a la que viaja una onda, se calcula multiplicando la frecuencia por la longitud de onda

wavelength the distance between one peak and the next in a wave, or between one trough and the next

longitud de onda distancia entre una cresta de una onda y la siguiente, o entre un valle y el siguiente

weak nuclear force the force responsible for radioactive decay

interacción nuclear débil fuerza responsable de la desintegración radiactiva

weathering   the physical or chemical breakdown of rocks and minerals into smaller pieces or aqueous solutions on Earth's surface

meteorización   desintegración física o química de rocas y minerales en trozos más pequeños o en soluciones acuosas en la superficie de la Tierra

---

white dwarf   a relatively small, dense star at the end of its life cycle, which generates little or no energy and has contracted to its densest state

enana blanca   estrella pequeña, relativamente densa, que está al final de su ciclo de vida y que genera poca energía o ninguna y que se contrajo a su estado más denso

---

work   the change in a system's kinetic energy due to being acted on by a force

trabajo   cambio en la energía cinética de un sistema debido a la actuación de una fuerza sobre él

X

x-ray   a form of short-wavelength, high-energy electromagnetic radiation

rayos X   forma de longitud de onda corta, radiación electromagnética de alta energía

A

Absolute age, 327
Absolute magnitude, 464
Absolute zero, 262
Absorption spectroscopy, 119
Absorption spectrum, of stars, 466–467
Acceleration
  action/reaction forces and, 25–26
  average, 58–59
  of charged particles, 280
  defined, 58
  due to gravity, 66, 163
  effects of perpendicular force on, 42–43
  force as cause of, 20–21, 29
  mass and, 21, 29
  motion, speed, and, 11
  Newton's third law and, 27
  in one dimension, 74–75
  position, velocity, and, 53–59, 74–77, 79–80
  for projectiles, 64, 65, 67
  for satellites in orbit, 168
  in two dimensions, 76–77
  uniform, 59
  universal gravitation and, 165, 166
  vector quantities for, 34
  from velocity vs. time graph, 62–63
Action forces, 23–28
  canceling out of, 26–28
  identifying, 23–25
  and mass, 25–26
Addition of vector quantities, 35–41
AEC (Atomic Energy Commission), 136
Aerospace engineering
  Newton's laws of motion in, 30
  satellites in, 200–201, 472
  superfast commercial aircraft in, 73

Age

Age
  absolute, 327
  of Earth, 334–336, 447
Airbags, automobile, 86, 103
Air conditioners, 260, 263–264
Airplanes
  electrostatic charge in, 146
  flight paths of, 44–45
  speed of, 73
Air resistance, 71
Air track, 100
Alpha decay, 308–309
Alpha particles, 308, 313, 316
Amplitude
  defined, 349
  of electromagnetic vs. mechanical waves, 356, 364
  and interference, 372
Antimatter, 450
Aphelion, 192
Apparent magnitude, 464, 467
Applied forces, electric and, 140–142
Architecture
  energy efficiency in, 265–266
  and seismic building codes, 433–434
Asteroids, 180–181
Astronomy, 12, 285
Astrophysics, 470
Athletes
  conservation of momentum for, 104–105
  motion of, 58
Atomic bomb, 130, 132–133
Atomic Energy Commission (AEC), 136
Atomic model, 328
Atomic nucleus
  strong nuclear force in, 115, 307–308
  subatomic particles in, 328
Atomic number, 328, 462
Atomic spectroscopy, 119–120

Atoms

Atoms
  energy in, 213–214
  identifying, 118–120
  nuclear forces in, 115, 307–308
  radioactive decay of, 309
  in radiometric dating, 328
Attractive force
  in atomic nuclei, 307–308
  Coulomb's law and, 275–279
  mass, distance, and, 156–157
Aurora borealis, 271
Average acceleration, 58–59
Average speed, 51–53, 57
Average velocity, 56, 60–61
Axes, 5, 187

B

Bands, wavelength, 357–361
Barycenter, 181, 190
Baseball, kinetic energy and velocity of, 215
Batteries, 210–211, 243
Beta decay, 129, 309
Big bang theory, 378, 448–455
Billiards, 42–43, 90–93
Birds, on electrical wires, 289
Black dwarfs, 464
Black holes, 169, 465
Blueshift, 368, 452, 467
Bobsledding, 15, 22
Bouncing ball, energy for, 228–230
Bowling, 227, 238
Bracketing method, 338
Brahe, Tycho, 182
British thermal unit (Btu), 229
Building codes, seismic, 433–434
Bullet train, 52
Bumper car collisions, 94–96

C

California, USS, 130
Cameras, laparoscopic, 402
Cancer
  and electromagnetic radiation, 360–361, 374
  treatment, 133, 315

Carbon, isotopes of, 307, 329

Carbon-14 isotope
radioactive decay of, 332
radiometric dating with, 311–312, 333

Car collisions, 86, 103

Carnot engines, 262

Center of gravity, 159–162, 173–176

Center of mass, 158–159, 161–162

Centripetal force, 42

Chain reaction, 314

Charge
and electric force, 142–143
electrostatic, 146–147, 276–277
on insulators, 297–298
negative, 140–141, 145
positive, 140–141

Charged particles
acceleration of, 280
electric potential energy of, 237–238

Cheetah, evolution of, 50

Chemical potential energy
in batteries, 243
described, 210
energy conversions involving, 219–220
from food, 221
from fossil fuel combustion, 231–232

Classical mechanics, 122

Clock, pendulum of, 239

Closed systems
momentum in, 88, 103
thermodynamics in, 256–257

CMB radiation. See Cosmic microwave background radiation

CMEs (coronal mass ejections), 461

Collisions
bumper car, 94–96
car, 86, 103
elastic, 92–99
football tackle, 96–99

inelastic, 93–99
in space, 180–181

Color
and Doppler effect, 368
and reflection, 369, 390, 391
and refraction, 370, 402
of stars, 464, 466, 467
and wavelength of light, 119, 360, 452

Communication plans, earthquake, 435

Compasses, 278

Component vectors, 39–41

Compression, at reverse faults, 429

Compressional (longitudinal) waves, 347, 355, 356, 411

Compton, Arthur, 273

Compton effect, 273

Computer chips, 299, 404

Computer repair technicians, 147

Concave lenses, 397, 404

Concave mirrors, 394, 398

Conduction, 213

Conductivity, 290, 292

Conductors, 288–302
and birds on electrical wires, 289
electric charge on, 297
and Faraday's law, 302–303
insulators, semiconductors, and superconductors vs., 290–291
magnetic induction and electric current in, 294–296
materials for, 292–293
STEM in Action, 299–301

Conservation of energy, 226–251
in conversion of kinetic and potential energy, 216, 217, 234–239
in elastic and inelastic collisions, 92–99
elastic potential energy, 249
electric potential energy, 250
and first law of thermodynamics, 259

gravitational potential energy, 232–234, 248
kinetic energy, 227, 234–239, 251
law of, 228–232, 239–242
measuring energy using, 246–247
STEM in Action, 243–245
and using energy, 227

Conservation of Energy and Energy Transfer, 226, 252, 288

Conservation of momentum, 88–101
defined, 88–90
demonstrating, 100–101
in elastic and inelastic collisions, 92–99
sample problem, 90–92
STEM in Action, 104–105

Constant speed, 51–53, 78

Contact forces, electric and, 140–142

Continental crust, 426

Convection, 214

Convergent boundary, 429

Convex lenses, 396–401, 404

Convex mirrors, 395

Cooling devices, 263–265

Coordinate systems, 3–5

Copper wiring, 293

Core, Earth's, 335, 418–419

Coronal mass ejections (CMEs), 461

Cosmic microwave background (CMB) radiation
characteristics of, 378
in cosmology, 457
as evidence for big bang theory, 450–451, 455

Cosmology, 455–457

Coulomb, Charles-Augustin de, 113, 142

Coulomb's law, 286–287
and attractive/repulsive forces, 275–277
electromagnetic force in, 113
and strength of electric force, 142–144, 148–149

Crane, net force applied by, 30
Craters, impact, 180
Crust, Earth's, 426, 431
Curie, Marie, 134
Curie, Pierre, 134
Curiosity rover, 8
Current, electric. See Electric
   current
Curved mirrors, 391, 394–395

D
Dance, momentum in, 105
Dark matter, 456
Daughter isotopes, 308, 331–332
Decay, radioactive. See
   Radioactive decay
Decay series, 311
Defining and Delimiting
   Engineering Problems, 84
Definitions of Energy, 205, 226
Developing Possible Solutions,
   226, 342, 388
Diffraction, 357, 372
Diffuse reflection, 393
Digitization, 375
Direction of motion,
   perpendicular force and,
   42–43
Directly proportional (term), 7
Direct orbits, 179
Disaster plans, 435, 437
Displacement
  determining, 53–54
  distance vs., 44–45, 55
  graphs of time vs., 81–82
  from velocity vs. time graph, 63
Distance
  center of gravity and, 160
  Coulomb's law and, 275
  displacement vs., 44–45, 55
  elastic potential energy
   and, 235
  electrical force and, 274
  electric force and, 142–143
  gravitational field and, 155–156
  gravitational force and, 153
  inclined planes and, 17
  in law of universal gravitation, 7

mass, force of attraction and,
   156–157
mass, gravity and, 185–186
motion sensors' measurement
   of, 69
in Newton's law of universal
   gravitation, 154, 156–157,
   162, 166
of projectiles, 66, 72
scalar quantities for, 34
speed and, 51–53, 78–80
with uniform acceleration, 59
Divergent boundary, 428
Doppler effect, 367–368,
   378, 452
Drag force, 45
Drag racing, 29
Draw-down, 439

E
Earth
  age of, 334–336, 447
  equinox and solstice on,
   192–194
  as frame of reference, 6, 12
  gravitational force on, 112, 153
  gravitational potential energy
   near surface of, 232–234
  gravity for objects near
   surface of, 162–164
  gravity's effects on, 152
  investigating past of, 326
  perihelion and aphelion in
   orbit of, 191–192
  planetary motion of, 181
  studying interior of, 418–419
  sun's energy on, 460
  tides on, 189–191
  universe and future of, 457
Earth and the Solar System, 177
Earth Materials and Systems, 408
Earthquake hazard map,
   431–432
Earthquakes, 424–444
  damage due to, 409, 425
  elastic rebound theory, 430
  fault types, 428–430
  hazards of, 431–434

intensity vs. magnitude of,
   415–417
preparing for, 434–436
safety during, 437
seismic waves as cause of, 409
STEM in Action, 442–444
S waves in, 412
and tectonic plate motion,
   426–427
and tsunamis, 438–441
wave characteristics and, 379
Eclipses, 195–197
Einstein, Albert
  mass–energy conversion
   equation, 130
  photoelectric effect
   explanation, 272, 273
  photon's energy calculation,
   376
  theory of general relativity,
   113, 117, 122, 123, 169, 455
  theory of special relativity, 122
Elastic collisions, 92–99
  described, 92
  sample problems, 94–99
  solving problems with, 93–94
Elastic potential energy, 249
  and conservation of energy
   for a spring, 241–242
  defined, 209, 232
  transformation of kinetic
   energy and, 234–235
Elastic rebound theory, 430
Electrical conductivity, 290, 292
Electrical energy
  from fuel cells, 222
  from generators, 284
  in human body, 221
  from hydroelectric power
   plants, 244–245
  from wind energy, 207, 219, 220
Electrical wires, birds on, 289
Electric charge, on insulators,
   297–298
Electric current
  in conductors, 290, 292,
   294–297
  in electricity, 282

Electric current (*Cont.*)
  and electric potential energy, 211
  and electromagnetic force,
    113–114, 283
  in generators and motors, 284
  and magnetic forces, 278–279
  and magnetic induction, 280,
    281, 294
  and magnetism, 282
  and photoelectric effect, 272
Electric fields
  and electrical forces, 274
  and electromagnetism,
    281–283
  energy storage in, 211–212
  generating electromagnetic
    waves with, 280
  and magnetic fields, 278–279
Electric forces, 138–149
  applications of, 274–275
  and contact forces, 140–142
  in force fields, 139
  STEM in Action, 145–147
  strength of, 142–144, 148–149
Electricity, 269–287
  applications of electric forces,
    274–275
  Coulomb's law, 275–277,
    286–287
  and electromagnetism,
    281–283
  magnetism's interactions
    with, 271
  from nuclear power, 131–132,
    135–136
  photoelectric effect, 272–273
  STEM in Action, 284–285
Electric motors, 294
Electric potential energy, 250
  examples of, 210–211
  sample problems with,
    236–238
Electromagnetic force, 113–114
Electromagnetic radiation
  energy of, 362–363, 380–381
  and expansion of universe, 448
  and spectrum, 357–358
  wave-particle duality of, 357

Electromagnetic Radiation,
    269, 342, 445, 458
Electromagnetic spectrum, 281
  and radiation, 357–358
  in study of universe, 447
  wavelength bands of, 357–361
Electromagnetic waves
  energy stored in, 211–212, 283
  generating, 280–281
  mechanical vs., 355–357
  wave speed and media for, 369
Electromagnetism, 280–283, 285
Electromagnets, 279
Electromotive force (EMF), 295
Electrons
  charge on, 140–141
  identifying atoms based on,
    118–119
  and ions, 111
  mass of, 328
  in photoelectric effect, 272
  and strong nuclear force, 128
Electrostatic charge, 146–147,
    276–277
Electrostatic forces
  and Coulomb's law, 276–277
  and Newton's third law, 28
Electrostatic generators, 146
Elements
  isotopes of, 306–307 (*See
    also* Isotopes)
  periodic table of, 328
  from stars, 454, 462
  transmutation of, 309
Ellipses, 182–183
Emergency kit, 436
Emergency plans, 434
EMF (electromotive force), 295
Emission, of radiation, 330
Emission spectroscopy, 120
Energy, 205–225. *See also*
    Conservation of energy;
    specific types
  conversions between types
    of, 216–221, 225
  and Coulomb's law, 276
  of electromagnetic radiation,
    362–363, 380–381

  of electromagnetic waves, 283
  in fields, 211
  from fossil fuels, 231–232
  mass, velocity, and, 214–216,
    223–224
  matter and, 109–110
  measuring, 229–230,
    246–247
  of mechanical waves,
    363–367, 386–387
  in nuclear fusion and fission,
    129–130
  in particles, 213–214
  and photoelectric effect, 272
  power, intensity of waves,
    and, 363–367
  from radioactive decay, 309
  scalar quantities for, 34
  from stars, 460–461
  STEM in Action, 221–222
  in systems, 256–258
  transfer of, in waves, 346–347
  using, 227
  work or heat and transfer of,
    255–256
Energy efficiency, 265–266
Energy in Chemical Processes,
    205, 252, 269, 342
Energy in Chemical Processes
    and Everyday Life, 458
Engines
  reversible and irreversible
    processes in, 262
  vehicle, 220–221, 254
Entropy, 261
Epicenter, 412, 414–415
Equilibrium
  for spring, 209, 347
  for system, 19
  thermal, 213, 256, 259
Equinox, 192
Evaporative cooler (swamp
    cooler), 265
Evolution
  of the cheetah, 50
  stellar, 463–466
Exoplanets, 185
Extension, at normal faults, 428

External forces, 16, 101–103
Eye, lens of, 396
Eyeglass lenses, 404–405

F
Falling objects
  conservation of energy with, 239–240
  energy conversion for, 217, 218
  kinetic energy of, 216
Faraday, Michael, 114, 280
Faraday's law, 295–296, 302–303
Fault blocks, 410, 428–430
Fault(s), 410
  and earthquake hazards, 432
  and focus of earthquake, 412
  formation of, 427
  modeling movement at, 442–443
  monitoring of, 421
  strain at, 422
  types of, 428–430
Fermi, Enrico, 129
First law of thermodynamics, 259–260, 267–268
Fission, nuclear. See Nuclear fission
Fission track dating, 338–339
Flight, forces in, 24, 45–46
Fluids, friction in, 71
Fluorescent lamps, 123
Flux, magnetic, 295
Focal length
  defined, 396, 397
  and image location, 398–400, 406–407
  and magnification, 401
Focus(--i)
  of earthquake, 412, 418
  of ellipse, 182
Football tackle collisions, 96–99
Footwall, 428
Force fields, 139
Force(s). See also specific types
  in flight, 24, 45–46

frame of reference and, 7, 11
  magnitude and direction of motion, and, 42–43
  motion and, 20–22
  Newton's first law and, 18–19
  in projectile motion, 64
  two-dimensional vectors for, 37–38
  in universal gravitation problems, 165
  vector quantities for, 34
Forces and Motion, 1, 14, 32, 48, 84
Forest fires, 231
Fossil fuels, 131, 231–232, 316
Fossils, dating with, 327, 337–338
Frames of reference
  and forces on objects, 7, 11
  and rotational motion, 11–12
  types of, 3–6
Franklin, Benjamin, 145–146
Free fall, objects in, 72, 217
Frequency
  of CMB radiation, 378
  defined, 349
  and Doppler effect, 367–368
  of electromagnetic and mechanical waves, 356, 358, 362–363
  and energy in photons, 212
  of light, 273
  resonant, 373
  of seismic waves, 420
  and wave speed/wavelength, 351–354, 382–385
Friction forces
  and gravitational potential energy, 231
  motion problems on, 70–71
  and Newton's third law, 28
Frisch, Otto, 313
Fuel cells, 221–222
Fundamental forces, 106–125
  discovery of, 112–116
  identifying atoms and molecules with, 118–120

magnitude of gravitational force, 117–118, 124–125
  and matter–energy interactions, 109–110
  and plasmas, 110–112
  recognizing, 108
  STEM in Action, 121–123
Fusion, nuclear. See Nuclear fusion

G
Galaxies, 458–472
  4414, motion of, 164
  gravity's effects on, 181
  Milky Way, 459, 467–468
  and origin/nature of universe, 453
  STEM in Action, 470–472
  types of, 468–469
Galileo Galilei, 17
Gamma decay, 309
Gamma rays, 361, 374
Gases
  in air conditioners, 263–264
  atomic spectra, 119
  internal energy of, 258
  mechanical waves in, 350–351, 369
  and origins of stars, 453, 454, 463
  and plasmas, 110, 111
Geiger counter, 116
General relativity, theory of. See Theory of general relativity
Generators, 146, 284
Geologists, 442–443
Geophones, 444
Geostationary orbits, 199
Giant impact hypothesis, 335–336
Giant star phase, 464
Glaciers, movement of, 2
GOES-13 satellite, 199
Graphs, in motion problems, 60–63, 81–82
Gravitational fields, 155–157, 161, 171–172

Gravitational force. *See also* Newton's law of universal gravitation
  and center of gravity, 159
  discovery of, 112–113
  electrical forces vs., 274
  as fundamental force, 109
  magnitude of, 117–118, 124–125, 153
  and mass, 8
  and Newton's first law, 18, 30
  and Newton's third law, 27
  for objects near Earth's surface, 163
  for satellites in orbit, 167
  on stars, 121
  and tides, 189–191
Gravitational potential energy
  conversions of kinetic and, 217, 218
  defined, 209–210
  for falling objects, 240
  at hydroelectric power plants, 244
  measuring, 229–230
  near Earth's surface, 232–234
  problems involving, 248
Gravitational waves, 169–170
Gravity, 150–176
  acceleration due to, 66, 163
  and big bang theory, 449
  center of, 159–162, 173–176
  discovery of, 112
  distance, mass, and force of attraction, 156–157
  distance, mass and, 185–186
  effects of, on Earth, 152
  inclined plane and, 17
  lift force and, 45
  magnitude of gravitational force, 153
  Newton's law of universal gravitation, 7, 9, 154–157, 162–168
  and Newton's third law of motion, 27, 30
  for objects near Earth's surface, 162–164

  orbital motion of satellites and, 167–168
  planetary motion and, 179–181
  solving problems involving, 164–168
  speed, direction, and, 42
  on stars, 121
  STEM in Action, 169–170
  theory of general relativity and, 110, 113, 117, 122, 169

H
Hahn, Otto, 313
Haiti earthquake (2010), 420, 430
Half-life, 321–322, 340–341
  calculating, 331–333
  defined, 310
  in radiometric dating, 312, 331–333, 340–341
  as time scale, 333–334
Hands, rubbing to warm, 208
Hanging wall, 428
Hawking, Stephen, 455
Headlights, 394
Head-to-tail method, 37–39
Heat. *See also* Thermal Energy
  in closed system, 256
  energy transfer by, 255–256
  in first law of thermodynamics, 259
  types of, 213–214
Helium, 450, 453, 462
Hertz (Hz), 349, 358, 362
Hertzsprung-Russell diagram, 463
The History of Planet Earth, 325
Hockey, momentum in, 89
Horizontal motion, of projectiles, 64–65, 67
Hubble, Edwin
  discovery of distant galaxies by, 468
  observations of expanding universe by, 122–123, 448, 451–452
Hubble space telescope, 455, 457, 470
Hydroelectric power plants, 244–245

Hydrogen
  emission spectrum of, 120
  formation of, 450, 453, 462
  isotopes of, 306, 330
Hydrogen bomb, 317

I
Igneous rock, 327, 337
Images
  in curved mirrors, 394–395
  formed by reflection, 391–395
  location of, 398–400, 406–407
  magnification of, 401
  real vs. virtual, 394, 398
Impact craters, 180
Incans, 178
Inclined planes, 17
Induction
  in conductors, 294, 295
  law of, 280–281
Inelastic collisions, 93–99
  defined, 93
  sample problems, 95–99
  solving problems with, 93–94
Inertia
  in Newton's first law, 18, 19
  and planetary motion, 180
  and wave speed in media, 351
Inertial frames of reference, 5–6, 11
Information Technologies and Instrumentation, 269, 342, 388
Infrared rays, 359
Inner core, of Earth, 419
Instantaneous speed, 51–52, 57
Instantaneous velocity, 56, 61
Insulators, 288–302
  and birds on electrical wires, 289
  conductors, semiconductors, and superconductors vs., 290–291
  electric charge on, 297–298
  and Faraday's law, 302–303
  materials for, 292–293
  STEM in Action, 299–301

Intensity
 of earthquakes, 417
 of electromagnetic waves, 359
 of mechanical waves,
  363–367, 386–387
Interference, 371–372
Internal energy, 258–260, 313
International Thermonuclear
 Energy Reactor (ITER), 222
Inversely proportional (term), 7
Inverse square law, 143
Ionizing radiation, 360, 361
Ions, 111
Iron, 454, 462, 465
Irregular galaxies, 468, 469
Irreversible processes, 260–262
Isla Del Sol, altar on, 178
Isolated systems, 258
Isotopes, 306–307. *See also*
 Radioactive isotopes
 daughter, 308, 331–332
 half-lives of, 331–332
 in nuclear fission, 313
 parent, 308, 331–332
 radioactive decay of, 307–311,
  333–334
 in radiometric dating, 311,
  329–330
ITER (International
 Thermonuclear Energy
 Reactor), 222

J

Jack-in-the-box, 235
James Webb space telescope
 (JWST), 471–472
Japanese tsunami (2011), 438
John Day Fossil Beds, 337
Joule (J), 214, 229
Joule, James, 242
JWST (James Webb space
 telescope), 471–472

K

Kepler, Johannes, 113, 182–185,
 202
Kepler's laws of planetary
 motion, 113, 182–185, 202
Kicked ball, 102, 215

Kinetic energy, 251
 in collision problems, 99
 and conservation of energy,
  227, 234–239, 251
 conversions of potential and,
  216–221, 225, 234–239
 defined, 208
 at hydroelectric power
  plants, 244
 mass, velocity and, 214–216,
  223–224
 measuring change in, 229–230
 momentum and, 88
 of particles, 213
 in perfectly elastic collisions, 92
Kinetic friction, 70
Kuiper belt, 181

L

Laparoscopic cameras, 402
Laser Interferometer
 Gravitational-Wave
 Observatory (LIGO), 170
Law of conservation of energy
 and big bang, 449
 demonstrating, 239–242
 described, 228
 examples of, 229–232
Law of conservation of
 momentum, 88–101
 defined, 88–90
 demonstrating, 100–101
 in elastic and inelastic
  collisions, 92–99
 solving motion problems with,
  90–92
 STEM in Action, 104–105
Law of induction, 280–281
Law of reflection, 392–393
Laws of thermodynamics,
 267–268
 applying, 262–266
 described, 255, 258–262
 and internal energy, 258
Lenses, 396–397
 applications of, 402–405
 concave, 397, 404
 convex, 396–401, 404

Life cycle of stars, 463–464
Lift force, 45–46
Light. *See also* Reflection;
 Refraction
 and cosmic background
  radiation, 378
 diffraction of, 357, 372
 Doppler effect for, 368
 dual nature of, 272–273, 357
 and electromagnetic force, 113
 and electromagnetic waves,
  355
 emission/absorption of, 118–120
 polarizing, 370–371
 quanta of, 110
 speed of, 354, 356, 358,
  360, 362
 from stars, 121
 wavelength and frequency
  of, 354, 360
Lightning, 111–112, 236
Lightning bells, 145–146
LIGO (Laser Interferometer
 Gravitational-Wave
 Observatory), 170
Liquefaction, 433
Lithium, 450, 453, 462
Little Ice Age, 461
Location, predicting, 33
Logarithmic scales, 415
Longitudinal waves, 347, 355,
 356, 411
Lowell Observatory, 447
Lunar eclipse, 196–197
Lunar rocks, dating of, 335–336

M

Maglev technology, 301
Magnetic fields
 and electric fields, 278–279
 and electromagnetic force, 114
 and electromagnetism,
  282, 283
 energy storage in, 211–212
 as force field, 139
 generating electromagnetic
  waves with, 280
 in generators, 284

Magnetic fields (*Cont.*)
  and magnetic induction, 294
  of superconductors, 301
Magnetic flux, 295
Magnetic forces, applications
    of, 278–279
Magnetic induction
  in conductors, 294, 295
  law of, 280–281
Magnetic resonance imaging
    (MRI), 301
Magnetism, 269–287
  applications of magnetic
      forces of, 278–279
  electricity's interactions
      with, 271
  and electromagnetism,
      282–283
  STEM in Action, 284–285
Magnets
  industrial, 114
  permanent, 278, 279
Magnification, image, 401
Magnifying glass, 401, 402
Magnitude
  absolute, 464
  apparent, 464, 467
  of earthquakes, 413, 415–416,
      420, 423
  of gravitational force, 117–118,
      124–125, 153
  of motion, 42–43
  of stars, 463, 464, 467
Main sequence phase, 463–464
Mass
  acceleration and, 21, 29
  action/reaction forces and,
      25–26
  center of, 158–159, 161–162
  in collision problems, 94
  distance, force of attraction
      and, 156–157
  distance, gravity and, 185–186
  gravitational field and, 155–156
  gravitational force and, 8, 153
  gravitational potential energy
      and, 218, 233

in Newton's law of universal
    gravitation, 154, 156–157, 162
Newton's third law and, 27
in nuclear fusion and fission,
    129–130
in problems with universal
    gravitation, 165
for satellites in orbit, 168
scalar quantities for, 34
in systems, 256–258
velocity, kinetic energy and,
    208, 214–216, 223–224
Mass number, 329
Materials engineers, 300–301
Matter
  antimatter and, 450
  dark, 456
  energy and, 109–110
  fundamental forces and, 121–123
  and origins of universe,
      449–450
  states of, 110–111
MAVEN satellite, 165
Maxwell, James Clerk, 114
Maxwell's equations, 114, 281
Maxwell's wheel, 209
Mechanical engineers, 245
Mechanical waves. *See*
    also specific types, e.g.:
    Seismic waves
  electromagnetic vs., 355–357
  energy, power, and intensity
      of, 363–367
  wave speed and media for, 369
Mechanics
  classical, 122
  quantum, 110, 116, 123
Medicine
  electromagnetic and
      mechanical waves in,
      373–374
  nuclear energy in, 133–134
Medium(--a) for waves, 357
  defined, 345
  refraction at boundary of, 396
  and wave speed, 350, 369
Meitner, Lise, 313

Metals
  conductivity of, 290, 292
  extraction of, 293
Metamorphic rock, 327
Meteorites, 336
Metric units, 229
Microchips, 299
Microwaves, 359
Milky Way galaxy, 453, 459,
    467–468
Minerals, 335, 339
Mining, 293
Mirrors
  applications of, 402
  concave, 394, 398
  convex, 395
  curved, 391, 394–395
  plane, 390–393
Modified Mercalli Intensity
    Scale, 417
Molecules
  energy in, 213–214
  identifying, 118–120
Momentum, 84–105
  in car collisions, 86
  in elastic vs. inelastic
      collisions, 92–99
  and kinetic energy, 87–88
  law of conservation of
      momentum, 88–101, 104–105
  and net external forces,
      101–103
  for satellites in orbit, 167
  STEM in Action, 104–105
  vector quantities for, 34
Moon (Earth's)
  age of Earth and, 335–336
  gravitational force on, 153
  phases of, 194–195
  and planetary motion of
      Earth, 181
  and tides, 189–191
Moons, as satellites, 188
Motherboard, computer, 147
Motion, 1–13
  and acceleration, 11
  causes of, 16–19

in cheetah's evolution, 50
defined, 7
forces applied perpendicular
    to, 42–43
force's effects on, 20–22
frames of reference for, 3–6
friction force and, 70–71
of glaciers, 2
inclined planes for studying, 17
measuring, 68–69
Newton's laws of (See
    Newton's laws of motion)
orbital, 167–168
planetary, 113, 179–185, 202
predicting, 7–10
projectile, 64–68, 72–73, 83
rotational, 11–12, 187–188
of satellites, 188–189
scalars for describing (See
    Scalars)
in space (See Space, object
    movements in)
STEM in Action, 11–13
uniform circular, 42
vectors for describing (See
    Vectors)
Motion problems, 48–83
conservation of momentum in,
    88–92
displacement vs. time in, 81–82
friction in, 70–71
graphs in, 60–63, 81–82
Newton's first law, 19
Newton's second law, 22
position, velocity, and
    acceleration in, 53–59,
    74–77, 79–80
with projectile motion,
    64–68, 83
speed and distance in, 51–53,
    78–80
STEM in Action, 72–73
Motion sensors, 68–69
Motorboats, forces on, 20
Motors, 284, 294
MRI (magnetic resonance
    imaging), 301

Musical instruments, resonant
    frequencies of, 373

N
National Aeronautics and Space
    Administration (NASA), 13
Negative charge, 140–141, 145
Net external forces, momentum
    and, 101–103
Net force, 20, 29–30
Neutrons
    discovery of, 110
    in isotopes, 306
    mass of, 328
    in nuclear fission, 313, 314
    and nuclear forces, 115, 116,
        128, 129, 308
Neutron stars, 465
Newton, Issac
    on acceleration–force
        relationship, 20, 21
    description of gravity by, 112,
        113, 169
    ideas about motion of, 18
    law of universal gravitation, 7,
        122, 154, 185
    observation of action and
        reaction forces by, 23
Newton's Cradle, 100–101
Newton's law of universal
    gravitation, 154–157
    in classical mechanics, 122
    gravitational fields and,
        155–156
    gravitational force and, 112,
        113, 117–118
    mass, distance, and attractive
        force according to, 156–157
    motion of objects and, 7–9
    object movements in space
        and, 185–186, 203–204
    for objects near Earth's
        surface, 162–164
    solving problems involving,
        164–168
Newton's laws of motion, 14–31
    action and reaction forces,
        23–28

in bobsledding, 15
forces and objects' motion
    according to, 20–22
and inertial frames of
    reference, 5
with law of universal
    gravitation, 164
Newton's first law, 18–19, 31
Newton's second law, 21–22,
    25, 26, 163, 167–168
Newton's third law, 23–24,
    27–28, 30
and object interactions, 16–19
and orbital motion of
    satellites, 167–168
predicting motion of objects
    with, 7–10
STEM in Action, 29–30
validity and usefulness of, 9–10
Non-inertial frames of
    reference, 6, 11
Normal faults, 428
Northern lights, 271
NRC (Nuclear Regulatory
    Commission), 136, 137
Nuclear energy, 127, 131–137, 316
Nuclear engineers, 316–317
Nuclear fission
    benefits of, 136
    electricity from, 131–132, 316
    fusion vs., 313–314
    mass and energy in, 129–130
Nuclear force(s), 126–137
    discovery of, 115–116
    mass and energy in fusion
        and fission, 129–130
    in positron emission
        tomography, 127
    and radioactive decay,
        307–308
    STEM in Action, 135–137
    strong, 109, 115, 121, 128–129,
        307–308, 313
    technological applications of,
        131–134
    in universe, 121–122
    weak, 116, 128–129

Nuclear fusion
developing, 136
electricity from, 131
energy from, 222
fission vs., 313–314
manmade, 317
mass and energy in, 129–130
for nucleosynthesis, 462
in stars, 454, 460, 462
Nuclear physics, 304–324
fission vs. fusion, 313–314
half-life, 321–322
isotopes, 306–307
radioactive decay, 307–311,
318–320
radiometric dating, 311–312,
323–324
and solar energy, 305
STEM in Action, 315–317
Nuclear Processes, 126, 304, 325
Nuclear reaction, 308
Nuclear reactor, 313
Nuclear Regulatory
Commission (NRC), 136, 137
Nuclear weapons
energy in, 130
fission in, 132–133, 135
Nucleosynthesis, 462, 465
Nucleus, atomic, 115,
307–308, 328
Number line, 54
Nutation, 188

O

Oceanic crust, 426
Oceanographers, 379
Open systems, 257
Optimizing the Design Solution,
84, 226, 342
Orbital motion, of satellites,
167–168
Orbit(s)
acceleration due to gravity in,
160
defined, 179
direct, 179
of Earth's satellites, 198–200
of electrons, 328

geostationary, 199
gravitational force in, 152, 154
perihelion and aphelion in,
191–192
period of, 183–185
retrograde, 179
Oscillation, in waves, 346–348
Outer core, of Earth, 418

P

Paddle wheel, 241
Paintball, 72–73
Parallelograms, for vector
addition, 38, 40
Parent isotopes, 308, 331–332
Particle accelerators, 129, 280
Particles. See also Subatomic
particles
alpha, 308, 313, 316
charged, 237–238, 280
electric potential energy of,
237–238
energy in, 213–214
wave-particle duality of light,
272–273, 357
Pendulum clock, 239
Penzias, Arno, 450
Perfectly elastic collisions, 92
Perihelion, 191, 192
Period
of planetary orbit, 183–185
of wave, 348
Periodic table, 328
Periodic waves, 347–348
Permanent magnet, 278, 279
Phases
of moon, 194–195
of waves, 371–372
Photoelectric effect, 272–273
Photogates, 68–69
Photons, 119, 212, 273, 356, 376
Photovoltaic effect, 375
Photovoltaics, 375–377
Physicists, 123
Planck, Max, 110
Plane mirror, reflection off,
390–393
Planes, inclined, 17

Planetary motion, 179–185, 202
Planetary nebula, 464, 465
Plasmas, 109–112, 317
Plate tectonics
determining Earth's age with,
334–335
and earthquakes, 426–427, 432
Plate Tectonics and Large-
Scale System Interactions,
408, 424
Pocket billiards (pool), 42–43,
90–93
Polarization, 370–371
Poles, magnetic, 278, 282
Position
graphing time vs., 60–61
velocity, acceleration, and,
53–59, 74–77, 79–80
Positive charge, 140–141
Positron emission tomography,
127
Potential energy. See also
specific types
and conservation of energy,
227, 234–239
conversions of kinetic and,
216–221, 225
at hydroelectric power
plants, 244
Power
of mechanical waves,
363–367, 386–387
scalar quantities for, 34
Precession, 187–188
Pressure, 427, 428, 430
Primary waves. See P waves
Projectile motion
applications of, 72–73
describing, 64–66
equations of, 67–68, 83
Protons
and atomic number, 328, 462
charge on, 140
discovery of, 110
and nuclear forces, 115, 116,
128, 129, 307–308
P waves (primary waves), 411,
414, 418, 419

Q

Quantum(--a), 110, 116
Quantum mechanics, 110, 116, 123

R

Racing athletes, motion of, 58
Radiation. *See also*
    Electromagnetic radiation
    cosmic microwave background,
        378, 450–451, 455, 457
    emission of, 330
    heat transfer via, 214
    ionizing, 360, 361
    and radioactivity, 327
Radiation therapy, 134
Radioactive decay, 307–311
    dating objects based on,
        311–312
    decay series, 311
    and nuclear force, 116, 307–308
    products of, 318–320
    in radiometric dating, 330–331
    rate of, 309–310, 333–334
    types of, 308–309
Radioactive isotopes
    decay of, 307–311, 330
    half-lives of, 331–333
    medical and industrial
        applications of, 315–316
    in radiometric dating, 311–312
    rate of decay for, 309–310
Radioactivity, 327, 330, 331
Radiometric dating, 325–341
    half-life calculations for,
        340–341
    investigating Earth's past
        with, 326
    radioactive decay and, 311–312
    solving problems involving,
        323–324
    STEM in Action, 337–339
    techniques for, 327–336
Radio waves, 358
Rafting, whitewater, 23
Reaction forces, 23–28
    canceling out of, 26–28
    identifying, 23–25
    and mass, 25–26

Real images, 394, 398
Red giants, 464
Redshift, 368, 452, 467
Reflection, 388–407
    causes of, 389
    defined, 390
    diffuse, 393
    images formed by, 391–395
    law of, 392–393
    regular, 393
    of sound waves, 369
    STEM in Action, 402–405
    and wave characteristics, 369
Reflection seismology, 379
Refraction, 388–407
    defined, 395–396
    focal length and image
        location/magnification,
        398–401, 406–407
    lenses and, 396–397
    STEM in Action, 402–405
    and wave characteristics, 370
Refractive index, 396
Refrigerant, in air conditioners,
    265
Regular reflection, 393
Relativity, theory of, 9, 130, 449
    theory of general relativity
        (*See* Theory of general
        relativity)
    theory of special relativity, 122
Renewable energy, 243–245
Repulsive force, 140–142,
    275–279
Resistance
    air, 71
    electrical, 290, 299
Resonance, 373
Retrograde orbits, 179
Reverse faults, 429
Reversible processes, 262
Revolution, 179, 189
Richter scale, 415–416, 443
Robots, 11–12
Rock cycle, 334–335
Rockets, with satellite
    payloads, 200

Rock(s)
    balancing, 16
    igneous, 327, 337
    layering of, 326
    lunar, 335–336
    metamorphic, 327
    sedimentary, 327, 337–338
Roller coasters, 35, 238–239
Room, frame of reference in, 4
Rotational motion, 11–12, 187–188

S

Satellites
    in aerospace engineering,
        200–201, 472
    MAVEN, 165
    motion of, 167–168, 188–189
    orbits of, 198–200
    tidally locked, 188
    TOPEX/Poseidon, 200
Scalars (scalar quantities)
    and distance vs.
        displacement, 55
    effects of perpendicular force
        on, 42–43
    predicting location with, 33
    STEM in Action, 44–46
    vector quantities vs., 34–36
Seasons, cause of, 194
Secondary waves. *See* S waves
Second law of
    thermodynamics, 260–261
Sedimentary rock, 327, 337–338
Seismic waves, 408–423
    as cause of earthquakes, 409
    and earthquake intensity vs.
        magnitude, 415–417
    measuring, 412–415, 423
    STEM in Action, 420–422
    studying Earth's interior with,
        418–419
    types of, 410–412
Seismograms, 413–414, 416
Seismograph (seismometer)
    defined, 413, 443
    seismologists' use of, 421–422
    studying Earth's interior
        with, 418

Seismology
  defined, 379, 413
  responsibilities of
      seismologists, 421–422
  technologies used in, 443–444
Semiconductors, 291, 292, 299
Sensors, motion, 68–69
Shadow zones, 418–419
Shallow-water waves, 439
Shear wave velocity, 444
Shrapnel, deflecting, 105
Silicates, 335
Singularity, 448, 449
Skiing, 217, 231
Skydiving, 71, 108
Smoke detectors, 316
Soccer, 102, 215, 345
Solar eclipse, 195–197
Solar energy, 305, 377
Solar system, center of mass in,
    158–159
Solstice, 193–194
Sonar, 379
Sound waves
  Doppler effect, 367–368
  energy, power, and intensity
      of, 364, 366–367
  reflection of, 369
  speed of, 350–351, 353–354
  wavelength and frequency,
      353–354
Space, object movements in,
    177–204
  in ancient civilizations, 178
  categorizing, 179–197
  during eclipses, 195–197
  and equinox/solstice on Earth,
      192–194
  motion of satellites, 188–189
  and Newton's first law, 19
  and Newton's law of universal
      gravitation, 185–186,
      203–204
  perihelion and aphelion in
      Earth's orbit, 191–192
  and phases of the moon,
      194–195
  planetary motion, 179–185, 202

rotation, 187–188
  STEM in Action, 198–201
  and tides on Earth, 189–191
Spacecraft, 4, 13
Speakers, 366
Spectroscopy, 119–120, 466–467
Spectrum(--a)
  absorption, 466–467
  electromagnetic (See
      Electromagnetic spectrum)
Speed. See also Wave speed
  acceleration, motion, and, 11
  average, 51–53, 57
  of commercial airplanes, 73
  constant, 51–53, 78
  defined, 51, 351
  distance and, 51–53, 78–80
  friction and, 71
  gravity's effect on, 42
  instantaneous, 51–52, 57
  of light, 354, 356, 358, 360, 362
  and Newton's laws of motion,
      5, 9
  of objects on inclined planes, 17
  in one dimension, 79–80
  perpendicular force and, 42–43
  planetary motion and, 183
  from position vs. time graph, 60
  scalar quantities for, 34
  of universe, 457
  velocity vs., 44, 56–57, 79–80
Speedometer, 51
Speed skating, 87
Spiral galaxies, 468, 469
Spring
  demonstrating conservation
      of energy with, 240–241
  elastic potential energy in,
      209, 234–235
Sputnik 1 satellite, 189
Standard model, 110, 116, 118
Stars, 458–472
  death of, 464–466
  elements from, 462
  energy from, 460–461
  fundamental forces on, 121–122
  gravity's effects on, 181
  life cycle of, 463–464

movement of, 459
  and origin/nature of universe,
      454
  plasma in, 111
  STEM in Action, 470–472
  studying, 466–467
States of matter, 110–111
Static electricity
  and electric force, 140–141,
      275
  electric potential energy, 236
  for engineers and computer
      repair technicians, 146–147
  insulators and, 297
  interactions of electric and
      magnetic forces in, 357
Static friction, 70
Steady state theory, 448, 455
STEM in Action
  conductors and insulators,
      299–301
  conservation of energy,
      243–245
  conservation of momentum,
      104–105
  earthquakes, 442–444
  electric forces, 145–147
  electricity and magnetism,
      284–285
  energy, 221–222
  fundamental forces, 121–123
  gravity, 169–170
  motion problems, 72–73
  Newton's laws of motion,
      29–30
  nuclear forces, 135–137
  nuclear physics, 315–317
  object movements in space,
      198–201
  radiometric dating, 337–339
  reflection and refraction,
      402–405
  seismic waves, 420–422
  stars and galaxies, 470–472
  thermodynamics, 263–266
  universe, 455–457
  vectors and scalars, 44–46
  waves, 378–379

Strain, at faults, 410, 422
Strassmann, Fritz, 313
Stress, at faults, 428, 430
Strike-slip faults, 430
Strong nuclear force
  in atoms, 128–129
  discovery of, 115
  as fundamental force, 109
  and nuclear fission, 313
  and radioactive decay, 307–308
  on stars, 121
Structural engineering, 105,
  420–421, 433–434
Subatomic particles
  discovery of, 110
  fundamental forces for, 123
  identifying atoms/molecules
    based on, 118
  nuclear forces for, 116, 128–129
Subduction, 426, 432
Summer solstice, 193, 194
Sun
  energy from, 460
  fundamental forces on, 121
  gravitational force of, 152
  nuclear fusion on, 454
  and tides on Earth, 190–191
Sunspots, 461
Superconductors, 291, 299–301
Supernova, 454, 462, 465
Surface waves, 412
Swamp cooler, 265
S waves (secondary waves),
  412, 414, 418
Systems
  closed, 88, 103, 256–257
  coordinate, 3–5
  defined, 256
  isolated, 258
  open, 257

T

Tectonic plates, 410, 426–428
Telegraph cables, 290
Telescopes, 466, 468
Temperature
  and laws of thermodynamics,
    261–262
  of stars, 463, 465

Theory of general relativity
  expansion of universe and, 455
  gravity and, 110, 113, 117, 122, 169
Theory of special relativity, 122
Thermal energy, 208, 219
  in air conditioners, 263
  from chemical potential
    energy, 231
  conservation of energy and,
    228, 239
  creating plasmas with, 111
  electromagnetic spectrum
    and, 359, 361
  in first law of thermodynamics,
    259–260
  as kinetic energy, 238
  in second law of
    thermodynamics, 261
  from stars, 121
  in systems, 256
  transfer of, 255–256
Thermal equilibrium, 256, 259
Thermodynamics, 252–268
  and energy transfer by work
    or heat, 255–256
  internal energy, 258
  laws of, 255, 258–262,
    267–268
  in open, closed, and isolated
    system, 256–258
  reversible vs. irreversible
    processes, 262
  STEM in Action, 263–266
  in vehicle engines, 254
Third law of thermodynamics,
  262
Throwing, momentum in, 104
Thrust faults, 429
Thrust force, 45
Tidal bulge, 191
Tidally locked satellites, 188
Tides, 189–191
Time
  displacement vs., 81–82
  measuring, 178
  position vs., 60–61
  velocity vs., 62–63
Tokamak, 222

TOPEX/Poseidon satellite,
  200
Topography map, 33
Trains, 6, 52
Trajectory, projectile, 64–66
Transform boundary, 430, 432
Transmutation, 309
Transverse waves
  amplitude of, 349
  defined, 347, 355
  electromagnetic and
    mechanical, 356
  polarization of, 370
  S waves as, 412
Trump Globe, 274
Tsunamis, 438–441
Tsunami Warning Centers, 440
Two-dimensional vectors,
  36–41
Types of Interactions, 1, 106,
  126, 138, 150, 269

U

Ultrasound, 373–374
Ultraviolet (UV) rays, 360
Uniform acceleration, 59
Uniform circular motion, 42
United States Geological
  Survey (USGS), 339
Universal gravitation. See
  Newton's law of universal
  gravitation
Universe, 445–457
  electromagnetism in study
    of, 285
  expansion of, 122, 378–379,
    448, 452
  and fundamental forces,
    121–123
  investigating, 446
  origins of, 447–454
  STEM in Action, 455–457
The Universe and Its Stars,
  445, 458
Uranium-238 isotope, 311,
  312, 339
USGS (United States
  Geological Survey), 339
UV (ultraviolet) rays, 360

V

Vectors (vector quantities), 32–47
  manipulating, 36–41, 47
  for motion, perpendicular
    force and, 42–43
  predicting location with, 33
  scalar quantities vs., 34–36
  STEM in Action, 44–46
  two-dimensional, 36–41
Vehicle engines, 220–221,
  254
Velocity, 5
  acceleration and, 20
  average, 56, 60–61
  in collision problems, 94–98
  graphing time vs., 62–63
  instantaneous, 56, 61
  kinetic energy and, 208,
    214–216, 223–224, 238
  mass and, 208, 214–216,
    223–224
  of objects on inclined planes, 17
  in one dimension, 79–80
  perpendicular force and, 42–43
  position, acceleration, and,
    53–59, 74–77, 79–80
  shear wave, 444
  speed vs., 44, 56–57, 79–80
  two-dimensional vectors for, 36
  vector quantities for, 34
Vertical motion, of projectiles,
  65, 67
Virtual images, 395, 398
Visible light, 360
Vision, 404–405

W

Washington Monument, 389
Water, hydrogen isotopes in,
  330
Waterfalls, gravitational
  potential energy in, 233

Water waves, tsunami
  formation and, 438–439
"The wave," in crowds, 345
Wavelength, 348
  of CMB radiation, 378
  diffraction and, 372
  Doppler effect and, 367, 452
  of electromagnetic and
    mechanical waves, 356–363
  wave speed, frequency, and,
    351–354, 382–385
Wave-particle duality, of light,
  272–273, 357
Wave Properties, 269, 342,
  388, 408
Waves, 342–387
  bands of electromagnetic
    spectrum, 357–361
  characteristics of, 344, 347–351
  defined, 345
  Doppler effect and frequency
    of, 367–368
  electromagnetic vs.
    mechanical, 355–357
  energy, power, and intensity
    of mechanical waves,
    363–367, 386–387
  energy of electromagnetic
    radiation, 362–363, 380–381
  energy transfer via, 346–347
  interactions of, 369–373
  light, 273
  media type and speed of, 369
  seismic (See Seismic waves)
  STEM in Action, 378–379
  technological applications of,
    373–377
  and tsunami formation,
    438–439
  wave speed, wavelength, and
    frequency relationship,
    351–354, 382–385

Wave speed
  defined, 350
  Doppler effect and, 367
  of electromagnetic and
    mechanical waves, 356, 362
  media type and, 369
  refraction and, 370, 395
  for seismic waves, 379, 418
  wavelength, frequency, and,
    351–354, 382–385
Weak nuclear force, 116, 128–129
Weapons, nuclear, 130, 132–133,
  135–136
Weathering, 335
Weight, 8, 160
White dwarfs, 464, 465
Whitewater rafting, 23
Wilson, Robert, 450
Wind energy, 207, 219, 220
Wind towers, 263
Work
  in air conditioners, 263
  in closed systems, 256
  energy transfer by, 255–256
  in engines, 262
  in first law of thermodynamics,
    259–260
  scalar quantities for, 34
World's Strongest Man
  competition, 21

X

x-axis, 5
X-rays, 361, 374, 403–404

Y

y-axis, 5

Z

z-axis, 5
Zeroth law of thermodynamics,
  258–259